WEATHER MAPS
- Third Edition -

How to Read and Interpret
All the Basic Weather Charts

by

Peter R. Chaston

Chaston Scientific, Inc.
P. O. Box 758
Kearney, MO 64060
telephone: 816-628-4770
fax: 816-628-9975

Meteorology is the study of the redistribution of air.

Unless otherwise labeled, the source for all weather maps in this book is the National Centers for Environmental Prediction (NCEP) of the National Weather Service.

Books written or co-written by Peter R. Chaston:

- WEATHER MAPS, THIRD EDITION - How to Read and Interpret all the Basic Weather Charts (ISBN: 0-9645172-7-2)
- TERROR FROM THE SKIES! (ISBN: 0-9645172-1-3)
- HURRICANES! (ISBN: 0-9645172-2-1)
- JOKES AND PUNS FOR GROAN-UPS, co-authored with James T. Moore (ISBN: 0-9645172-3-X)
- WEATHER BASICS, co-authored with Joseph J. Balsama (ISBN: 0-9645172-5-6)
- THUNDERSTORMS, TORNADOES AND HAIL! (ISBN: 0-9645172-6-4)

These books are available from select bookstores or directly from Chaston Scientific, Inc.; P.O. Box 758; Kearney, MO 64060; phone: 816-628-4770; fax: 816-628-9975.

ABOUT THE AUTHOR

PETER R. ("Pete") CHASTON became fascinated with weather as a young boy. His personal affinity for the science of meteorology began when he experienced a few hurricanes while growing up along the East Coast. He was fascinated by having the eye of a tropical storm named Brenda go right over his home weather station, followed some two months later by Hurricane Donna's 100+ mph winds and driving sheets of horizontal rain. Winter snowstorms and blizzards also thrilled him, and weather grew to be Pete Chaston's main interest.

Having weather as an intense hobby eventually led to a career in meteorology. Pete started reading college texts and everything else he could find on weather through secondary school, and then served as a weather observer in the Air Force for four years, saving money for college.

Pete Chaston received his Bachelor of Science degree in Meteorology and Oceanography from New York University, and later, while a National Weather Service (weather bureau) forecaster, was selected for the weather service Fellowship to graduate school, underwhich he earned his Master of Science degree in Meteorology from the University of Wisconsin. It was at Wisconsin where he met Mary Gabrielski and they married almost two years later.

Pete Chaston served as a National Weather Service meteorologist from 1971 through 1995, afterwhich he took advantage of an early retirement option to found Chaston Scientific, Inc., under whose auspices this book is written.

In the weather service, Pete served at Binghamton, New York and at Hartford, Connecticut before transferring to the forecast office at Pittsburgh, Pennsylvania. He then was the Meteorologist-in-Charge of the National Weather Service Office at Rochester, New York and later became Technical Project Leader for the National Weather Service Training Center in Kansas City, Missouri.

Pete has written several books on meteorology, had a weekly newspaper column on weather, did television and radio weather and numerous talk shows, and is a regular lecturer and speechgiver. He played the role of a meteorologist in the movie, "Water", filmed for the PBS TV network and...for something different... even appeared in a Stephen King movie, "Sometimes They Come Back", and has a popular Kansas City radio program called "The Pete Chaston Doowop Show". He has taught at the State University of New York, the University of Missouri at Kansas City, the University of Kansas at Lawrence, Kansas, William Jewell College at Liberty, Missouri and lectured at other colleges. Pete Chaston has also worked with several grants involving training the nation's earth science teachers in meteorology, and has presented seminars to the National Science Teachers Association and various Academies of Science. He also gives training seminars on weather. Pete was also President of the Kansas City Chapter of the American Meteorological Society for two terms.

Pete Chaston has published scientific research articles in magazines and journals, including the National Weather Digest and Weatherwise. He developed a technique for forecasting heavy snow amounts that is widely used by forecasters nationwide. The technique is called "The Magic Chart" because it is straightforward and easy to use. He also pioneered new operational forecasting procedures now commonplace in contemporary meteorology. Some of the books Pete has written include "WEATHER MAPS - How to Read and Interpret all the Basic Weather Charts", "TERROR FROM THE SKIES!", "HURRICANES!" and "THUNDERSTORMS, TORNADOES AND HAIL!". With fellow meteorologist Dr. James Moore he co-authored a humorous book entitled, "JOKES AND PUNS FOR GROAN-UPS", and with science educator Joseph Balsama, he co-authored the compendium, "WEATHER BASICS", which is a preferred introduction to meteorology book. Thus, Pete Chaston has varied interests and derives great fun and enjoyment from all of them.

TABLE OF CONTENTS

Why is Forecasting so Difficult?

Consider a rotating spherical envelope of a mixture of gases -- occasionally murky and always somewhat viscous.

Place it around an astronomical object nearly 8000 miles in diameter.

Tilt the whole system back and forth with respect to its source of heat and light.

Freeze it at the poles of its axis of rotation and intensely heat it in the middle.

Cover most of the surface of the sphere with a liquid that continually feeds moisture into the atmosphere.

Subject the whole to tidal forces induced by the sun and a captive satellite.

Then try to predict the conditions of one small portion of that atmosphere for a period of one to several days in advance.

Introduction to the Third Edition

To the great satisfaction of all of us who enjoy the fascinating topic of weather, be it as a professional meteorologist, teacher, student or weather enthusiast, the personal computer makes weather maps and weather satellite imagery readily available. Virtually every weather observation, weather forecast, statement, warning, weather map, satellite picture, radar data and historical climatological data are accessible via the internet.

The main comprehensive weather data sources are the National Weather Service and universities with meteorology programs. Other data distributors provide enhanced graphics, colorization and movie-loops, for a fee. Thus, there is plenty to choose from, depending on your personal interests.

More of us are looking at weather data now than ever before. Thus, a need arose for a comprehensive text to explain the variety of weather maps. Beyond that, information on how to interpret and use the most common weather charts is also required. Moreover, the information needed to be written in an easily understandable manner so that the book could be used as both a reference and educational textbook. This books contains much technical information; however, great care has been taken to try to present this information as understandably as possible without surrendering technical correctness and completeness.

It was necessary to write this book. This project has grown over many years and has been an exhilarating endeavor because of the knowledge that many people have waited a long time for a comprehensive text on the basic weather maps.

This book, "WEATHER MAPS - Third Edition - How to Read and Interpret All the Basic Weather Charts", therefore fills the need for this information and represents a necessary advance in weather education. It is hoped that this book is for you a valuable reference on the most commonly-used weather maps.

For a comprehensive weather training, this author recommends to you the companions to this book: "Weather Basics", "Tornadoes, Thunderstorms and Hail!" and "Hurricanes!", which are available from the address below and in selected bookstores.

Chaston Scientific, Inc.
P. O. Box 758
Kearney, MO 64060
telephone: 816-628-4770
fax: 816-628-9975

1. SOME INTERESTING HIGHLIGHTS IN THE HISTORY OF WEATHER

●weather - the word "weather" comes from the Indo-European words "we" for wind and "vydra" for storm, in the Sanskrit language, first codified about 3000 B.C. In Anglo-Saxon and Middle-English, the word became "weder" and later evolved into "weather".

●Approximately 500 B.C. - In Greece, the first routine weather observations were started after the rain gauge was invented to measure the amount of rainfall, and the wind vane was invented to give the wind direction. These weather observations were written down and displayed publicly in the cities and for farmers.

●Approximately 350 B.C. - In Greece, because of the great interest in following the weather and trying to predict what will happen by looking at signs in the sky, such as cloud types, some real research was done trying to understand how weather evolves. Eventually, the famous scientist Aristotle wrote his book called "Meteorologica", which was the first major treatise on the weather. The title of that book gives the science of meteorology its name, since the term comes from the Greek word root "meteoron" and its plural, "meteora", meaning "things in the air". "Meteor" and "meteorite" also come from the same word root.

●1593 - The thermometer is invented by Galileo Galilei (1594-1642) of Italy. He used glass globes in an enclosed column of liquid, and used the principal that the density of a liquid changes with temperature. Thermometers use mercury as the liquid of expansion and contraction as the temperature changes. However, because mercury freezes at about 40 below zero Fahrenheit (which is also minus 40° Celsius), alcohol, which has a much lower freezing point, is used in thermometers for places in the world where the temperature could fall below -40°F. Nowadays, digital-type thermometers have replaced most liquid-in-glass thermometers. New generation thermometers use a sensor that expands as the temperature rises and contracts as the temperature falls. These sensors are typically made of certain metal alloys or ceramics.

●1643 - The barometer is invented by one of Galileo's students, Evangelista Torricelli (1608-1647) of Italy, to measure the weight of a column of air from where the barometer is to the top of the atmosphere. This weight or force per unit area is known as the pressure of that column of air. At sea-level, the average pressure reads about 29.925" on the barometer, which is about 14.7 pounds of air pressure pushing on every square inch. You might ask, why doesn't the human body get crushed or pushed in by the air pressure weighing on every square inch of us? The reason the air does not start to crush us is that we also have air inside of us, which helps to push out at 14.7 pounds per square inch also, so that the net pressure effect on our body is zero. However, we still notice rapid pressure changes when the body has not quite had enough time to adapt, such as when you take a rapid elevator ride to the top of a tall skyscraper. You are going higher in altitude to where there is somewhat less air (the air pressure is then less on you because the total weight of the column of air from you on up is less). You might have 14.5 pounds of pressure per square inch on you, but the pressure from inside your body is still 14.7 and needs up to few seconds to decrease to 14.5. The result is that your ears "pop". Air is pushing out and it is easily sensed in your ear channels.

The original barometers used liquids, using the scheme illustrated below:

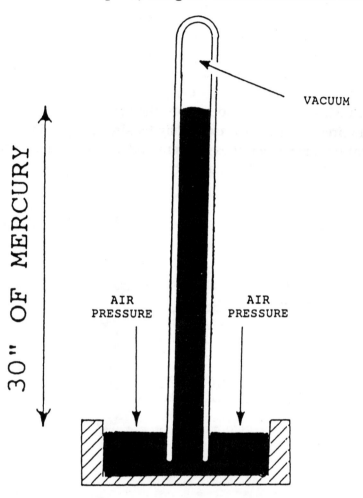

Figure 1. The Principle of the Barometer. A fluid such as colored water would take a tube over thirty feet high to make a barometer; however a very heavy fluid, mercury, requires a tube of about three feet long. First, fill the bowl with a few inches of mercury. Next, fill a narrow tube with mercury so that no air is left in it. Then turn the tube over into the mercury and the column of mercury will fall to the current air pressure level. For example, if the height of the mercury column is 30.00", then the barometric pressure is reported as 30.00". If denser air is moving in (higher pressure since it weighs more than lighter air), then the air pressure will push down with more force on the open bowl, forcing the mercury to rise in the column. Thus, three hours after reading a pressure of 30.00", the pressure could rise to 30.10". When the pressure falls, less air weight is pushing down on the mercury in the bowl, with the response in the column being the height of the mercury will fall, e.g. to 29.90" a few hours later. Later in this book, the meaning of this for weather forecasting will be discussed.

Pressure is force per unit area, and is measured in pounds per square inch, or newtons per square meter, or dynes per square centimeter or in millibars, also known as hectoPascals. One millibar equals 1000 dynes per square centimeter. We use the height of the mercury column in the mercurial barometer to measure the pressure, and then keep track of its changes since they relate to the kind of weather we are experiencing and expecting.

The modern barometers do not use mercury at all. Instead, they use a small metal container such as a cylinder, which has all the air taken from it. Thus, there is a vacuum inside the cylinder, and if the metal is soft enough, this cylinder will slightly compress inward as the air pressure rises, and slightly expand when the air pressure falls. A spring and dial are attached to this cylinder so that the dial moves in one direction when the pressure rises, and the opposite direction when it falls. The other end of the dial moves across a calibrated scale which uses the same units as does the mercurial barometer, e.g., 30.10", 29.45", 30.74", etc. This type of barometer is called an aneroid barometer.

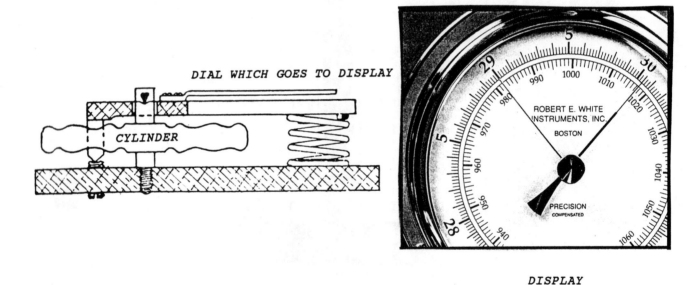

Figure 2. An Aneroid Barometer. As the air pressure changes, the vacated cylinder expands or contracts, causing the dial to move.

●1648 - Blaise Pascal of France carried a barometer up a mountain to show that atmospheric pressure decreases with increasing altitude. If you are at sea-level, you have all the air parcels from you to the top of the atmosphere weighing down on you at about 14.7 pounds per square inch. But if you are on top of a 10,000-foot high mountain, then you have only the atmosphere from 10,000 feet up to the top weighing down at you, and at that elevation you'd have a force of about 10.3 pounds per square inch.

If the air pressure at sea-level happens to be 30.00", then:

ELEVATION:	PRESSURE WOULD BE:
sea-level	30.00"
5,000 feet	about 25.50"
10,000 feet	about 21.00"
18,000 feet	about 15.00"
29,000 feet	about 9.00"
39,000 feet	about 6.00"

Thus, there is not a linear relationship between the altitude and the pressure except for the first few thousand feet. That is, the pressure does not decrease at the same rate for the same increase in altitude. Only in the first few thousand feet can we say that the air pressure decreases about one inch on the barometer for every 900 feet increase in elevation. As we go above 5000 feet, then the pressure decreases more and more slowly as we keep going up. This is because most of the heavier molecules of gasses that comprise the mixture of gasses we call the atmosphere are found in the lowest parts of the atmosphere, and as we go up we find the lighter gasses such as hydrogen and helium which gradually thin out until there are no more molecules and atoms of the lightest gas, hydrogen. The top of the atmosphere varies from about 600 to about 1000 miles out.

Dry air is heavier than moist air: Moist air contains more water vapor (water in the form of a gas) than does dry air. We know that (liquid) water weighs more than air; however, here we are concerned with water vapor. Let us assume that dry air is comprised of about 99% by volume of oxygen and nitrogen, and ignore the other gasses. The molecular weight of dry air is about 29. The molecular weight of water vapor is about 18 (i.e., 2 for 2 atoms of hydrogen, each weighing 1 atomic unit, and 1 atom of oxygen, weighing 16 atomic units).

Most of the time, the percentage by volume of water vapor in the lower atmosphere over any local area varies from near zero to about 4%. Thus, wherever and whenever the percentage of water vapor increases, we are replacing some dry air, which has a molecular weight of 29, with water vapor, which has a molecular weight of 18. Because the total number of molecules in a column of both dry or moist air remains the same, the moist air, which is comprised of dry air plus water vapor, weighs less than does all dry air, which is comprised mostly of nitrogen and oxygen.

At the bottom of the atmosphere we find that almost 99% of our air, if it were completely dry, is comprised of nitrogen and oxygen, with the other about 1% being argon, with traces of other gasses. However, when the air is moist, as stated earlier, water vapor can comprise up to about 4 percent of the volume.

The atmospheric pressure, therefore, is the sum total of the individual or partial pressure exerted by each component gas of the atmosphere.

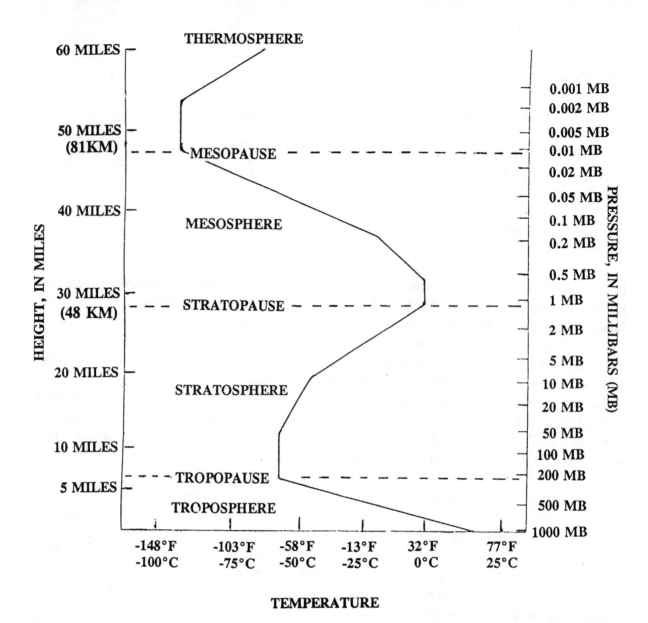

Figure 3. Composition of the Atmosphere. The figure is not drawn to scale, because half of the atmosphere is in the lower 18,000 feet above the earth's surface, and the other half is from 18,000 feet (about 3½ miles) to about 600 miles! The top of the troposphere layer is called the tropopause, the top of the stratosphere layer is called the stratopause and the top of the mesosphere layer is called the mesopause. The thermosphere layer eventually cools off and becomes outer space at about 600 miles up where the last hydrogen atoms are extremely far apart.

•1714 - Gabriel Daniel Fahrenheit (1686-1736) of Germany invented his temperature scale which has 32° for the freezing point of water and 212° for the boiling point of water.

•1742 - Anders Celsius (1701-1744) of Sweden invented his temperature scale which has 0° for the freezing point of water and 100° for the boiling point of water. Celsius' temperature scale is also known as the Centigrade temperature scale. (Originally, Celsius designated 0° as boiling and 100° as freezing, of water, but later inverted the scale.)

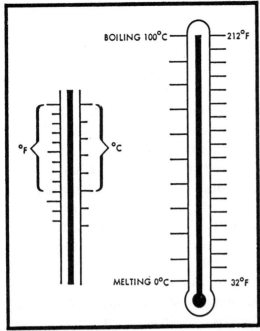

BOILING 100°C — 212°F

°F   °C

MELTING 0°C — 32°F

$$C = \frac{5}{9}(F - 32)$$

$$F = \frac{9}{5}C + 32$$

Figure 4. The Fahrenheit and Celsius Temperature Scales. By comparing both scales, note that a temperature change of one Celsius degree is a temperature change of 1.8 Fahrenheit degrees.

● 1743 - Benjamin Franklin (1706-1790) of the American Colonies became the first American meteorologist. Franklin talked his friends and colleagues into taking weather observations at the same time and sending him their reports. He concluded that there are organized weather systems and that these systems move. He discovered, for example, that a storm along the coast that brought rain to Georgia and the Carolinas would by the next day move up the coast to bring snow to New Jersey, New York, Pennsylvania and New England.

Franklin is also famous for discovering that lightning is electricity. He flew a kite into a thunderstorm and attached a key to the end of the wire where he held it. When lightning struck the kite, Franklin was jolted by the electric charge he received by touching the key. Thus, Benjamin Franklin was fascinated by the weather, and kept diaries about it. Some other Founding Fathers of our nation, including Thomas Jefferson and George Washington, also kept weather diaries.

Figure 5. Benjamin Franklin, the first American Meteorologist. This sketch illustrates Franklin sending a kite into a thunderstorm to determine some properties of lightning. (His kite was probably more box like.)

• 1803 - Luke Howard of England named all the clouds, using Latin names. Thus, puffy clouds caused by convection (rising air currents of 20 to 40 mph or more) were called cumulus clouds. The more straight-looking clouds were named stratus clouds. The high thin wispy clouds comprised of ice crystals, and often looking feathery, were called cirrus clouds. Thus, cumulus, stratus and cirrus are the three main cloud families. Combinations of types led to cirrostratus, stratocumulus and cirrocumulus. Clouds were also categorized by the height of their bases above the ground. Clouds bases from zero to about 6500 feet high are called low clouds, from about 6500 to about 20,000 feet high are called middle clouds, and clouds bases from about 20,000 feet high and higher are called high clouds. The middle clouds are given the Latin prefix, alto; thus, if cumulus or stratus clouds have their bases between about 6500 and 20,000 feet, we call them, respectively, altocumulus and altostratus clouds. Thunderstorm clouds are cumulonimbus. These names cover most of the clouds. Fog is a stratus cloud whose cloud base is on the ground. Thus, when you are in fog, you are in a stratus cloud.

• Early 1800s - Emperor Napoleon Bonaparte of France issued a decree that the Fahrenheit temperature would no longer be used throughout the Empire; it was to be replaced by the Centigrade (Celsius) scale. The Celsius scale is still the standard in much of the world.

• 1812 - During the War of 1812, United States Army hospital surgeons started taking and recording weather observations.

• 1819 - H. W. Brandes at the University of Breslau drew the first weather map from observations taken across Europe at the same time, and sent to him by mail. He was able to identify areas of high and low pressure and warm and cold areas.

• 1837 - Samuel Finley Breese Morse invented the telegraph. Its importance for meteorology is that weather reports could now be transmitted across the country.

• 1849 - The U.S. Department of War's Army Signal Corps started taking weather observations, transmitting them via telegraph.

• 1850 - The Smithsonian Institution in Washington, D.C. started using telegraphed weather observations to produce the first daily weather maps.

• 1855 - The first officially sanctioned national weather service was begun by France.

• Early to mid 1860s - President Abraham Lincoln was approached by a weather scientist proposing the establishment of a national weather service. President Lincoln challenged him to make a forecast to prove his point. The scientist predicted fair weather and it rained, so Lincoln refused to see him a second time. Lincoln's successor, President Ulysses Grant, was convinced that the establishment of a weather bureau would be good for the country.

●1870 - The weather bureau of the United States was established with 20 original weather offices, in the Army Signal Corps, and in 1890 was moved as the United States Weather Bureau to the Department of Agriculture, and in 1940 to the Department of Commerce. In 1970 the weather bureau had its name changed to the National Weather Service.

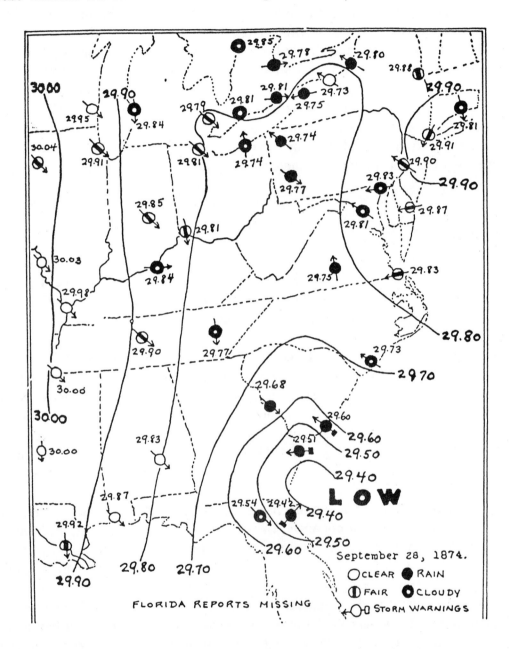

Figure 6. One of the first "Daily Weather Maps". This surface weather map was plotted and analyzed by hand by the then-called United States Weather Bureau. Local weather offices printed forecasts on post cards and then took them to the post office which was sometimes co-located with the weather bureau office, in the morning for delivery the same day to local subscribers.

●1876 - The word "cyclone" was coined by Henry Piddington of England, meaning "coil of a snake", to be used to mean a storm. Piddington was President of the Marine Courts at Calcutta, India.

●1899-1902 - Teisserence deBort sent up kites and balloons with thermometers attached to profile the temperature changes in the vertical in the lower atmosphere. Based on his findings, he named the first atmospheric layer "the troposphere", meaning "sphere of mixing", and the next layer "the stratosphere", for "sphere of stratification".

●1914-1918 - During World War I, Norwegian meteorologists discovered that there is a boundary between a warm and a cold air mass, and they named such a boundary a "front", after the battlefronts of the war. When the cold air is advancing, the front is a cold front; when the warm air is advancing, the front is a warm front.

Also during this war, Lewis F. Richardson of England, while on war duty in France as a medical corpsman, wrote a manuscript describing how data of current weather parameters at the surface and aloft could be used with the equations of motion of the atmosphere to make a forecast "by the numbers". Inotherwords, Richardson showed that we could forecast the state of the atmosphere say 12 and 24 hours later by taking the current conditions of the atmosphere and using them in the governing equations of the atmosphere, solving those equations for out in time.

This scheme is known as "numerical forecasting" and requires a mathematical "model" of the atmosphere to start with. Richardson's manuscript was lost in a coal bin but recovered several months later, refined, and published in 1922 as "Weather Prediction by Numerical Process". (Earlier, in 1900, Vilhelm Bjerknes postulated that the state of the atmosphere could be forecasted using numerical computations.) These basic equations defining atmospheric motions and processes became known as the "primitive equations" of the atmosphere.

Richardson determined that by using mechanical hand calculators, it would require some 6000 persons, all working simultaneously, to perform the necessary computations to generate a 12- to 24-hour forecast. Computers were not even a viable concept at that time.

●1948 - John von Neumann, a Hungarian mathematician, working at Princeton University, used one of the very first vacuum-tube computers to successfully make a numerical forecast. Most of the prognostic (called "prog") charts or forecast weather maps are created by computer models. Many counties run these "numerical forecast models". In the United States, a branch of the National Centers for Environmental Prediction, a part of the National Weather Service, outside Washington, D.C., runs several numerical models to generate forecast weather maps for the surface, aloft and for layers of the atmosphere. This book includes all the commonly used weather charts, including the charts produced by these computer models.

●Weather History: Worst Weather Disasters

Until the 20th century, the worst weather disaster in recorded history, in terms of human lives lost, was the great hurricane of October 7th, 1737, which hit at the mouth of the Hooghly River on the Bay of Bengal. The storm surge was forty feet. It is recorded that some 300,000 people died in that single hurricane. However, in that same general area, a major hurricane struck the islands and coastline of Bangladesh in November 1970 and killed an estimated 500,000 people. The storm surge came over the islands that were only several feet above sea-level, drowning residents by the thousands.

In the United States, the greatest weather disaster in terms of lives lost was the Galveston, Texas hurricane of September 8th, 1900, which killed over 6000 people, mainly from the storm surge.

As a hurricane approaches land, a surge of water from the sea grows higher and higher as the center of the hurricane, known as the eye, approaches the shore. When the winds are on the order of 150 mph or more, and the hurricane is a massive one, these violent winds and the force of the air pressure cause the shallow water near the shore to rise up to great heights. By the time the storm surge from major hurricanes reaches landfall, it is typically over 20 feet high.

For example, in 1969 Hurricane Camille hit the Mississippi coast. This storm grew into one of the most powerful hurricanes ever recorded as it strengthened over the warm waters of the Gulf of Mexico. Its highest sustained winds around the nearly calm "eye" were 200 to 210 miles per hour, and gusts were higher. As it smashed into the Mississippi gulf coast, a group of people ignored the warning and had a "hurricane party" in the three-story Richelieu Garden Apartments. All but one person died as a 27-foot high storm surge smashed ashore. On top of this 27-foot storm surge were waves up to fifteen feet high. The only survivor was a woman who floated out the third story on a mattress. After the storm subsided and the water level dropped, she was rescued from the top of a tree.

2. THE SURFACE WEATHER MAP

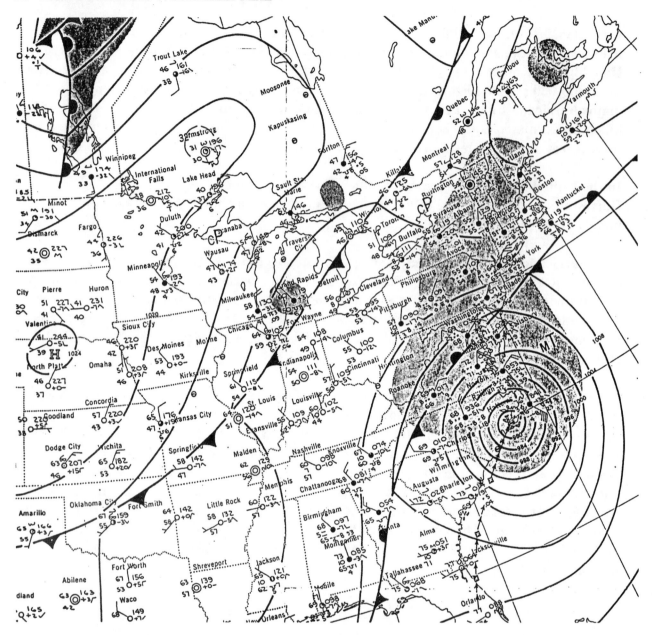

Figure 7. A Surface Weather Map. Here is a section of a U.S. surface weather map. Each weather station has a circle and some characters around the circle that describe the weather at that location. Lines of equal air pressure, called **isobars**, are drawn and the centers of highest and lowest air pressure are located. Boundaries that separate warm and colder masses of air are drawn; these boundaries are called **fronts**.

In the following pages, the weather reporting stations' plotting symbols are explained, as are the isobars, high and low pressure systems, fronts, etc. First, we need to start with an explanation of weather observations and how to read them.

2a. READING PLOTTED WEATHER OBSERVATIONS

Most weather observing stations across the country are located at airports, because the pilots need to know vital weather conditions for safety consideration. Most weather observations are taken just before each hour, with special observations (which are called just that -- special observations) at any time when the weather changes importantly.

WEATHER OBSERVATION
STATION MODEL

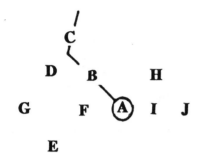

EXAMPLE OF A PLOTTED
WEATHER OBSERVATION

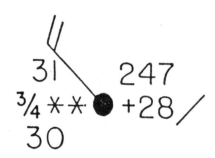

Figure 8. How to Read a Plotted Weather Observation. Listed below is the most common style for plotting weather observations on a surface weather map. On the following few pages are the detailed explanations of the various coded weather elements.

A = Total Cloud Cover. A clear sky has an open circle, with the circle filled in as more clouds occur. In the sample, the sky is overcast.

B = Wind Direction. The arrow points into where the wind is coming from. In the example, the wind is coming from the northwest.

C = Wind Speed. A half-barb is five knots; a full barb is 10 knots; a flag is 50 knots. This is explained later. In the example, the wind is 20 knots (2 barbs). A knot is approximately 1.15 miles per hour, so 20 knots is about 23 mph.

D = Temperature. In the example, the temperature is 31°F. Celsius is plotted outside the U.S. Thus, temperature and dewpoint are given either in degrees Fahrenheit or Celsius.

E = Dewpoint. This is explained later. In the example, the dewpoint temperature is 30°F.

F = Current Weather. The weather symbols are explained later. In the example, the two asterisks mean a continuous fall of steady light snow.

G = Visibility. This is the average distance the observer can see, horizontally. In the example, the visibility is three-quarters of a mile.

H = Sea-level Pressure. This is given in a unit called millibars, which is explained later. In the example, the pressure is 1024.7 millibars (the first digit or digits is/are a 9 or a 10, and are left out). At sea-level, 1024.7 millibars would be about 30.15" on the barometer.

I = Pressure Change, usually within past 3 hours. Example shows 3-hour change of plus 2.8 millibars.

J = Pressure Tendency, usually within past 3 hours. Example shows steady 3-hour rise.

DETAILED EXPLANATIONS OF EACH CODED WEATHER ELEMENT

A. TOTAL CLOUD COVER

Circle over station location

Amount of cloud cover:

Figure 9. Total Cloud Cover Plotted on a Surface Weather Map for Each Weather Observation Site. If the sky is clear, then the station circle is clear. As each one-eighth of cloud cover occurs, the station circle is gradually filled in.

For example, if about a quarter (two-eighths) of the sky) is covered by clouds, then the station circle is filled in (shaded-in) a fourth. If the sky condition is partly cloudy with four-eighths cloud cover, then half the station circle is filled in. An overcast sky has the circle completely filled in. If the sky or clouds cannot be discerned at all because of an obscuration (e.g., dense fog), then the sky report is "obscured" and an X is drawn into the station circle.

The sky cover total is cumulative from the surface up. That is, the lowest cloud deck is then added to by the next higher cloud deck, and then the next higher, and so forth. For example, if the first cloud deck has its base at 2000 feet high and covers 2/8ths of the sky, and the next deck is 8000 feet high and covers 2 eights more, then the total sky cover is 4/8ths which is partly cloudy. When the clouds cover 1 to 2 eighths of the sky, the sky condition is reported as "few clouds", 3 through 4 eighths sky cover is called "scattered", 5 through 7 eighths is "broken", 8/8ths "overcast". If the sky is partially obscured due to a surface-based phenomenon such as fog, haze or smoke, or partially obscured due to heavy precipitation, then the sky condition is called just that: a "partial obscuration", and it may also be partly cloudy or overcast, for example, since the sky cover is cumulative from the surface up. If the sky cannot be seen at all due to one or more obscuring phenomena (even cloud decks cannot be seen), then the sky is called "obscured".

B. WIND DIRECTION
C. WIND SPEED

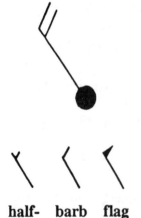

Figure 10. The Plot of the Wind Direction and Wind Speed. In meteorology, the convention is to report the wind in the direction **from which** it comes. Thus, a northwest wind means that the air is coming from the northwest. The top of the station circle is north, the right is east, the bottom is south and the left is west. In the example given, the wind is coming from the northwest. The speed is in knots (nautical miles per hour), a knot being approximately 1.15 mph. A half barb is 5 knots, a full barb is 10 knots and a flag is 50 knots. The example shows a northwest wind at 20 knots (23 mph). Thus, the wind is plotted to the nearest 5 knots.

half-barb   barb   flag

Calm

At left is a report of an obscured sky with the wind coming from the southeast at 75 knots (86 mph). This may be a report from a location in a hurricane. The 86 mph wind is the average wind typically over the minute up to observation time, and there may be higher gusts. For example, the weather report may say the wind is southeast at 75 knots with gusts to 100 knots. (In a hurricane the sky would probably be obscured with blinding rain with these winds.)

Sometimes, the gust report is plotted at the end of the wind barb on a weather map. An example is given below:

The wind is coming from the northeast at 35 knots with gusts to 55 knots.

D. TEMPERATURE
E. DEWPOINT

Figure 11. The Temperature is Plotted in the Upper Left of the Station Plot and the Dewpoint Temperature in the Lower Left. On a surface weather map in the United States, the temperature and dewpoint temperature are plotted in degrees Fahrenheit. Outside the United States, they are usually plotted in degrees Celsius.

In our example, the temperature is 31°F and the dewpoint is 30°F.

The dewpoint is the temperature that the air would have if the atmosphere were allowed to locally cool off to the coldest it could get with that local air. For example, if the early evening temperature is 60 degrees and the dewpoint is 40 degrees with light winds and clear skies expected overnight, then the atmosphere can radiate heat (infra-red radiation) out into space at night until it cools off to its dewpoint. Dew would then form on grass and other surface objects. If the dewpoint is 32 degrees F or lower, frost would form.

The dewpoints over hundreds of areal miles define the type of air mass we are in. If the dewpoints are high in the summer, e.g., 70° or higher, then we are in a soppy, moist warm air mass; if dewpoints are low, such as well below zero degrees F in the winter, then we are in a cold polar or arctic air mass. When dewpoints are rapidly increasing or decreasing, e.g., changing by two or more degrees per hour for several hours, then either moister or drier air is moving in.

The closer the temperature and dewpoint are to each other, the more moist is the air (the higher is the relative humidity). When the temperature and the dewpoint are the same, then the relative humidity is 100%; that is, when both temperature and dewpoint temperature are identical, the air at that pressure is holding 100% of the moisture that it can hold.

F. CURRENT WEATHER

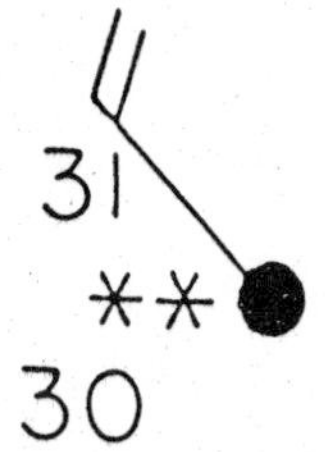

Figure 12. The Symbol for the Current Weather is Plotted to the Left of the Station Circle, Beneath the Temperature and Above the Dewpoint.

In our example, the two asterisks represent steady light snow. The next page gives all the present weather symbols used. On some surface weather maps, simplified symbols are used, especially for precipitation. For example, just one asterisk might be plotted, which would stand for snow. The snow could be light, moderate or heavy. One dot would represent rain; a comma stands for drizzle. All the standard symbols are in the table on the next page.

There are precise definitions for precipitation intensities. For snow, the rate of fall will lower the visibility. This gets confusing if something else, such as fog, is also contributing to a lower visibility. (Visibility is the average distance you can see in the horizontal.)

When snow is occurring alone (no other precipitation mixed in and no other visibility-limiting parameter such as fog, haze or smoke), then light snow is snow that does not reduce the average visibility to less than 5/8ths of a mile. The next lower reportable visibility value is 1/2 mile. When the visibility in snow is one half mile or less but not lower than 5/16ths of a mile, then the snowfall is reported as moderate snow. When the visibility in snow is below 5/16ths of a mile (i.e., 1/4 mile or lower), then the snow is reported as heavy snow. We are referring here to the rate of snowfall, not the total accumulation. For accumulation purposes, a heavy snowstorm is generally one which dumps greater than 6 inches of snow in 12 hours or less, although regions of the country that infrequently receive significant snows typically set lower threshold values for defining a heavy snowfall.

For weather observation purposes, when the visibility is reduced by moderate snow (under 1/2 mile down to 5/16ths of a mile), the snow is falling at a rate of typically an inch an hour. At visibilities of 1/4 mile or less, the rate is in excess of an inch an hour.

Light rain is not drizzle. Drizzle is very fine drops of water and occurs in fog. Fog is a stratus cloud whose cloud base is resting on the ground. Thus, when you are in fog, you are inside a stratus cloud. When enough cloud particles combine to form a drizzle drop, the drizzle precipitates out. Raindrops are larger than drizzle, and fall out of clouds such as stratocumulus, cumulonimbus and nimbostratus.

Drizzle drops are generally not larger than 0.02" in diameter (about 0.5 mm maximum diameter). Raindrops are larger.

Figure 13. The Symbols for Present Weather, as Authorized by the World Meteorological Organization (WMO)

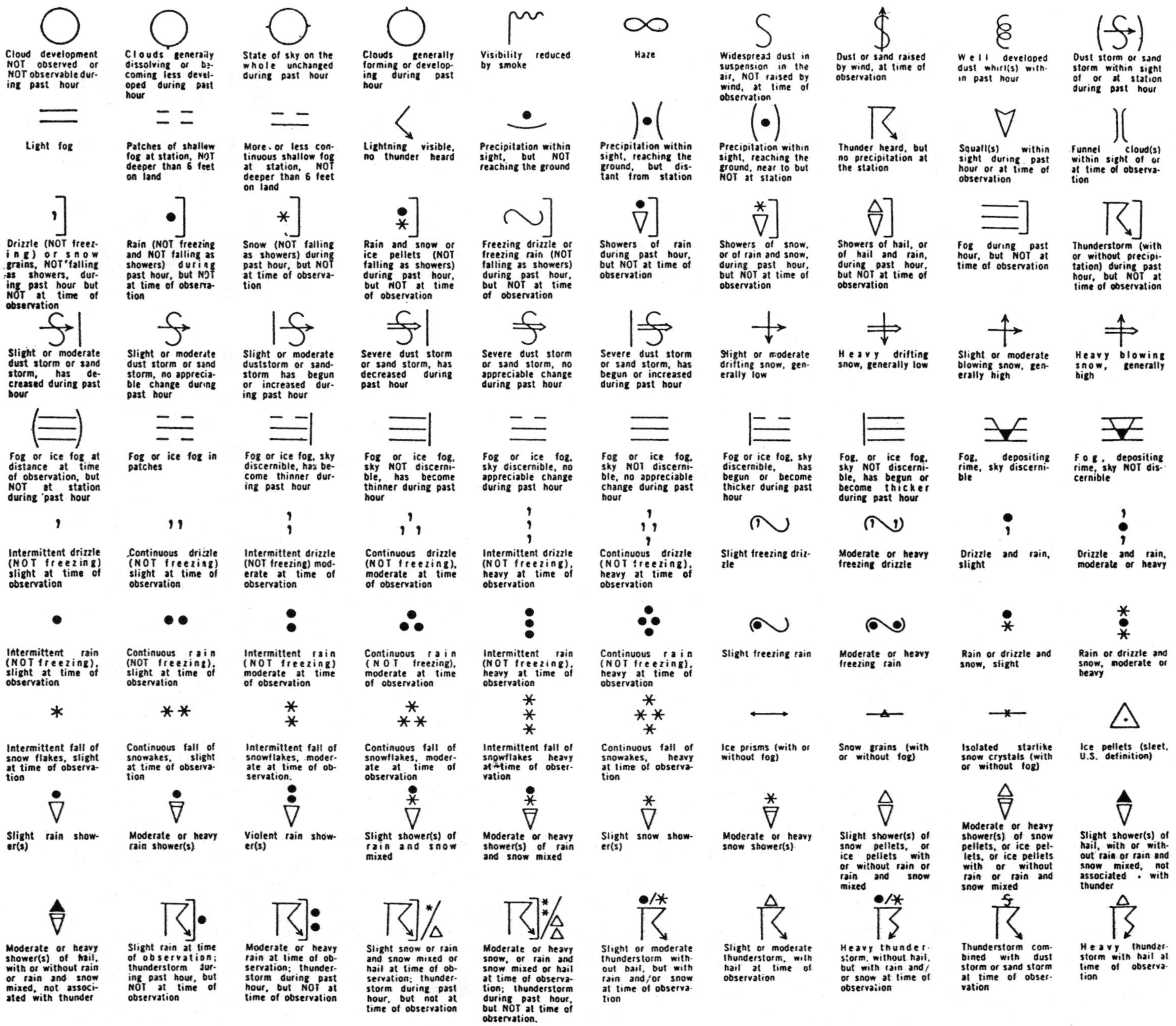

G. VISIBILITY

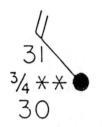

Figure 14. The Visibility is Reported in Whole Miles or Fractions and is Plotted to the Left of the Symbol for the Current Weather. In our example at the left, the visibility, or the average distance for how far one can see in all directions, is 3/4ths of a mile. The visibility in this case is reduced due to snow, which the symbol for the current weather shows is occurring at this reporting station at observation time. Fog, haze or smoke are not reported unless it or they by themselves reduce the visibility to under 7 miles.

H. SEA-LEVEL PRESSURE

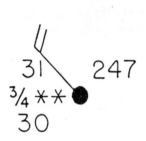

Figure 15. The Sea-Level Pressure is Reported to the Nearest Tenth of a Millibar and is Plotted in the Upper-Right of the Station Plot. Most sea-level pressures will lie between 930 and 1050 millibars, or from over 28.00" to over 31.00", with the pressure most of the time between 29.20" and 30.80". The average sea-level atmospheric pressure around the world is about 29.92" which corresponds to 1013 millibars. In our station model plot at the left, the 9 or 10 is left off. Therefore, the plotted 247 stands for either 924.7 millibars or 1024.7 millibars. Since pressure generally lie between 930 and 1050 millibars except for rare events, our 247 is very likely 1024.7 millibars. This term for pressure, millibars, is abbreviated **mb** in data reports and on weather charts.

I. PRESSURE CHANGE

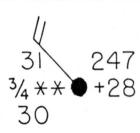

Figure 16. The Pressure Change is Plotted to the Right of the Total Cloud Cover (Sky Condition) Symbol and is Given to the Nearest Tenth of a Millibar. Thus, in our example, the +28 means that the pressure has risen 2.8 millibars since the last pressure change report, which typically is three hours ago. Thus, pressure changes on most weather maps are for three-hours. A zero pressure change is plotted as just 00.

J. PRESSURE TENDENCY

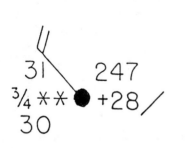

Figure 17. The Pressure Tendency is Plotted to the Right of the Pressure Change. The pressure tendency is for the same time period as the pressure change, usually for the past three hours. This plot tells **how** the pressure has been changing. For example, has it been a steady rise, or a rise then a fall, or a steady fall, or a fall then a rise?

Z-TIME or UTC TIME

Usually, the time put on a weather map to designate the time of the observation or the time of the forecast conditions, is given in Greenwich (for Greenwich, England) mean time; that is, the time at the 0° longitude meridian. This is because except for local-use regional maps, weather maps are distributed throughout the country and the world, especially maps that cover up to an entire continent or hemisphere. Therefore, the whole world's weather community refers to the same time zone when recording and archiving some of its weather data.

Z-time is commonly referred to in weather circles as "ZULU TIME", from an older version of the phonetic alphabet. (Alpha bravo charlie delta means A B C D in old-style radio reports, in order to make sure the listener was being given a C and not a B, for example, in a radio transmission that involved giving letters.) Zulu time or Z-time is also called UTC for Universal Temps Coordinee, or French for Universal Coordinated Time. This time is the time if you were on the 0° meridian in England.

For example, if a weather observation for JFK Airport in New York City says it is the 1500Z observation, then it is 1500 o'clock (3:00 p.m.) at 0 degrees longitude in England, but it is the 10 a.m. observation in New York City, because New York City is five hours earlier than England (in daylight savings time it would be four hours earlier). Thus, all weather observation sites such as airports that take an observation at that hour all around the globe, would report that observation as the 15Z observation (1500Z or 1500 UTC). If an observing site were to take a special observation a half-hour later, then that report would have the time 1530Z.

2b. WHAT ARE ISOBARS?

After all the data from the data sites are plotted on a map, the meteorologist then starts to draw the analysis so that a snapshot or picture of the weather at that observation time is drawn. This is why the weather observatories record and transmit their observations every hour around the world, and reference their observations to Z-time (UTC time).

The **surface weather map** is drawn from these observations which give the weather parameters at the earth's surface. The temperature is read from thermometers in an instrument shelter that allows the air to flow through it, but protects the sensors from sunlight and precipitation. The thermometers are typically six feet above the ground. Lines of equal temperatures can be drawn (these are called **isotherms**), but usually these lines are drawn on the so-called **upper-air charts**. Upper-air charts are weather maps showing conditions, including air flow, well into the atmosphere above the surface. The lines connecting points of equal atmospheric pressure are called **isobars**. Isobars are critical to analyzing the weather because from them we can determine where are the highest air pressure regions and the lowest air pressure regions. The air flows from high to low pressure. and as we shall see later, most of the time a region of high pressure is one of sinking "diverging" air and dry, fair conditions, whereas a region of low pressure is one of storminess.

Figure 18. Isobars and Fronts on a Surface Weather Map.

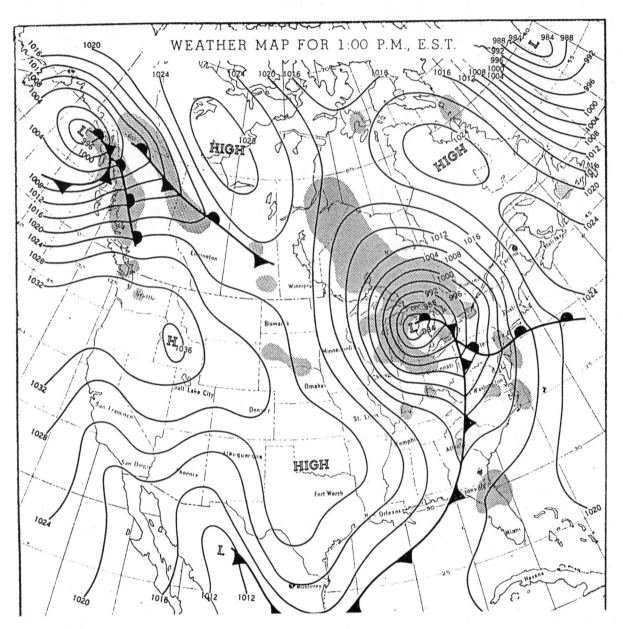

On this weather map, the isobars are lines of equal air pressure. An H identifies the center of the high pressure system (the highest pressure) and an L is the center of lowest pressure. A region of highest pressure is called a **high pressure system**, and of lowest pressure, a **low pressure system**. Highs and lows evolve, move and die, because the air is in motion and unequally warming and cooling in different regions. Thus, weather maps are excitingly active, because weather never stands still. The weather map depicts the state of the atmosphere for that level or environment at a specific time. On some surface weather maps, areas receiving precipitation are shaded in, as in the example above. Time-lapse animation of surface weather maps show the movements and evolutions of the highs, lows and fronts.

2c. WHAT ARE HIGH AND LOW PRESSURE CENTERS AND SYSTEMS?

The surface weather map on the previous page shows the locations of the highest and lowest barometric pressures, as reported by the weather observations all taken at that same time. As you see, the lines of equal air pressure, the isobars, are drawn and labelled for every four millibars. On some surface maps, the first "9" or "10" left off.

A pressure of 1024 millibars is significantly higher than a pressure of 980 millibars. The 1024 mb reading means that the air in a column from the observation point to the top of the atmosphere is pushing down on the surface with a total pressure (force per area) of 1024 millibars. This would be a force of about 15 pounds pushing down on every square inch at the surface. Thus, the air pressure's force is simply the weight of that column of air pushing down on what is at the bottom of the column of air. The 980 mb pressure would be pushing down at about 14 pounds per square inch.

You might ask. "If the air is pushing on me at 14 to 15 pounds for every square inch of my body, why am I not crushed?" The answer is, there is also air **inside** our bodies, pushing **outward** at the same pressure, so that the pressure is equalized pushing both on your body and out from your body. However, you can detect pressure changes if you ride a fast elevator from the ground floor to the top of a tall skyscraper such as the World Trade Center in New York City. The pressure is lower at the top, so your ears will "pop" as the elevator ascends. As you are rising, the pressure is decreasing fast, and the pressure inside your body pushing out is not decreasing as fast. Therefore, when you are in an elevator going up fast, the pressure inside you pushing out is temporarily higher than the air pressure pushing on you, and since air moves from high to low pressure, the air inside your body is trying to push out through all available openings, and your ears sense that readily; thus, your ears "pop" as you ascend to the top of a skyscraper in an elevator. You don't experience as drastic a popping on the way down because it takes longer for more air to reenter your body.

Sometimes a fast-climbing airplane will not pressurize the inside cabin fast enough to keep it at the pressure you had at the surface when the plane took off. Your ears would then "pop" as the plane flies to higher elevations, and the popping stops when the air pressure pushing out in your body is equal to the air pressure pushing on your body.

Notice that the weather map for the surface uses the sea-level pressure. But most locations are above sea-level. For example, at Denver, your **station pressure** would be the pressure at your elevation of about 5,280 feet high. In reality, then, the real pressure you experience is the STATION PRESSURE, or the pressure at that observation station. For Denver, the atmosphere's pressure pushing on you would mostly be about 12.5 pounds per square inch, but higher when high pressure is moving in, and lower when low pressure is moving in. However, all surface weather maps convert the pressure report to what the air pressure would be if location were at sea-level. This makes it easier to use the data to find the highs and the lows.

2d. WHAT CAUSES THE WIND? (WHAT IS THE PRESSURE GRADIENT FORCE?)

It is easy to picture why air blows from high to low pressure. In a high pressure system, the air weighs more --it is heavier. In a low pressure system, the air weighs less because there is less of it to weigh. Wind is created because of these pressure differences. As an analogy, if we created a local environment half of which was comprised of a blob of molasses syrup, and right next to it was an equal-volume blob of water, the heavier syrup would start moving into the water. Similarly, higher pressure forces the air to move into regions of lower pressure. The difference in pressure from one place to another nearby is called the **pressure gradient.** We can define the horizontal **pressure gradient force** as the difference in pressure between points A and B where the pressure at A is higher than at B, and also consider the distance between A and B.

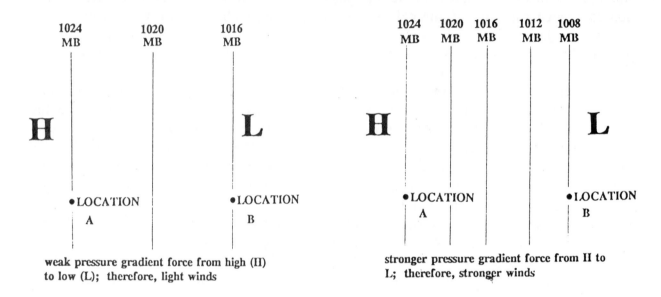

weak pressure gradient force from high (H) to low (L); therefore, light winds

stronger pressure gradient force from H to L; therefore, stronger winds

Figure 19.   The Pressure Gradient Force Changes as the Pressure Difference Between Points Varies and the Distance Between These Points Varies. This Diagram Would be True for a Nonrotating, Frictionless Earth.

Later, we will look at the real, rotating earth, with friction between the wind and the earth's surface. But for now, consider just the pressure gradient force by itself. We know that air blows from high to low pressure. This is the wind. Where the pressure difference is greater over the same distance, the pressure gradient force is greater and therefore the wind speed is stronger. Moreover, when the lines on the surface weather map that give the air pressure, the **isobars**, are closer together, the pressure gradient is stronger and therefore the winds in that region are stronger. Thus, in a major low pressure system such as a strong winter storm or a hurricane, the isobars are very close around the low center: these close isobars therefore indicate strong winds. A pressure difference of 4 mb every 60 miles would give winds of about 50 mph, whereas a pressure difference of 4 mb every 300 miles would give winds of about 10 mph.

However, the earth rotates. As we look down on the earth from over the North Pole, we would see the planet rotating from west to east. Since the circumference of the earth around the equator is about 25,000 miles, and we know that a day is about 24 hours long, then at the equator the earth must rotate at a little over 1,000 miles per hour. Why then don't we feel one thousand mile per hour winds? The reason is because the earth **and the atmosphere** are all rotating at that same speed. We are also in that frame of reference; therefore, at the equator we are moving at 1,000 mph along with the earth, its atmosphere and everything within the earth-atmosphere system.

So we know that pressure differences cause air to move. However, because the earth rotates from west to east, this moving air, the wind, is deflected to the right in the Northern Hemisphere, and to the left in the Southern Hemisphere. This deflecting force due to the earth's rotation is called the **Coriolis force**, named for the scientist who discovered the effect. It is analogous to placing a tiny ball in the middle of an old phonograph record on a turntable, and then pushing the ball towards the edge of the record. When the turntable is not moving, the ball will continue straight towards the record's edge, but when you repeat the experiment with a turntable moving from left to right, the ball will head towards the edge and systematically turn 90 degrees. On the earth, the pressure gradient force pushes the air from high to low pressure and it turns to the right in the Northern Hemisphere due to the Coriolis force.

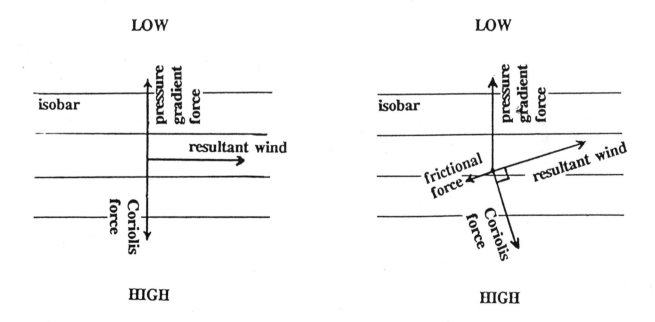

Figure 20. The movement of air due to the pressure gradient and Coriolis forces if there were no friction with the ground and objects on it, and the same air movement with the effect of friction between the air and the earth's surface and objects on the surface.

However, friction between the air and the surface it is flowing over will slow down the air flow and also change its direction. This frictional effect is significant in the first 1500 to 2000 feet from the surface up. This "frictional layer" of atmosphere is called the **planetary boundary layer.** Above the planetary boundary layer, the wind is steered by the net result of the pressure gradient and Coriolis forces, although a curved flow also introduces a centrifugal force ("fleeing" from the center of curvature) which will be discussed with the upper-level charts later.

Within the planetary boundary layer, the wind is the result of the effects of:
        a. the pressure gradient force,
        b. the Coriolis force, and
        c. the frictional force.

There are vertical motions too, and these are essential to the weather we get. However, we look at other causes of motion in the vertical, because the vertical pressure gradient force is suppressed by the weight of the atmosphere, so that upward and downward moving air needs to be instigated by other dynamical or mechanical forcings. This will be covered later in the book.

2e. WHAT ARE COLD, WARM, OCCLUDED AND STATIONARY FRONTS?

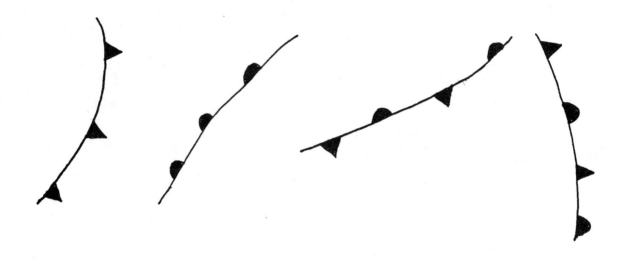

COLD FRONT   WARM FRONT   STATIONARY FRONT   OCCLUDED FRONT

Figure 21. The Symbols for the Four Types of Fronts

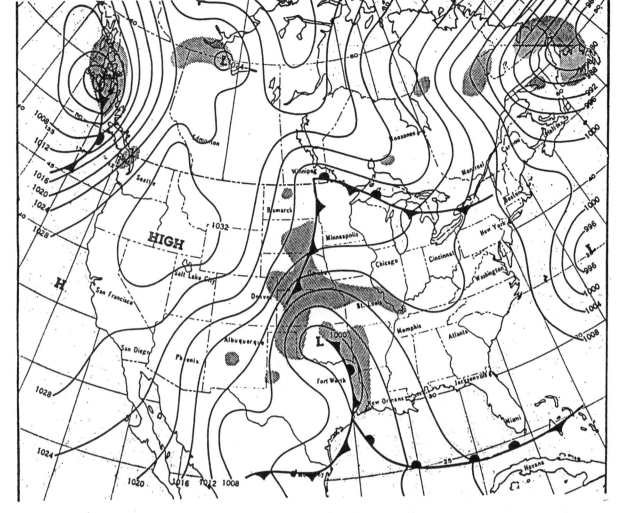

Figure 22. A Surface Weather Map with Cold, Warm, Occluded and Stationary Fronts

In the early 20th century, meteorologists discovered that boundaries exist separating different kinds of masses of air. For example, in wintertime in the Arctic, the earth there is losing more heat into space than it receives from the sun, so the net result is the formation of a massive cold, dense high pressure region. Large blobs of this cold air move down the globe toward lower latitudes. The leading edge of each blob or air mass as it pushes equatorward, displacing warmer air, is called a cold front. Similarly, when warm air masses form in low latitudes and expand poleward, its leading edge at the surface is called a warm front. However, as warm air advances to displace colder air, it advances aloft (say 20,000 to 30,000 feet up) first because it is lighter than cold air and therefore first rides up and over the colder dome of air it is trying to displace.

A front separates cold or cool air from warmer air. Where the boundary is not moving, the front is called a stationary front. Where the cold air is advancing at the surface, its leading edge is called a cold front. Where the warm air is advancing, its leading edge at the surface is called a warm front. Where a cold front catches up to and overtakes a warm front, that boundary is called an occluded front. The following figures illustrate what is happening.

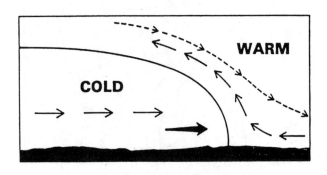

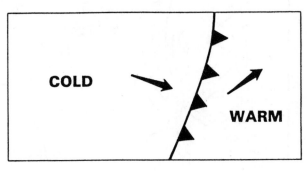

A

B

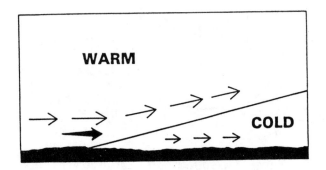

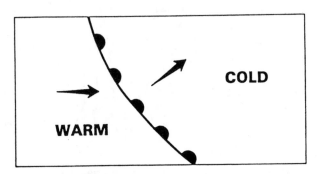

C

D

Figure 23. A. A cold front, illustrating denser, colder air advancing and lifting the warmer air ahead of it
B. How a cold front is depicted on a weather map
C. A warm front, showing the less dense warmer air first advancing aloft over the colder air, and eventually reaching the surface (where the front is placed on the weather map)
D. How a warm front is depicted on a weather map

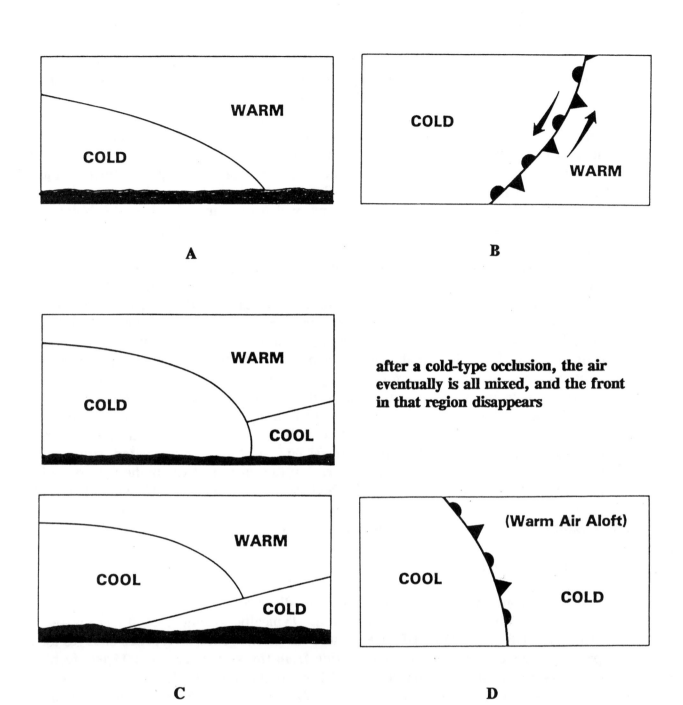

after a cold-type occlusion, the air eventually is all mixed, and the front in that region disappears

Figure 24. A. A stationary front, showing neither the cold air nor the warm air advancing
B. How a stationary front is depicted on a weather map
C. The two types of occluded fronts, where a cold front overtakes a warm front
D. How an occluded front is depicted on a weather map.

2f. INTERPRETING THE SURFACE WEATHER MAP

High and Low Pressure Systems: Because air has weight, it has pressure. Its weight over an area is that pressure. The more a volume of air weights, the higher its pressure. Therefore, a high pressure system is heavier than a nearby low pressure system. Air flows from the high pressure towards the low pressure. Typically, throughout much of the high pressure system, the air is sinking or "DIVERGING", and spreading out, flowing towards lower pressure. And typically throughout much of the low pressure system, the air is "CONVERGING" and rising. Converging and rising air cools and condenses any moisture it is carrying, which can form clouds and subsequent precipitation. Diverging and sinking air dries out the air and leads to dispersing clouds and fair skies. Thus, low pressure systems are usually associated with clouds and precipitation, and most high pressure systems are associated with fair weather. Some exceptions for highs include lake effect snow, which is a local effect caused by very cold air passing over the relatively warm waters of a Great Lake, and upslope or mechanical lifting of air which may ride up a region of increasing elevation to cause clouds and precipitation. Orographic lifting of air passing up a mountain is similar. For example, areas downstream from the Great Lakes in winter can experience some of their heaviest snowfalls as a high pressure system is moving in from Canada with cold Arctic air, setting up the lake effect snow mechanism, and eastern Colorado can experience precipitation as low-level northeasterly winds from a high passing to the north cause the air to move up the rising terrain, leading to clouds and precipitation. Therefore, except for local effects such as these, high pressure systems are typically associated with fair weather. In the Northern Hemisphere, the region to the west of the highest pressure in a high (to the west of the high pressure CENTER) is where the start of rising air usually occurs as the pressure lowers with the moving-in (also called ADVECTION) of the next low pressure system. Also, during the convective (thunderstorm) season, most thunderstorms tend to form away from the region within the high pressure system that is experiencing sinking, diverging air.

The air cannot converge and rise, as in a low, or diverge and sink, as in a high, throughout the entire depth of the atmosphere. Typically, around 15,000 feet up we find a LEVEL OF NONDIVERGENCE, where the convergence/divergence changes to its opposite: that is to say, if air is converging from the surface to about 15,000 feet, then it starts diverging above that level, and if air is sinking and diverging (spreading out) from about the 15,000-foot level to the surface, then it is converging above about the 15,000-foot level.

Thus, weather is truly four-dimensional: to fully appreciate the scope of the atmosphere's behavior, we must analyze what the air is doing in the horizontal, in the vertical, and over a period of time. The beauty of these weather maps at the surface and aloft, is that they give a picture of the atmosphere at that time, and next require our looking at a series of these maps over a time period to see the evolution of the weather.

Figure 25. Here is how a surface weather map would show, over time, the development of a low pressure system (CYCLOGENESIS) on a front, followed by its occlusion and death.

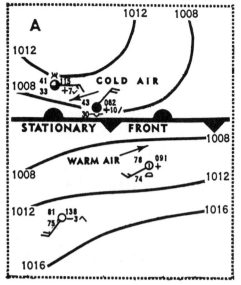

A stationary front, showing cold air to the north and warm air to the south. The arrows depict the wind flow.

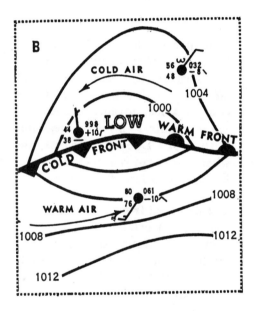

Some of the warm air tries to move northward while some of the colder air tries to move southward. This establishes a bend or kink in the front, which is called a "WAVE", which is an incipient cyclone. Some waves will continue to develop into a low pressure system.

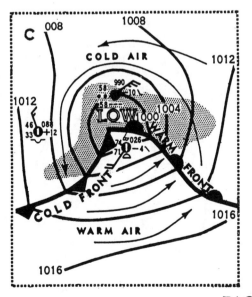

Now the warm air is advancing and rising northeastward while the cold air is sinking under the warm air as it advances southeastward. Thus, the stationary front is no longer quasi-stationary, but part of it is now advancing as a warm front and part of it is advancing as a cold front.

(cyclogenesis cycle continued on next page)

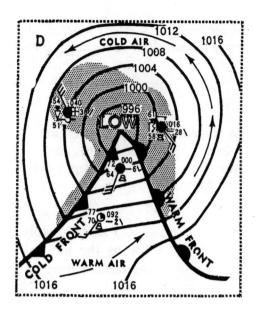

Now we have a well-developed counter-clockwise circulation with warm air being lifted over cold air, and cold air pushing under the warm air. This is our intensifying low pressure system, also called an "EXTRATROPICAL LOW". If sufficient moisture is present in at least the first 10,000 feet of the troposphere, then the region with the rising air experiences precipitation.

Now, just south of the low center, the cold front is catching up to the warm front, because the colder air is denser than the warm air and, being heavier, advances faster than the warm air. This is the beginning of the "OCCLUSION" process, and is when the storm is at its maximum intensity and lowest pressure.

The occluded front, which is the cold front overtaking the warm front, continues developing, which gradually ends the lifting required for precipitation, and also slowly terminates the cyclonic (counter-clockwise in the Northern Hemisphere) circulation about the center of the low pressure. The storm is dying. The air is mixing.

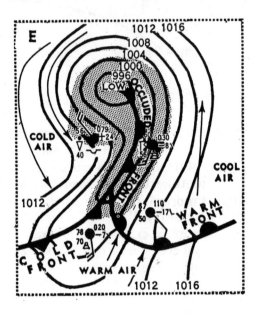

The storm ends, and we wait for another wave on the front to intensify into a low pressure system.

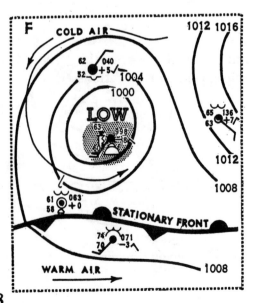

3. WHAT CAUSES WEATHER?: MOISTURE DISTRIBUTION AND VERTICAL AIR MOTIONS

All of those weather maps that are related to weather forecasting must ultimately lead us to conclude whether we will have fair or stormy weather, or a little of both, for the time period under consideration.

To have clouds and subsequent precipitation, we must have ample moisture in the lower atmosphere, and that moisture-laden air must be raised so that the air CONDENSES or "squeezes out" the moisture as precipitation.

When the air is saturated, it is holding as much moisture (water vapor) as it possibly can at that temperature and pressure. Thus, its dewpoint is the same as the air parcel's temperature. If the air parcel is forced to rise, it will cool. Since the temperature cannot be lower than the dewpoint temperature, the water vapor becomes liquid (rain or drizzle) or solid (snow, etc.). This process also releases some heat, known as the latent heat of condensation.

Typically, for a major rain or snow storm, we would want the average relative humidity in the storm area to be 90% or greater from the surface up to about 18,000 feet (the approximate average of the 500 millibar level, which we will study later). We also require a vertical velocity of air which is upward through that saturated layer, so that the condensation/precipitation process occurs. A typical upward velocity at about 10,000 feet up (around the 700 millibar level) is on the order of 3 to 10 centimeters per second, sometimes more. This vertical component of the wind is not even one-fifth of a mile per hour! However, this slight yet steady lift over hundreds and hundreds of miles out to the north and the east of a low pressure center is sufficient to cause precipitation if the air being lifted is saturated or nearly saturated. This motion is known as SYNOPTIC-SCALE vertical motion. It is not the same as CONVECTIVE-SCALE vertical motion which is what causes most of the convective weather (showers and thunderstorms). Typical upward vertical motion speeds, known as UPDRAFTS, in a thunderstorm can be over 50 miles per hour. Indeed, to sustain hail the size of grapefruits, the updrafts must be at least 125 mph!

Later in this book, we will explore the "1000-to-500 Millibar (mb) Average Relative Humidity Chart" and the "700 Millibar Vertical Velocity Chart" for synoptic-scale precipitation considerations.

4. SOME ESSENTIAL TERMS

BAROTROPIC: As a first approximation, a barotropic atmosphere is an area in which the isotherms are parallel to the contours. Thus, there is no temperature advection to try to cause vertical motion. (However, vertical motion may occur from other causes, such as differential positive vorticity advection. See the chapter on the Omega Equation.)

SOLID LINES ARE CONTOURS, DASHED LINES ARE ISOTHERMS.

A BAROTROPIC REGIME

More rigorously defined, a **BAROTROPIC REGION** of the atmosphere is one in which the density of the air depends upon only the pressure (i.e., density is a function of pressure), so that isobaric surfaces are surfaces of constant density. In a barotropic region, the isobaric surfaces are also isothermal.

BAROCLINIC: As a first approximation, a baroclinic atmosphere is an area in which the isotherms are out of phase with the contours. Thus, we have baroclinicity and likely vertical motion when isotherms cross the contours at any angle.

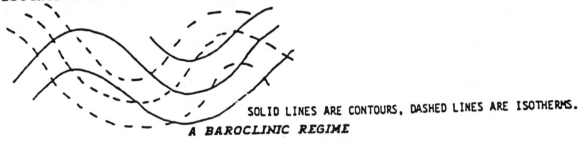

SOLID LINES ARE CONTOURS, DASHED LINES ARE ISOTHERMS.

A BAROCLINIC REGIME

More rigorously defined, a **BAROCLINIC REGION** of the atmosphere is one in which the density depends on the temperature and the pressure (i.e., density is a function of temperature and pressure); thus, the geostrophic wind generally changes with height because it is related to the horizontal temperature gradient by the thermal wind equation.

EQUIVALENT BAROTROPIC: Below is a diagram of a barotropic section of the atmosphere. However, if the entire pattern is translating in any direction, then the isotherms are also moving, which in effect is a thermal advection. Thus, a moving barotropic field is called equivalent barotropic because there is, in fact, thermal propagation; however, this is not temperature advection across the contours, so no significant vertical motions result as they do in a truly baroclinic regime.

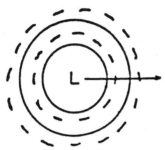

WHEN A BAROTROPIC
PATTERN IS MOVING,
IT IS TERMED :
EQUIVALENT
BAROTROPIC

SOLID LINES ARE CONTOURS, DASHED LINES ARE ISOTHERMS.

GEOSTROPHIC WIND: In a geostrophic assumption in non-curved flow, the effects of friction on the wind field are absent. The wind then is a balance between the pressure driven air from higher to lower pressure (the pressure-gradient force) and the deflecting force caused by the rotation of the earth (the Coriolis force). A geostrophic wind blows parallel to the isobaric contours on a constant pressure level. All this applies outside the tropics because the Coriolis force is too small in low latitudes.

AGEOSTROPHIC WIND: If the pressure gradient force is temporarily greater than or less than the Coriolis force, then the excess of one of these accelerations (forces per unit mass of air) over the other is an ageostrophic component of the wind. The forces are not in balance. (See the chapter on the jet-stream for examples.) The significance of this is that when an ageostrophic acceleration exists, the wind is blowing across the contours in that area and may result in vertical motions. This is because when cross-contour (ageostrophic) flow occurs, the air is being depleted from one area (divergence) and piling up (converging) in another. Diverging air is replaced by air from above and/or below, and converging air rises and/or sinks.

GRADIENT WIND: When the air flow is curved (curved contours), then centripetal force (toward the center of curvature) develops, and in response to it, centrifugal (center "fleeing") force occurs. In curved flow above the friction or earth's boundary layer (above the first approximately 50 millibars), curved contours imply a balance among three forces: pressure-gradient, Coriolis and centifugal.

Meteorologists have gotten into the habit of calling all upper-level flow geostrophic and ageostrophic, when much of the time the flow is actually gradient and agradient because the air flow has some curvature to it which introduces centrifugal accelerations.

CYCLOSTROPHIC WIND: When the pressure gradient is intense over a small curved flow, the Coriolis force is greatly overpowered and cannot increase to the great values of the pressure-gradient and centrifugal forces. Examples are in a tornado and near the center around the eye of an intense hurricane. Thus, cyclostrophic flow is essentially a balance between the pressure-gradient and centrifugal forces.

In these examples, the pressure-gradient force drives air toward the center of the tornado or intense hurricane (from higher to lower pressure), and the centrifugal force drives it out from the center; the balance between these forces is the resultant wind, called cyclostrophic, which flows essentially around the center of low pressure.

MOMENTUM: In Newtonian physics, simple momentum of an object is the product of its mass and its velocity. If we treat it as a scalar rather than a vector, then momentum is a product of mass and speed, mv. Thus, if we double the object's mass, m, or if we double its speed, v, we double its momentum. If the object is a parcel of air, it would have zero relative momentum if it were not moving, but the same parcel would have a value of absolute momentum if viewed from above the earth because the earth is rotating.

ANGULAR MOMENTUM: Because our planet can, as a first approximation, be considered a sphere, it is necessary to speak of angular momentum in relation to the latitude and the radius of the earth from the center of rotation to the point on or just above the earth's surface. The cosine of the latitude includes the equatorial radius and the radius from the equator to the latitude point in question. Because the earth rotates, its angular momentum, Ω, is considered.

Ω, the angular velocity of rotation of the earth, is:

$$\Omega = 7.292 \times 10^{-5} \text{ radians/second}$$

DEFINITION OF RADIAN AND THE EARTH'S ANGULAR VELOCITY:
The following is included for the nonscientist reading this text who may not be familiar with the terminology. A radian is a convenient unit of measure which is an arc of a circle equal in length to the radius of that circle. A radian is about 57.295 degrees of a circle. Thus, if the angular velocity (rate of rotation) of the earth is 7.292 x 10 to the minus 5 radians per second, substitute 57.295 degrees of the 360 degrees circle for radians and convert per second to per day and we get 360 degrees per day, or a complete rotation, for the earth. Thus, the angular velocity of the earth is the rate at which the earth rotates in order to make one complete (360 degrees) rotation in 24 hours.

As in simple momentum, angular momentum involves the wind. Because the earth is rotating from west to east, when we look "down" at the earth from above the North Pole, we consider the west-to-east component of the wind for angular momentum. If this component, the "u" wind, increases at the same latitude, then angular momentum increases. It follows from Newton's second law of motion that changes in angular momentum occur only because of torques. The atmospheric torques are those caused by east-west pressure gradients and by friction. (Torques are tangential forces having a moment about the axis of rotation.)

Momentum and angular momentum involve products of mass and speed. If we divide the angular momentum by the mass of the air parcel under consideration we obtain an expression for this momentum per unit mass.

The absolute angular momentum per unit mass of air is:

$$M = (\Omega\, a \cos\phi + u)\, a \cos\phi$$

When we multiply out we obtain:

$$M = \underset{A}{\Omega\, a^2 \cos^2\phi} + \underset{B}{u\, a \cos\phi}$$

(a is the radius from the earth's center to the point on the surface or above the surface in the lower atmosphere.)

Term A is the angular momentum due to the earth's rotation and is sometimes called the Omega-momentum; term B is the angular momentum due to the zonal motion of the air relative to the earth and is called the relative momentum. A and B are components of a property; by themselves they are not physical properties, just mathematical properties.

Term A, the omega-momentum, is the absolute angular momentum that would occur if the atmosphere were in solid rotation with the earth; term B, the relative angular momentum, is associated with the motion relative to the earth.

Understanding absolute angular momentum and its flux gives us insight into why air spins and rotates. Friction between the earth and its atmosphere appears to transfer horizontal momentum in the vertical direction.

Omega-momentum, term A, is altered by a torque, such as at the top of the atmosphere and at the bottom of the atmosphere, and relative angular momentum, term B, is altered by a torque if the Coriolis torque is included.

If we assume that the flux of angular momentum across the equator is negligible, then there is a meridional poleward flux of angular momentum, at least in the 1000-to-100 mb layer. Over a long time period, the total angular momentum for the entire atmosphere remains unchanged, or else the mean atmospheric circulation would be changing. Thus, angular momentum plays a role in the maintenance of the mean atmospheric circulation. Therefore, the upward flux of angular momentum in low latitudes must be balanced by a downward flux in higher latitudes. Most of the angular momentum must therefore be transfered poleward by atmospheric processes, the eddies (short-waves). Atmospheric eddies feed the larger-scale flow and the larger-scale flow feeds the eddies.

5. GENERAL CIRCULATION OF THE ATMOSPHERE

For the most part, the sun does not directly heat the lowest part of the atmosphere. The troposphere is essentially transparent to most of the incoming solar radiation. This radiation heats and ground, and the ground heats the air above it through infrared radiation (heat). The tropospheric heating occurs because water vapor and carbon dioxide have absorption bands for this returning long-wave radiation from the earth.

There is unequal heating of the earth's lower atmosphere (differential heating). On an annual average, there is a net excess of incoming radiation to outgoing terrestrial radiation in the lowest latitudes, and a net loss of radiation by the earth in polar regions.

Thus, temperature differences are established across the planet. Temperature differences result in pressure differences. Therefore, pressure gradients are established which drive the wind. Wind normally blows from high pressure to lower pressure, driven by the pressure gradient force, and is deflected to the right in the Northern Hemisphere and left in the Southern Hemisphere by the Coriolis Force caused by the earth rotating from west to east. In the lowest 50 millibars (roughly 1500 to 2000 feet), which is called the planetary boundary layer, friction prevents this deflection from being 90 degrees. Over ocean areas, the total deflection may exceed 70 degrees with relatively smooth seas, but over land the effect of friction in the planetary boundary layer is to reduce the deflection to typically between 50 and 70 degrees.

The vertical temperature regime of the atmosphere is available in any basic meteorology textbook. The temperature generally cools as we ascend through the troposphere to the tropopause, and generally warms through the stratosphere to the stratopause. Cooling again occurs through the mesosphere with warming in the thermosphere.

The stratospheric warming is caused by ultraviolet solar radiation causing some of the atmosphere's oxygen molecules to divide into oxygen atoms, and then these oxygen atoms combine with other oxygen molecules to form ozone:

$$O_2 \xrightarrow{\text{ULTRAVIOLET}} O + O$$

$$O_2 + O \longrightarrow O_3$$

Ozone has absorption wavelengths for incoming ultraviolet radiation and thus warms up. The greatest concentration of ozone in the stratosphere is at approximately 25 to 30 kilometers up.

As we rise higher in the atmosphere, the lighter gases in the atmosphere comprise a greater ratio to the heavier components. In the thermosphere, which is above about 80 km, monatomic oxygen is found. This also absorbs short-wave solar radiation and warms up, which is why the thermosphere warms.

The top of the earth's atmosphere is about 1000 km. **PAGE 44**

In 1735, HADLEY postulated that solar heating would lead to a general rising motion in lower latitudes, and that cooling in very high latitudes would result in a sinking motion there, with the circuit being completed by equatorward motion at low levels and poleward motion aloft. But he rejected the idea that motion toward the sun would lead to any average westward or eastward air movement. He then noted that in the absolute sense, the earth's surface moves most rapidly eastward at the lowest latitudes, and he maintained that if the air were initially moving equatorward with no relative eastward or westward motion, it would, in attempting to conserve its absolute velocity, arrive at lower latitudes moving westward relative to the earth.

He found, in fact, that air travelling considerable distances would acquire a much greater westward velocity than any ever observed, and assumed that the frictional drag of the earth's surface would, in the course of a few days, reduce the velocities to those actually found --thus, the trade winds.

He next noted that the required counter-drag of the air upon the earth would continually slow down the earth's rotation unless opposed by an opposite drag in other regions; this he assumed to occur in the belt of prevailing westerlies in middle latitudes. To account for the westerlies, he maintained that the air initially moving directly poleward at high levels would soon acquire an eastward relative velocity, and upon reaching higher latitudes and being cooled would sink and become the prevailing westerlies.

HADLEY'S BIG ERROR: In 1857, Thompson showed that in the absence of eastward or westward forces, air moving equatorward or poleward conserves its absolute angular momentum rather than its absolute velocity. This tendency to conserve angular momentum is now recognized to be the east-west component of the deflective force. (Note: the definition of angular momentum is given later in this chapter.)

HADLEY'S CONTRIBUTION: Because there is continuity of mass (the air is not created or destroyed), the general equatorward motion at one level requires general poleward motion at some other level; because of conservation of total angular momentum, the general westward motion dragging upon the earth's surface at one latitude requires a general eastward motion at some other latitude.

Hadley's major contribution is the development of the concept of a global circulation, no one of whose major branches can be explained independently of the other branches. Also, he recognized that the prime forcing mechanism of the atmospheric circulation is the pole-to-equator density gradient caused by differential solar heating.

GENERAL CIRCULATION MODELS

HADLEY (1735)

DOVE (1837)

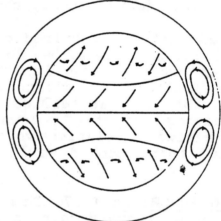

FERREL (1856)

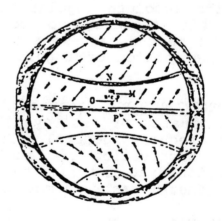

In 1837, DOVE (pronounced "Dove-ay") accepted Hadley's ideas for low latitudes, but he postulated that the predominating southwesterly winds in the middle latitudes are a continuation of the southwesterlies above the trade winds because , he believed, their warmth and humidity demanded an equatorial origin. He argued that at higher latitudes, alternating currents transported various properties. Unlike other atmospheric scientists at that time, Dove did not treat the general circulation as being completely symmetrical with respect to the earth's axis.

DOVE'S CONTRIBUTION: Dove introduced the concept of eddies within the generalized flow. It was not until well into the 20th century before it was shown that in the mid-latitudes, eddies feed the westerlies aloft and the westerlies aloft also feed the eddies.

In 1856, FERREL postulated that there must be three general circulation cells in each hemisphere. He stated that these were demanded by virtue of the known observations.

FERREL'S ERROR: The way he drew his model, there should be easterlies aloft in mid-latitudes.

FERREL'S CONTRIBUTION:
  1. His 3-cell model shows an indirect cell in the mid-latitudes which is forced, at least in part, by the direct tropical and polar cells;

  2. Ferrel gave a correct account of the north-south component of the Coriolis Force;

  3. He gave a quantitative description of the geostrophic wind and explained how it came about;

  4. Ferrel showed that it is possible for the pressure field to adjust itself to fit the wind field (a point overlooked by many contemporary meteorologists), besides the wind adjusting to the pressure field.

! !

Hadley explained the trade winds and prevailing mid-latitude westerlies by noting that heating should produce a direct meridional cell in each hemisphere. The equatorward current at low levels should be deflected by the earth's rotation to become the trade winds. The returning poleward current aloft should be deflected to become the upper-level westerlies,which upon sinking should become the surface westerlies.

However, Hadley's circulation, and any other zonally-symmetric circulations, are not observed, because they are unstable with respect to small-amplitude wavelike disturbances of the large scale.

The observed circulation must therefore possess eddies. The transport of angular momentum by these eddies largely determines the distribution of surface easterlies and westerlies.

A **DIRECT CELL** is a circulation cell in which warm air rises and cold air descends; examples are the tropical and polar Hadley Cells; an **INDIRECT CELL** is a circulation in which warm air sinks and cold air rises; an example is the mid-latitude Ferrel Cell.

| | | | | | | | | | | | | | | | | | | | | | | | | | | | | | | | | | | |

In 1855, **MAURY** postulated that instead of the single meridional cell in either hemisphere, or opposing currents side by side, there are two cells --a direct cell like Hadley's within the tropics, and an indirect cell in higher latitudes. The surface flow above the northeast trades is from the southwest, and the upper-level flow at higher latitudes is apparently supposed to be from the northeast. Maury could not offer an explanation for the indirect cell in higher latitudes.

In 1857, **THOMPSON** noted Hadley's error concerning the conservation of absolute velocity. (An example of relative vs. absolute is: if you are an observer on the earth watching the motion of a very small parcel of air, you are observing its relative motion; if, however, you are above the earth at a fixed point watching the motion of the same parcel, you are observing its absolute motion. The absolute motion is its actual relative motion plus the motion caused by the rotation of the earth in this sense.)

In 1888, **OBERBECK** represented the effects of friction by a simple coefficient of viscosity. He was the first person to represent the global circulation by solutions of the dynamic equations, rather than using the equations simply to deduce general properties.

EXCEPT FOR DOVE, THE GENERAL CIRCULATION WAS TREATED AS BEING COMPLETELY SYMMETRIC WITH RESPECT TO THE EARTH'S AXIS, BY THESE RESEARCHERS THROUGH 1888.

Also in 1888, **HELMHOLTZ** introduced the concept of turbulent viscosity. The principal deterrent to stronger winds aloft than what is actually observed is not surface friction but is the mixing of layers of different velocities by means of vortices forming on surfaces of discontinuity.

In 1926, **JEFFREYS** stated that in the long-run, angular momentum need not be conserved, because its net transport is proportional to the net mass (air) transport.

The net angular momentum transport is proportional to the product of the eastward and northward wind components.

Jeffreys was the first to state the need for a horizontal angular momentum transport and also for correctly identifying the mechanism through which it is accomplished. The angular momentum transport across middle latitudes is accomplished mainly by the eddies.

Through the 1930's and '40's, ROSSBY promoted the concept of 3 atmospheric general circulation cells in each hemisphere. In 1939 he showed that the large scale horizontal mixing, i.e., wave motion, could explain the high altitude westerlies.

Later in the 20th century, some interesting work by KUO, ELIASSEN, LORENZ, D. JOHNSON and others show, mathematically, how the westerlies are produced and maintained against the effects of friction by employing the transport relations for mass and absolute angular momentum. (Interestingly, when viewed in the isentropic coordinate system, there is one direct cell.)

What is important is that in any coordinate system used (cartesian, isobaric, isentropic, spherical, natural, etc.), the frictional stresses in tropical latitudes in the region of surface easterlies transfer angular momentum from the earth to the atmosphere; the frictional stresses in the region of surface westerlies at higher latitudes transfer angular momentum back to the earth from the atmosphere. There must therefore be a transport of angular momentum from the source at low latitudes to the sink in mid-latitudes.

DISH-PAN EXPERIMENTS:
An interesting approach to demonstrating qualitatively the large-scale general circulation is through dish-pan experiments. These were very popular in universities in the 1940s before computer modelling was developed.

Take a large dish-pan --about a foot or a little more in diameter-- which is about a few inches deep, and place it on a turntable or Lazy Susan which can be rotated. Fill it with about two inches of water. The dish-pan represents the Northern Hemisphere as we look down on it, and the water medium represents our atmosphere. Now cool the center of the dish-pan from below with ice or, much better, "dry ice" (solid carbon dioxide). Heat from below the pan around the rim to about a third of the way in towards the center. The cooling in the middle represents the North Pole and polar region, with its net radiative loss to space, and the warming along the edge represents the tropics with its net radiative warming from the sun.

Now rotate the dishpan in a counterclockwise sense, simulating the rotation of the earth. Recall that we are looking down on the Northern Hemisphere from above the atmosphere.

Inject blue die into the polar region wherein the water is being cooled, and inject red dye into the tropics wherein the water is being warmed.

What you should observe is the development of long waves and short waves in the fluid motion, showing advection of warm water poleward and cold water equatorward, and subsequent wrap-around occlusions.

Although the earth's rotation rate (the vorticity rate of the earth) is considered constant, you can vary the rate of rotation to observe the effects on the general circulation.

These simple experiments are excellent introductions for new students of meteorology for a first-approximation conceptualization of elements of dynamics that force and maintain the large-scale general atmospheric circulation.

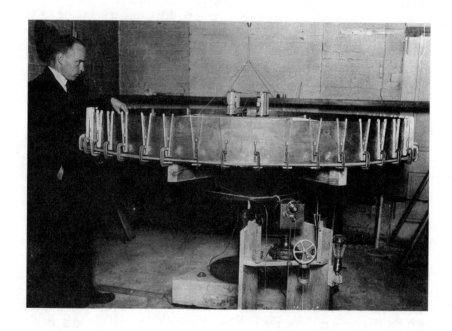

An old photograph discovered in the files of the National Weather Service, then known as the United States Weather Bureau, shows one of these dish pans. The writing on the back of the photo reads, "Dr. C. G. Rossby and the rotating tank constructed for him by the U. S. Weather Bureau in 1926-27 for use in making model experiments of atmospheric movements by means of liquids of different densities...".

6. POLAR FRONT THEORY

Consider the Northern Hemisphere. There is a southern limit to the polar Hadley cell, and northern and southern limits of the indirect Ferrel cell, and a northern limit of the tropical Hadley cell. In the summer, the low-level boundary between the polar Hadley cell and the Ferrel cell becomes rather diffuse at times, but a mesoanalysis reveals it is still there. (A dewpoint and wind direction analysis may at times be the only way to draw a surface frontal boundary.) Thus, according to the polar front theory, there is a continuous low-level front across the hemisphere, especially between the polar Hadley and the Ferrel cells.

Waves along the front form a family of cyclones across the hemisphere. The stronger low pressure systems, when occluding, deform the front from an east-west orientation to a more north-south one in that vicinity. Thus, the polar front fluctuates latitudinally because of the seasons and the waves along it.

The polar front model provides a straightforward four-dimensional visualization of the lower atmosphere on a synoptic scale, because it ties together the Hadley and Ferrel cells, the jet-streams associated with the cells' overlapping tropopauses and the extra-tropical low pressure systems.

When temperature contrasts are greater between the pole and the tropics, i.e., in winter, the polar front is stronger and the cyclones along it are stronger. Increasing the horizontal temperature gradient increases the baroclinicity of the atmosphere.

By extension of the polar front theory, it can be argued that a much more diffuse boundary should exist between the Ferrel cell and the tropical Hadley cell.

Drawback of the Polar Front Theory: It can be argued that there cannot be at all times a continuous frontal boundary because significant meridional air-mass exchange and air-mass conversions would be restrained. Polar Front supporters may counter that breaks need to occur at times along the polar front to allow for this exchange.

. . . .

In the winter and early spring, the polar front and its associated jet-stream jet-streaks, which are essentially thermally-driven, and the subtropical jet-stream jet-streaks, which are largely driven by angular momentum balance considerations, can approach each other and even overlap on infrequent occasions.

This is a significant event when the upper divergence part of the subtropical jet overlaps the upper divergent part of the polar jet, because each of these regions is a zone of upward motion and part of a circulation. Thus, synoptic-scale lift is enhanced, which leads to major, rapid cyclogenesis and/or setting the environment for severe convection, especially in the early Spring.

If both polar and sub-tropical jet-streaks are fairly straight, then the left-front and right-rear quadrants of each jet-streak would be the regions of upper divergence associated with rising air through the troposphere in those regions (see chapter 19). Thus, parts of both jet-induced circulations would be superimposed.

7. THE RADAR SUMMARY CHART

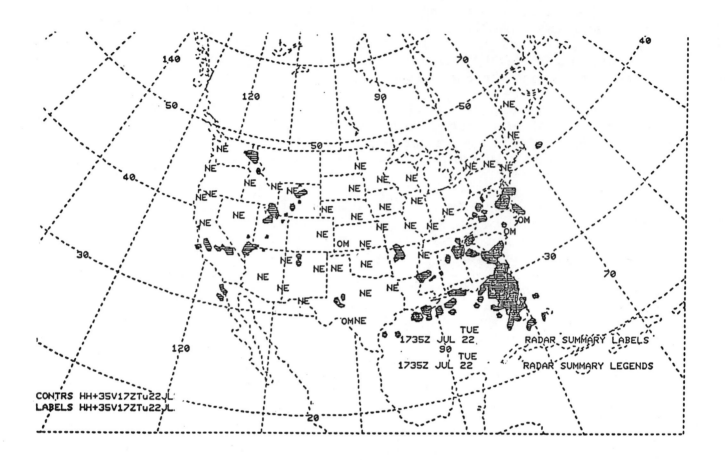

Figure 26. An Example of a Radar Summary Chart.

The radar summary chart is typically available every hour, and summarizes where the weather radars are detecting any precipitation. Some versions of this chart colorize the intensity levels of the precipitation. Typically, the lighter precip. is colorized green, with moderate to heavy precip. in yellow to orange, and the heaviest to extreme in red.

The movements of the precip. areas are also given, as well as the heights of the tops of the precip. Starting on the next page, a breakdown of radar chart information is given.

This type of radar presentation is called RADAR REFLECTIVITY, because it shows the precipitation detected by beams of radar energy reflecting to each local radar after hitting a precipitation target.

(continued)

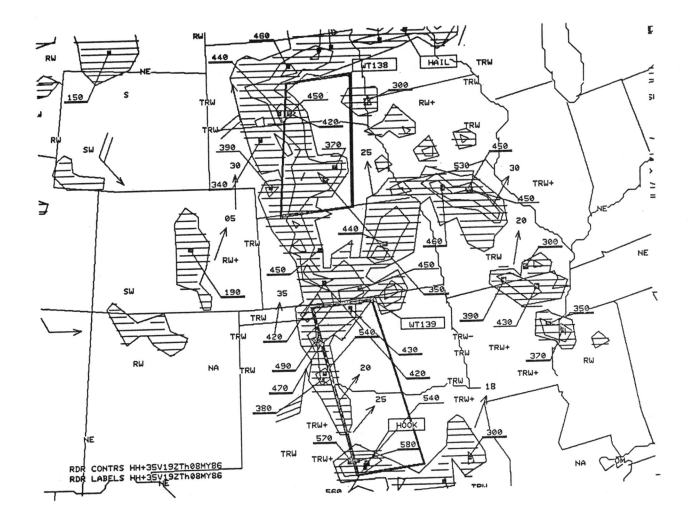

Figure 27. A Zoomed-in Portion of a Radar Summary Chart.

If the precipitation areas are not color-enhanced as described on the previous page, then they are usually contoured as in the example above. Consider the rain area detected over northern and central Missouri. The first contour represents light to moderate rainfall, with the next inner contour being heavy to very heavy, and the third or innermost contour being extreme (at least one to two inches per hour) rainfall rates.

The precipitation type is labeled, and T for thunderstorms is also given. Intensity TRENDS are given, not the intensities. A plus, such as RW+, means the cell, line or area is new or has increased in intensity; a minus means a decrease in intensity; no suffix means no change in intensity. These trends are for the past hour except that cells have fifteen minute intensity trends. Thus, to the right of the northern Missouri area we see a label "TRW+", which means that area is an area of thunderstorms which are producing rain showers which have increased in intensity; the actual intensity is indicated by the intensity contours.

(continued)

PAGE 53

The labels beside a precipitation area will be from this list:

```
  T = thunderstorm
  R = rain
  L = drizzle
  S = snow
 IP = sleet (ice pellets)
 RW = rain shower
 SW = snow shower
IPW = sleet shower
 ZR = freezing rain
ZRW = freezing rain shower
 ZL = freezing drizzle
  A = hail
```

Thus, it is possible to have combinations such as TIPW and TRWA, for example.

The cell movements are labeled with an arrow for direction, with speed printed just before the arrow's point. Movements of areas and lines are given with a flag, with a long stem for each 10 knots of movement and a half-stem for each 5 knots; a filled-in triangle on the flag would depict 50 knots. (One knot = 1.15 mph.)

The radars across the country also scan up and down into the precipitation areas, so that we can detect how high up into the clouds precipitation is occurring. This value is underlined and given in hundreds of feet above mean sea-level, with the last two digits left off. For example, the northern Missouri area has precipitation tops underlined with lines indicating where these highest tops are occurring. Notice some 450 values. This means that those areas are observing precipitation tops up to 45,000 feet high. In mid-latitudes during the warmer half of the year, showers become thunderstorms when the precip. tops exceed about 25,000 feet high. Tops in excess of 45,000 are typically associated with very heavy rainfall. Tops above 50,000 to 60,000 feet would typically also occur for severe, including tornadic, thunderstorms, although severe thunderstorms and tornadoes do occur with even lower tops when the updrafts inside a thunderstorm are intense. The criteria for a severe thunderstorm are wind gusts of 50 knots (58 mph) or greater and/or hailstone diameter of 3/4 inch or greater.

Sometimes, precipitation forms and falls into rather dry air, causing it to evaporate before reaching the ground. This phenomenon is called VIRGA. Eventually, the lower levels will become moistened by the water vapor and the rainfall or snowfall will reach the ground as precipitation. If precipitation bases are detected aloft by radar, they are overlined instead of underlined, and are given in hundreds of feet above the ground level.

If a severe thunderstorm watch or a tornado watch is in effect for an area, that area is boxed in as in our example, and labeled. WS means a severe thunderstorm watch is in effect, and WT is for a tornado watch. (continued)

PAGE 54

Note the tornado watches over parts of South Dakota and Nebraska, and over parts of Oklahoma and Texas. The number next to the WT may be given for the sequential box number for the calendar year.

Five mandatory remarks are also plotted, with a line extending from the remark to its reported location. These remarks are:

HAIL

HOOK = hook echo (radar signature of possible tornado)

BWER = bounded weak echo region

LEWP = line echo wave pattern

PCLL = persistent cell

A hook echo indicates a possible tornado. A bounded weak echo region is a dry area surrounded in the vertical and around by precipitation. This could be the beginning of a tornado. A line echo wave pattern is a wavy line of thunderstorms. Where two sections of this line merge, severe weather is probable. A persistent cell remark is used for very strong to severe thunderstorm cells that have been persisting for a long time (e.g., for several hours).

If no precipitation echoes are detected by radar, you may see on some radar charts an "NE" plotted for "no echoes", or "PPINE" for "plan position indicator no echoes". "OM" means "out for maintenance". "ROBEPS" means "radar operating below performance standards" and "RHINO" means "range height indicator not operating", so that the radar is not properly scanning in the vertical to obtain features such as precipitation tops. "NA" means a particular radar site's report is "not available".

READING PLOTTED CANADIAN RADAR REPORTS

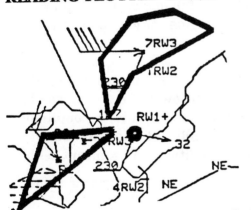

Figure 28. For Canadian radar reports, the alphanumeric code associated with each echo system shows, in this order, AREAL COVERAGE, PRECIPITATION TYPE, INTENSITY and INTENSITY TREND.

In the example to the left, we see a widely scattered area, less than one-tenth coverage, of very strong rain showers which are increasing in intensity: 1RW4+

The Canadian areal coverage code is:

BLANK = cells

1 = widely scattered area	(less than 1/10 coverage)	
4 = scattered area	(1/10 to 5/10 coverage)	
7 = broken area	(6/10 to 9/10 coverage)	
10 = solid area	(10/10 coverage)	

The Canadian intensity code is:

0 = very light

1 = light

2 = moderate

3 = heavy

4 = very heavy

8. THE WEATHER DEPICTION CHART

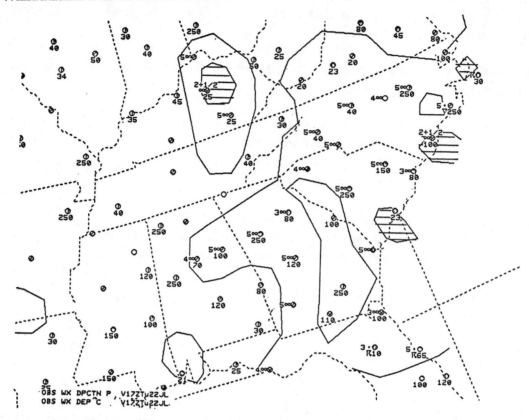

Figure 29. A Zoomed-in Portion of a Weather Depiction Chart.

Various forms of the weather depiction chart are available, showing essentially the same features. This chart is created primarily for weather briefings for pilots, so that they can see where the current inclement weather areas are, including regions of low ceilings and/or low surface visibilities.

Shaded areas depict IFR ("instrument flight rules") conditions. IFR means ceiling (for cloud bases) is below 1000 feet high and/or surface visibility is below 3 miles. Non-shaded regions within a contour depict MVFR ("marginal visibility flight rules") conditions. MVFR means ceiling from 1000 to 3000 feet and a surface visibility of 3 to 5 miles. Non-contoured areas are regions of VFR ("visibility flight rules") conditions. VFR means ceiling over 3000 feet and visibility over 5 miles.

Individual station circles are colored in, proportional to the amount of cloud cover. Ceilings, in hundreds of feet above ground level, are given in hundreds of feet above ground level. If the cloud amount is less than five-eighths sky coverage, that is, if the sky condition is not a ceiling, then the height of the first scattered deck is given. The standard weather symbols are given for the significant weather and are found to the left of the station circle. To the left of that is the surface visibility if five miles or less.

The chart is produced every hour.

9. THE SURFACE PRESSURE-CHANGE CHART

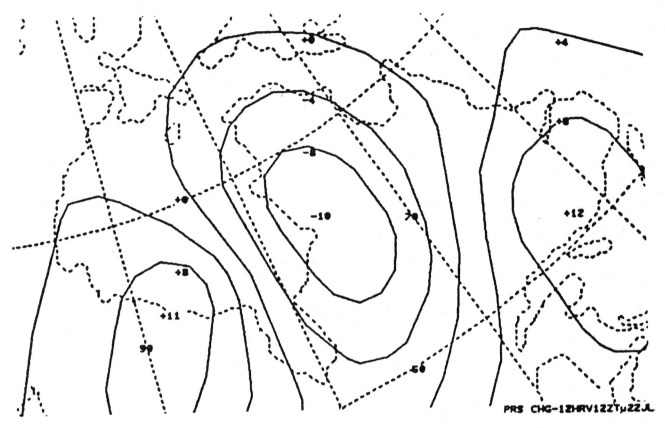

Figure 30. A Zoomed-in Portion of a 12-Hour Surface Pressure-Change Chart.

A pressure-change chart is useful because it shows where the greatest pressure falls and rises are occurring, and falls are associated with converging, rising air, with rises associated with sinking, diverging air. The greatest falls typically indicate toward where the low pressure center is moving. If the troposphere is moist, then pressure falls indicating rising air would cause cloudiness and subsequent precipitation.

Pressure falls are given in millibars of pressure over a time period. For forecasting, a one, two or three-hour pressure change chart is the most useful. Generally, rapidly developing storms and rapidly moving storms would have the greatest pressure falls ahead of their centers.

Lines or contours of equal atmospheric pressure change are called ISALLOBARS; therefore, the pressure-change chart is called an isallobaric analysis.

10. THE SURFACE "GEOSTROPHIC" WIND CHART

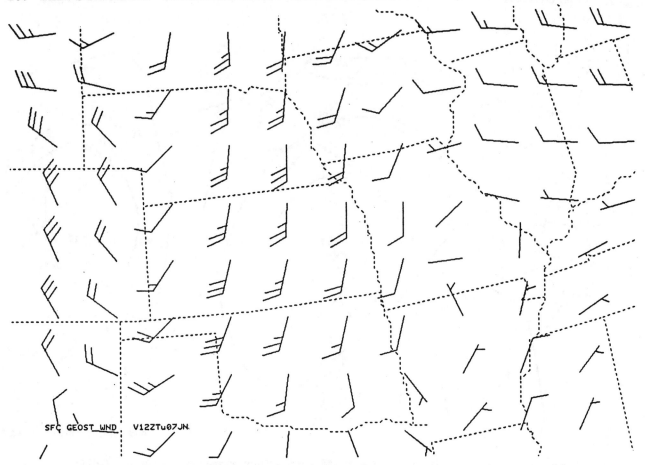

Figure 31. A Zoomed-in Portion of a Surface Geostrophic Wind Chart.

This chart shows what the wind would be if the frictional component of the wind were subtracted. It is useful in finding circulations around incipient low pressure systems and for finding wind-shift lines associated with boundaries such as fronts.

The plot uses standard notation with the wind barb pointing in the direction from which the wind is coming. Each half line on the barb represents 5 knots, and each full line 10 knots. A filled-in triangle represents 50 knots. Thus, a 65 knot sustained wind would have a triangle, line and half-line plotted on the wind barb. Calm or a wind of 1 or 2 knots has no lines on the straight wind barb.

One effect of friction is to slow down the surface wind somewhat and change its direction some. Thus, since this chart shows what the wind would be like if there were no friction, the wind speeds are some 20% higher than the actual wind, but are used to estimate the peak gusts that are likely. Thus, if a location shows a northerly wind at 30 knots, then the actual wind is probably around 25 knots with gusts to 30 knots. (One knot = 1.15 mph.)

(continued)

The cyclonic circulation (counterclockwise in the Northern Hemisphere) around a center of low pressure as the storm starts to develop, will show up on this chart sometimes before a closed isobar is analyzed on the surface weather map. The low often starts as a "kink" on a slow-moving or stationary part of a front.

A major use of this chart is in locating regions of WIND SPEED CONVERGENCE. A wind speed convergence zone is an area where strong winds are blowing into lighter winds.

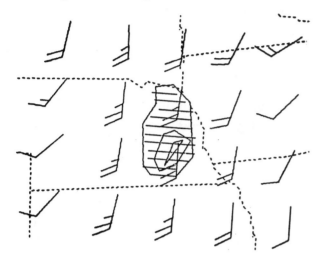

Figure 32. Radar echoes superimposed on a geostrophic wind chart, showing wind speed convergence and thunderstorms over eastern Nebraska.

Air parcels blow through the wind field which is set up by primarily the pressure field. To understand wind speed convergence and wind speed divergence, look at what must happen to the air parcels in the example to the left, as they move through the flow from southeastern Nebraska northward into eastern South Dakota.

In southeast Nebraska the wind is from the south at 30 knots. In northeast Nebraska the wind is from the south at 25 knots. And in southeast South Dakota the wind is from the south at 20 knots. Thus, as the air parcels move from south to north in the flow, they are moving at 30 knots in southeastern Nebraska and eventually slow down to 20 knots when they reach southeastern South Dakota. Thus, the air parcels are slowing down and piling up. This piling up is called CONVERGENCE of the air, and, since air cannot be created or destroyed (there is conservation of air), the air that is converging must go somewhere, and that is upwards. Thus, the important principle is: AIR BLOWING FROM STRONG WINDS INTO LIGHTER WINDS IS A REGION OF WIND SPEED CONVERGENCE AND, IF OCCURRING NEAR THE SURFACE, A REGION OF RISING AIR. Conversely, air near the surface blowing from light winds into stronger winds is a region of wind speed divergence and a zone of sinking air, since additional air parcels are supplied from aloft.

In our example (figure 32), the radar echoes showed thunderstorms forming in the zone of wind speed convergence, a region of rising air. The atmosphere there was also unstable and moist; therefore, thunderstorms, which require the LIFTING of moist, air in an unstable environment, developed.

(continued)

To understand wind speed convergence and divergence, consider cars approaching and leaving a toll booth. As cars approach the booth, they are travelling at say 65 to 70 mph, but they must slow down to pay the toll. Where they slow down, they converge. The analogy to air parcels is that when the air parcels near the surface slow down by moving from a region of relatively higher winds into a region of low wind speeds, they converge or "pile up" and rise.

As the cars leave the toll booth, they speed up and spread apart. When we are talking about air parcels near the surface moving from a region of light winds into a region of stronger wind speeds, they spread apart...diverge...and are replaced by air from above; thus the air sinks in a region of wind speed divergence.

The concepts of CONVERGENCE and DIVERGENCE are important in meteorology. When convergence or "piling up" of air occurs, some of it must go up and some of it down. If we are at the surface, then converging air has no place else to go but up. Diverging air, or air that is spreading out, is replaced by air from above or below. Thus, if we are at the surface, diverging air is replaced by air from above, and we find sinking air. Therefore, convergence and divergence are typically associated with VERTICAL MOTIONS in the troposphere. Since cloudiness and precipitation require upward vertical motion to cool the air to its dewpoint, making it saturated, forecasters are interested in interpreting weather data that can be used to detect low-level convergence.

Moreover, air that is converging in low levels cannot keep piling up and rising indefinitely in time and space. At some point...typically about 15,000 feet up...at about the 550 millibar level...the air stops converging and starts diverging outward. Similarly, divergence below about 550 millibars is accompanied by convergence above the divergence. This level where the convergence and divergence change is called the LEVEL OF NONDIVERGENCE. Thus, if we have convergence of air occurring in low levels of the troposphere, we will have divergence in the upper levels, and if we have divergence in the lower levels, we will have convergence aloft.

Although there are times when there is more than one level of nondivergence, the typical situation is as described in the previous paragraph.

11. VORTICITY: RELATIVE VORTICITY and ABSOLUTE VORTICITY

Vorticity is the spinning of a very minute air parcel about its own axis. The spinning refers to both the rate of rotation and the direction. If the mixture of gases we call the atmosphere is the fluid under consideration, then the vorticity of each minute air parcel is actually a three-dimensional spin. Vorticity in a fluid is caused by curvature of the flow and/or by shear. For synoptic-scale analysis and forecasting, we use the air parcels' horizontal vorticity about a vertical axis because it is related to vertical motion.

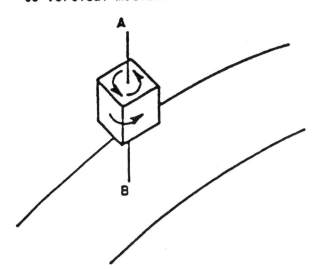

The sketch to the left shows an air parcel spinning about a vertical axis, AB. Thus, the parcel has vorticity. What we are observing is the horizontal vorticity about a vertical axis. An unspinning parcel has no relative vorticity.

Axis AB is perpendicular to the earth's surface.

When we speak of vorticity on a weather chart --say a 500 mb chart-- we are referring to a point on the chart, representing the vorticity of that parcel at that time. The 500 mb chart shows the absolute vorticity of the parcels. A discussion of relative motion vs. absolute motion is therefore appropriate.

Let us say you are observing a railroad train passing by. One of the cars is an open flatbed car which has a circus clown standing on it while the train is moving. The clown is about to throw a large ball straight up into the air. Neglecting air friction, will the ball land back into the clown's hands even though the train is moving? The answer is yes, as long as the train is not accelerating or decelerating while the ball is in the air. If the train is moving at 30 mph, then the clown and the ball are also moving at 30 mph. Thus, when the clown throws the ball in the air, it will come back into his hands. To the clown, the ball appeared to go just up and down. Thus, the relative motion of the ball (to the clown) is straight up and straight down. However, to you standing on the sidelines watching the train go by, the ball appears to go up as well as forward with the train, and then to descend as well as continuing forward with the train. You observe the absolute motion of the ball.

Thus, the absolute motion of the ball is the ball's relative motion to the clown plus the motion of the train. Another frame of reference allows you to determine absolute motion. Actually, this absolute motion is in itself relative because you can be observing the ball's motion from above the rotating earth and then you can add in the earth's motion to give you yet a higher order of absolute motion. Then you can observe the ball's motion from just outside the solar system, and so on.

Thus, for vorticity, the relative vorticity of an air parcel is its spin as observed from the earth; the absolute vorticity of the parcel is the parcel's relative vorticity plus the spinning (rotating) of the earth (the earth's vorticity).

$$\eta = \zeta + f$$

where η = the absolute vorticity of the air parcel

ζ = the relative vorticity of the air parcel

f = the earth's vorticity (the vorticity about the vertical, due to the earth's rotation)

. . . .

$$f = 2\Omega \sin \phi \qquad \text{where}$$

Ω = the angular velocity of rotation of the earth, and

ϕ = the latitude.

$\Omega = 7.292 \times 10^{-5}$ radians/second. A radian is about 57.3 degrees of a circle. For the earth to complete one rotation in 24 hours about its axis, Ω is the rate at which it must spin.

Contemporary 500 mb charts show absolute vorticity. Thus, because $\sin \phi$ is zero at the equator (because the sine of zero degrees latitude is zero) and increases with increasing latitude, the absolute vorticity, η, is higher at a higher latitude than a lower one if both locations have the same relative vorticity. The vorticity value is not as significant as the gradient of vorticity. Strong positive or negative vorticity advections are used to infer short wave motions. If the wind field has no divergence or convergence (that is, if we are at the level of nondivergence), then the waves move with the vorticity field. Since 500 mb is close to the level of nondivergence, this is why the vorticity field at 500 mb is used.

Another way to look at vorticity is mathematically in cartesian coordinates, where relative vorticity, ζ , is defined as:

$$\zeta = \frac{\partial v}{\partial x} - \frac{\partial u}{\partial y} + \frac{u \tan \phi}{a}$$

where a = the radius of the earth to that point over the earth, and
ϕ = the latitude.

The far right term is due to the convergence of the meridians (velocity convergence). ($\tan \phi/a$ is the horizontal curvature of the latitude circle and $(u \tan \phi)/a$ is the vorticity of uniform zonal flow. Thus, this term is a "correction" factor when using spherical coordinates.) This term is so small relative to the other terms that it can be neglected for practical usage.

Thus, $\zeta = \frac{\partial v}{\partial x} - \frac{\partial u}{\partial y}$

By simply dividing the wind into its u (west-to-east) and v (south-to-north) components and analyzing the spatial change of v in the x direction and the spatial change of u in the same absolute value of y direction, we obtain the relative vorticity of particles within that grid. It is easier to use a finite differencing approach:

Here is a simple local change in the west-to-east (u) component of the wind: What is the change at point 0 if we know u at points 1 and 2?:

$$\frac{\partial u}{\partial x} = \frac{U_1 - U_2}{2\Delta x}$$

If we want to solve for relative vorticity at point 0, then:

$\zeta = \frac{\partial v}{\partial x} - \frac{\partial u}{\partial y}$, so:

$\zeta = \frac{\partial v}{\partial x} - \frac{\partial u}{\partial y} =$
$\frac{V_1 - V_2}{2\Delta x} - \frac{(U_4 - U_3)}{2\Delta y}$

Another easy method, long favored by meteorology professors for meteorology lab exercises, is to use a coordinate system that you can move anywhere, to center it on the area of concern. This is the natural coordinate system.

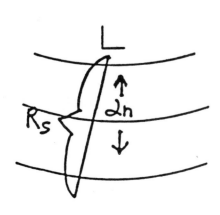

In this system, $\zeta = \frac{V}{R_s} - \frac{\partial V}{\partial n}$

where $\frac{V}{R_s}$ is the curvature contribution to relative vorticity and $\frac{\partial V}{\partial n}$ is the wind shear contribution to relative vorticity.

V is the wind speed, R_s is the horizontal radius of curvature of the streamline and d_n is the distance measured along the normal.

Thus, relative vorticity can be expressed as the sum of a contribution due to curvature of the contours and to the change of the wind speed along the normal (wind speed shear). To use this method, go along the normal from your starting to ending point from high to low heights or pressure.

(In today's weather forecasting environment, computer programs solve these problems, but it is important to know what we are doing physically and mathematically. It surprises many new students of meteorology, as it did this author when I first became enthralled with the science, how much mathematics and physics are a part of this science. But if you are as excited about weather as I, then the math and physics help to bring the science truly alive and enjoyable. So if you are weak in these areas, take the time and patience to understand them, for then you will be truly enriched in your understanding of this enjoyable science of meteorology.)

Does positive vorticity advection (PVA) at 500 mb mean that there is synoptic scale upward vertical motion occurring through that level? The answer is probably, but PVA at 500 mb does not by itself mean upward motion. As chapter 46 discusses, a contributor to upward motion is differential positive vorticity advection -- that is, PVA values that increase with height (or NVA values that decrease with height) so that air has to spin up.

. . . .

We can show mathematically that the rate of change of the absolute vorticity of a parcel is related to the rate of change of convergence or divergence:

$$\left(\frac{\Delta \eta}{\Delta t}\right)_{parcel} = (-)\ (\text{DIV TERM}) + (\text{TILTING TERM}) + (\text{BAROCLINIC TERM})$$

where   DIV TERM   = the rate of change of convergence or divergence relative to the level of nondivergence

TILTING TERM   = the amount of horizontal spin that is converted to vertical spin (lift)

BAROCLINIC TERM = the amount and type of temperature advection

Inferences from the above include:

Applying this equation at the level of nondivergence: if the absolute vorticity of the parcel is increasing with time, then minus divergence (i.e., convergence) occurs below the level of nondivergence and divergence occurs above. With converging air below and diverging air above, then upward motion is inferred through that column.

Conversely, decreasing absolute vorticity with time at the level of nondivergence implies downward motion through that column.

Thus, the divergence and vorticity fields are related; they are components of the wind.

Modern computer programs give us the divergence (convergence) fields at various levels in the atmosphere, and the weather forecaster needs to determine what is causing this divergence and convergence.

Keep in mind that a significant mesoscale system, such as a large, organized convective complex, will generate its own vorticity field, which then is superimposed on the synoptic scale vorticity field.

* * * * * * * * * *

If the relative wind is defined as the wind that an observer on earth records at his/her location, and the absolute wind is that same wind as observed from above the earth (which means that the movement (rotation) of the earth must be added to the wind), then relative vorticity is the vorticity of the relative wind, and absolute vorticity is the vorticity of the absolute wind.

* * * * * * * * * *

Something to think about: Have we been looking at vorticity analyses aloft wrongly for many decades?

At 500 mb we traditionally analyze for absolute vorticity, which is the actual (relative) vorticity of the parcel plus the rotation (vorticity) of the earth. Consider the equation for absolute vorticity. The earth's vorticity is much higher in high latitudes than in the low latitudes. Therefore, an absolute vorticity value of +20 units at Miami, Florida represents much more relative spin than a +20 would at Fairbanks, Alaska.

However, forecasters become familiar with representative units of vorticity for the local areas for which we forecast. Thus, a +20 in south Florida would excite a forecaster there more than a +20 would for a forecaster in interior Alaska.

Therefore, we may have been looking at vorticity wrongly for all these years, and should consider converting to relative vorticity on our upper-level charts.

The forum is open for honest discussion on this issue.

In conclusion, vorticity is the spin of a parcel about its own
axis, and in meteorology the vorticity of air parcels is important
because it is related to vertical motion.

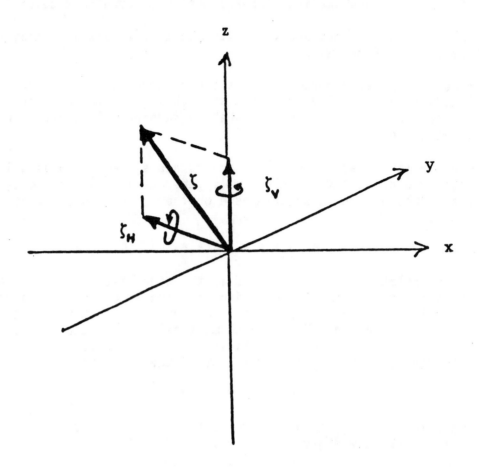

The diagram shows the 3-dimensional vorticity vector divided into
its horizontal (sub H) and vertical (sub V) components. We have
shown in fluid dynamics through the omega equation that we can
look at a component of vorticity, namely the vertical component,
to determine that increasing advection of vertical-component
positive vorticity with increasing height causes air to spin up.
Positive vorticity is defined as the air parcels rotating in a
counterclockwise sense when looking down at them. In the unusual
event of decreasing negative vorticity advection with increasing
height, air would spin up also, leading to the interesting
phenomenon of NVA aloft related to rising air.

Thus, the bottom line is: increasing PVA with height causes air
to spin up. The contributions to synoptic-scale vertical motions
in the troposphere by other dynamic factors and the mechanical
factors are added to the vorticity contribution to determine the
resultant vertical motions.

(Note: for notational purity, note that ζ throughout the text
is the conventional representation for the horizontal vorticity
about a vertical axis. In the diagram above, ζ_v is that ζ ,
and ζ in the diagram is the total 3-dimensional vorticity
vector.)

12. THE SURFACE "GEOSTROPHIC" VORTICITY CHART

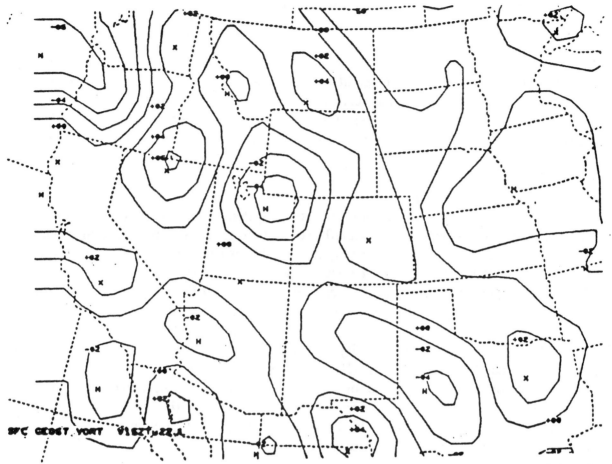

Figure 33. A Zoomed-in Portion of a Surface Geostrophic Vorticity Chart, showing values of relative positive vorticity and relative negative vorticity.

VORTICITY is a weather parameter usually analyzed at the surface and at the 500 millibar level. Vorticity is the rate of spin of a small parcel of air. Air parcels are forced to have some spin on them because of curvature of the wind flow, which causes turning of the air parcels blowing through the wind pattern, and because of changes of wind direction and speed in both the horizontal and the vertical. This latter cause of vorticity is called WIND SHEAR, which causes parcels to have spin.

Vorticity is a complicated meteorological parameter that arose from fluid dynamics. Mathematically, meteorologists take the three-dimensional spin of small air parcels and separate the spin into the rotation about a horizontal axis and the rotation about a vertical axis. The vorticity component about a vertical axis is what is depicted on vorticity charts, because it is related to synoptic-scale vertical motion. Looking down on the Northern Hemisphere, if the spin about a vertical axis is counterclockwise...left to right...this is called POSITIVE VORTICITY; if the component of spin or vorticity about a vertical axis is clockwise...right to left...this is called NEGATIVE VORTICITY.

(continued)

When values of positive vorticity are moving into an area, we say that POSITIVE VORTICITY ADVECTION, frequently referred to by its initials, PVA, is occurring, and when negative vorticity is moving into an area, we say that NEGATIVE VORTICITY ADVECTION or NVA is occurring there.

From a derived equation in meteorological dynamics called the omega equation, which gives the dynamic causes of synoptic-scale vertical motion, comes the statement that increasing positive vorticity advection with increasing height causes air to spin up. Thus, PVA is usually related to upward vertical motion. Since clouds and subsequent precipitation require moisture and upward motion, the analyses of vorticity charts are useful in weather forecasting.

PVA is typically associated with low pressure systems and their counterclockwise circulations, and NVA is typically associated with high pressure systems and their clockwise circulations. Thus, when we see on this map an area of positive vorticity, we can infer a low pressure system or "SHORT-WAVE TROUGH" (which is discussed in the section on upper-air ["upper-level"] charts). Areas of PVA can also be TRIGGERS that initiate convection, which does not necessarily require any organized low pressure system.

Values on the surface geostrophic vorticity charts are actually multiplied by 10 to the minus 5 power per second. GEOSTROPHIC means the frictional acceleration (frictional component) of the wind is factored out. Thus, this chart complements the surface geostrophic wind chart. The chart therefore shows what the relative vorticity would be if the surface wind had no friction. The friction is left out so that it is easier to see the vorticity field without frictional "contamination".

Note that this chart shows the RELATIVE vorticity. Compare this with the 500 millibar (500 mb) chart which shows the ABSOLUTE vorticity at 500 mb. The difference between relative and absolute is that the relative parameter follows the motion of the parcel, whereas the absolute parameter adds the affect of the earth rotating. Thus, absolute vorticity is relative vorticity plus the vorticity (rotation) of the earth. This is discussed later for the 500 mb chart description. In the earlier days of weather charts, especially in the 1940s, it became fashionable to look at 500 mb absolute vorticity, although it can be shown that relative vorticity works at least as well as absolute vorticity.

The difference between relative and absolute can be illustrated by this example. Consider an open flat-bed railroad car moving down the track at a steady speed. A clown is standing on the car and has a ball in his hands. You are observing the train a short distance from it. The clown throws the ball into the air as the train is moving. Will the ball land back in the clown's hands (neglecting air friction)? Yes, because the clown and ball are moving at the same speed. To the clown, the ball will appear to go up and then down; he is observing the RELATIVE motion of the ball; to you the ball will go up and down as well as forward with the train; you are observing the ABSOLUTE motion of the ball, because you are observing both the ball's and train's motions from another frame of reference.

13. THE LIGHTNING DETECTION SUMMARY CHART

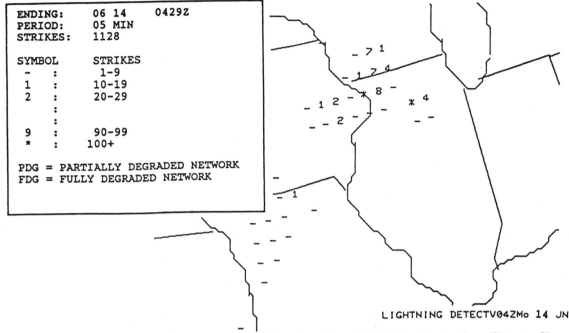

Figure 34. An Example of a Zoomed-in Portion of a Lightning Detection Chart, Showing the Number of Cloud-to-Ground Strikes Within a Five-Minute Period.

This chart may appear in various forms, and show lightning strikes for 5 minutes, 15 minutes or other time periods. Cloud-to-ground (CG) strikes detected by the lightning detection sensors are given. Other lightning, such as intracloud, cloud-to-cloud and cloud-to-air are not plotted.

In the above example, the grid spacing is 0.50 degrees of latitude and of longitude, so for middle latitudes the grid box is approximately 30 nautical miles by 30 nautical miles. Thus, for example, the 8 over northwest Illinois represents 80 CG strikes in the 5-minute period ending at 0429Z.

Over 95% of CGs are negatively-charged electrical bolts. The fewer than 5% positive charges are significantly more powerful and last longer than the negative lightning strikes. There is also a correlation between lightning frequency and heaviest rainfall: the heaviest rains tend to occur where the greatest frequencies of lightning are occurring.

Typically, during the convective season in mid-latitudes, as a rule-of-thumb in nonmountainous areas, showers become thunderstorms when their precipitation tops approach 25,000 feet above ground level. For winterlike thundersnow, slantwise convection, as in "lake-effect" thundersnow, will generally have radar precip. tops below 15,000 feet, even below 12,000 feet. (Typical nonthunderous lake-effect snow often has precip. tops below 6000 feet.) With this type of thunderstorm, the convection is occurring on an angle, which can be as low as about 30 degrees, so that the precipitation tops on radar may be, e.g., 12,000 feet high, but the actual stretch of convective cloud may be over 25,000 feet but at a slant rather than quasi-vertical.

14. WHAT ARE UPPER-LEVEL CHARTS?

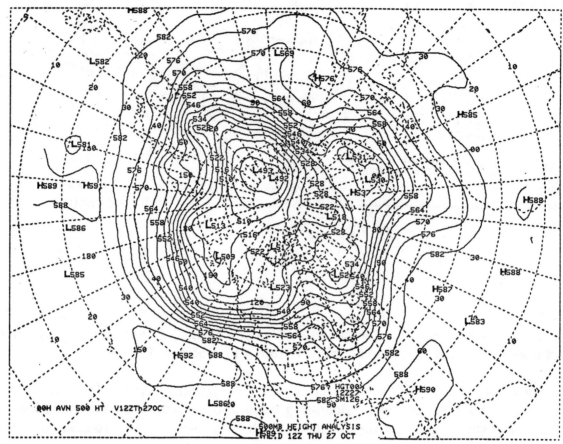

Figure 35. An Example of an Upper-Level Chart. This is a 500 millibar (500 mb) hemispheric chart showing the lines (contours) of equal heights of the 500 mb pressure level.

Weather is four dimensional: the two horizontal and the vertical realms, and the realm of time. Therefore, as soon as we generate a weather map of features at one level, or a cross-section of features in the vertical, that "snapshot" becomes old an instant later because the conditions are typically in a state of flux --always changing. Moreover, to understand what the atmosphere is doing, we do indeed need to look at weather at not only the surface where we live, but aloft, especially in the troposphere and stratosphere, because the surface weather is a part of what is happening aloft: the surface and upper levels are spatially and temporally connected.

As we rise away from the surface, we observe that the flow of air becomes more wave-like. This is a natural feature of the earth's atmosphere on a rotating Earth. As proof, we can devise a DISH-PAN EXPERIMENT to simulate the flow patterns of the mid and upper troposphere:

(continued)

PAGE 70

DISH-PAN EXPERIMENTS TO SIMULATE AIR FLOW PATTERNS IN THE UPPER TROPOSPHERE:

Take a large dish-pan --about a foot or a little more in diameter-- which is about a few inches deep, and place it on a turntable or Lazy Susan which can be rotated from left to right the way the earth rotates when looking down at it from over the North Pole. Fill the pan with about two inches of water. Thus, the dish-pan represents the Northern Hemisphere as we look down on it, and the water medium respresents our atmosphere. Now cool the center of the dish-pan from below with ice or, much better, "dry ice" (solid carbon dioxide). Heat from below the pan around the rim to about a third of the way in towards the center. This can be done with candles or bunsen burners. The cooling in the middle of the pan represents the North Pole and polar region, with its net radiative loss to space, and warming along the edge represents the tropics with its net radiative warming from the sun.

Now rotate the dish-pan in a counterclockwise sense, simulating the rotation of the earth.

Inject blue dye into the polar region wherein the water is being cooled, and inject red dye into the tropics wherein the water is being warmed.

What you should observe is the development of LONG WAVES and SHORT WAVES in the fluid motion, showing advection of warm water poleward and cold water equatorward, and susequent wrap-around occlusions.

Although the earth's rotation rate (the vorticity rate of the earth) is considered constant, you can vary the rate of rotation to observe the effects on the general circulation.

These simple experiments are excellent introductions for a first approximation conceptualization of elements of dynamics that force and maintain the large-scale general atmospheric circulation.

THE MILLIBAR STANDARD (a millibar is also known as a hectoPascal):

In the early days of weather maps, charts were developed for different height levels, based on data send back by weather kites, weather balloons, weather rockets and from aircraft weather reports. Charts were constructed to show the air flow at 5,000 and at 10,000 feet above the ground, and for other levels.

It was later realized that air flows not along height lines, but along what are called isentropic surfaces, but that isobaric surfaces can also be used as a good first approximation. Thus, surface charts are accompanied by 850 millibar charts, 700 millibar charts, 500 millibar charts, and others. Each of these charts has unique uses employing the atmospheric variables such as temperature, moisture, density, the wind and derived wind fields such as its divergence and vorticity to forecast the weather at the surface.

(continued)   **PAGE 71**

PRESSURE	HEIGHT
beyond 600 to 1000 miles is outer space	
0 mb	600 to 1000 miles
0.0000000001 mb $(1 \times 10^{-10}$ mb)	445 miles
0.01 mb	53 miles
0.1 mb	45 miles
1 mb	30 miles
10 mb	100,000 feet (19 miles)
50 mb	67,000 feet (13 miles)
100 mb	53,000 feet
200 mb	39,000 feet
300 mb	29,000 feet
500 mb	18,000 feet
700 mb	10,000 feet
850 mb	5,000 feet
1000 mb	near sea-level

Figure 36. Millibar Levels with an Average Height for Them. The height of a pressure level over a particular point at a certain time varies as the high and low pressure (high and low heights) systems pass over that point, but we can give long-time <u>average</u> height values, which are shown in the figure.

This millibar sketch is not drawn to scale, because a 100 millibar difference in low levels is much smaller than a 100 mb difference in high levels. For example, the vertical distance between 1000 and 900 mb is about 4,000 feet, but the distance between 300 and 200 mb is about 10,000 feet.

The average sea-level atmospheric pressure is 1013.25 mb (29.925" on the barometer). If we take, for round figures, 1000 mb (or about 30" on the barometer) as being the average sea-level pressure, then at 900 mb we have 90% of the weight of the atmosphere at that point still above us. The barometer at that 900 mb level would read about 90% of 30" or 27". At the 700 mb level, we have 30% of the atmosphere at that point below us and 70% above us, and the barometer would read 700 millibars or 21".

LONG WAVES AND SHORT WAVES ON UPPER-LEVEL WEATHER MAPS:

As described on page 47, the air flows through wave patterns as seen on the upper-air charts. Around the Northern Hemisphere, we see from 3 to 7 long waves, with the wave number changing over days or weeks, and through the long waves move the faster short waves.

Long waves have wavelengths of from 50 to 120 degrees longitude and are BAROTROPIC (no temperature advections: the isotherms are parallel to the height contours). The short waves have wavelengths of from 1 degree or less to 40 degrees longitude, and are BAROCLINIC (they have the thermal advections with warm air advection usually to the east of the trough axis and cold air advection to the west: isotherms cross the height contours at some angle).

Thus, the short waves are the significant "weather-makers". The short wave troughs are associated with the surface low pressure systems. Look for the evolution of strong short wave troughs (15 to 40 degrees longitude) since they are associated with organized cyclones.

The waves in the 40 to 50 degree range are transitory (a "gray" area).

PAGE 72

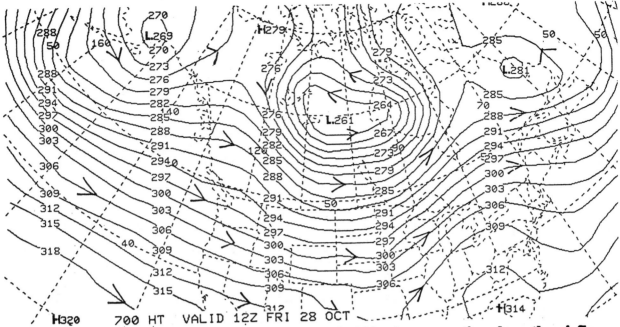

Figure 37. Arrows placed on the contours of this 700 mb map section show the airflow.

STATION PLOTS:

				250 &
850 mb:	700 mb:	500 mb:	300 mb:	200 mb:
+07 545	+00 045	-32 533	-44 934	-58 220
40●+01	5●-01	160-02	O+00	O+02
72340	72775	71722	72353	72201

Figure 38. When the actual data from weather balloons or other sources are plotted on the upper-level charts, they are plotted according to the station models above.

The station circle is shaded-in when the temperature-dewpoint spread is five Celsius degrees or less, which indicates a moist environment. The temperature in degrees C. is at the upper left with the temperature-dewpoint depression (difference) below it. Below the station circle is the station identification number (e.g., 72456 is Topeka, KS). The 12-hour height change in decameters is to the right of the station circle. The wind barb points in the direction from which the wind is coming, with the standard short line for five knots, long line for every 10 knots and flag for every fifty knots. On the station plot, the pressure-level heights, in meters, in the upper right, are given as follows:

> for 850 mb, the first digit is a 1 and is omitted;
> for 700 mb, the first digit is a 3 or 2 and is omitted;
> for 500 mb, the last digit is a 0 and is omitted;
> for 300 mb, the last digit is a 0 and is omitted;
> for 250 and 200 mb, the first digit is a 1 or 0 and the last digit
> is a 0 and both digits are omitted.

Example: our 700 mb example above shows: west wind at twenty knots, temperature of 0 degrees C., temperature-dewpoint depression of 5 (meaning dewpoint is minus 5°C), the height of the 700 mb pressure level at that station is 3045 meters, the height change is a drop of 10 meters in the past 12 hours, and the station identification # is 72775 which is Great Falls, Montana.

PAGE 73

15. ADVECTION

The term "advection" comes from the Latin, meaning "to convey". The wind advects (moves) an entity into an area. When the wind is moving warmer air into an area, for example, we call this warm air advection. It is interesting that we speak of vorticity advection, for PVA and NVA, by the wind, because vorticity can also be considered to be a part of the wind field itself.

Advection by the wind is three-dimensional; however, when using constant pressure charts, we operationally consider the horizontal advection of parameter J:

$$\frac{dJ}{dt} = \frac{\partial J}{\partial t} + V \cdot \nabla_H J = \frac{\partial J}{\partial t} + u \frac{\partial J}{\partial x} + v \frac{\partial J}{\partial y}$$

J can be temperature or thickness, pressure, stability (instability), mixing ratio and other relevant entities.

Any student of Basic Meteorology learns early that on upper-air charts, when the isolines of the parameter are parallel to the contours, there is zero advection of that parameter, assuming geostrophic or gradient flow. When the contours are at any angle to the parameter's isolines, horizontal advection of that parameter by the wind is occurring.

As a simple example of horizontal advection, consider the temperature change at an observation point, P:

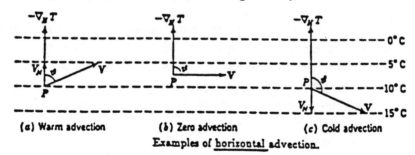

(a) Warm advection (b) Zero advection (c) Cold advection

Examples of horizontal advection.

(V sub N is the component of the wind vector normal to the isotherms in the direction of minus del sub H of T.)

$$\frac{dT}{dt} = \frac{\partial T}{\partial t} + V \cdot \nabla_H T = \frac{\partial T}{\partial t} + \left(u \frac{\partial T}{\partial x} + v \frac{\partial T}{\partial y} \right)$$

Thus, the change in temperature is caused by the local causes of heating and cooling with time, $\partial T/\partial t$, and the horizontal advection of warmer or colder air, $\left(u \frac{\partial T}{\partial x} + v \frac{\partial T}{\partial y} \right)$

If the total derivative of a field variable is zero, then the variable is a conservative quantity following the motion, which implies that any local change is due exclusively to advection of that variable. Variables that are conserved or nearly so, following the motion, allow for following them by their advection.

The concept of advection is also applicable, though it may be less accurate, for curved trajectories.

MOVEMENT OF AIR PARCELS:
Consider an air parcel moving horizontally. The pressure pattern will typically vary along the parcel's trajectory, even if the pressure field is steady, because contours are usually not straight or uniformly curved and are not parallel over large distances.

Therefore, an air parcel that at one instant is in geostrophic or gradient balance may soon be in a different pressure field. To readjust itself, the parcel is subjected to acceleration forces (e.g, a pressure gradient force that is temporarily stronger or weaker than the Coriolis force) and develops an ageostrophic component to its motion.

16. THE 850 MILLIBAR (mb) OR HECTOPASCAL (hPa) LEVEL CHART

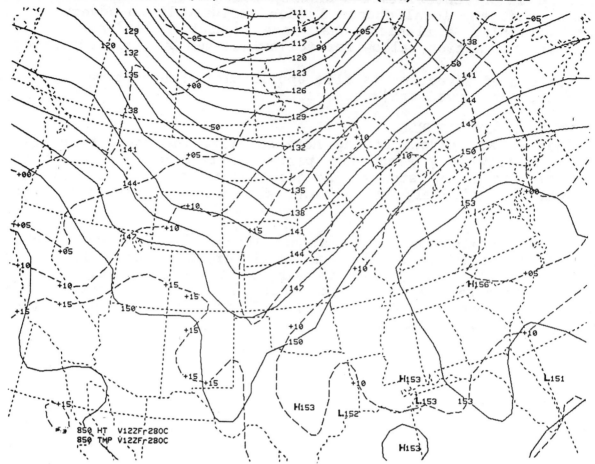

Figure 39. An 850 Mb Chart. The solid lines are height contours; the dashed lines are isotherms (lines of equal temperature) in degrees Celsius.

The height contour interval for the 850 mb chart is 30 meters and the isotherms are for every 5 Celsius degrees.

One use of the 850 mb chart is to find areas of warm air advection and cold air advection. By itself, warm air advection causes rising air and by itself cold air advection causes sinking air. If the temperature-dewpoint depression, or difference between the air temperature and the dewpoint temperature, is five Celsius degrees of less in the area of warm advection, then lifting this warm, moist air could result in clouds and subsequent precipitation. There can be other factors such as negative vorticity advection or a downslope (moving from high to lower elevation) flow that would cause downward motion to counteract the upward motion caused by the warm air advection. Therefore, all the dynamical and mechanical factors causing vertical motions must be combined in attempting to forecast the resulting vertical motion field. Warm air advection is probably the greatest dynamically-caused lifting mechanism over a large scale, that occurs in the troposphere.

(continued)

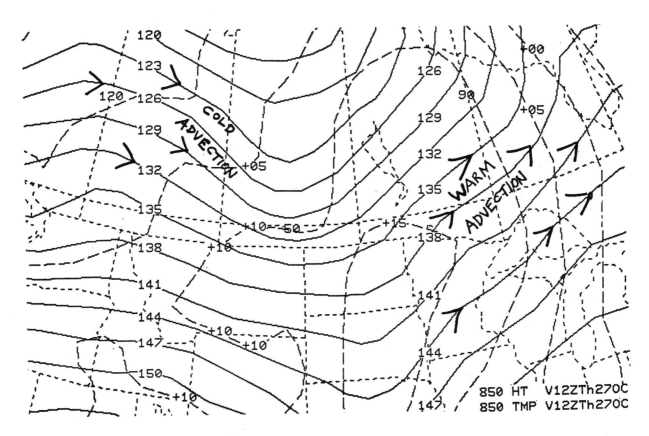

Figure 40. Warm and Cold Air Advections at 850 Millibars.

The arrows placed on the 850 mb height contours show the wind flow. Notice to the east how the wind flow is moving warmer and warmer isotherms downstream. This region is experiencing warm air advection. It can occur at day or night. If during the daylight, then heating by the sun would ALSO cause the temperature the rise, so that both solar heating AND warm air advection are combining to raise the temperature.

(An important aside: the sun does NOT heat the air! The sun's radiation...mostly the ultraviolet wavelengths...actually heat the ground, and then the ground heats the air above it by emitting chiefly infrared radiation [heat].)

Cold air advection, such as that which occurs in a wintry Arctic outbreak...a major blast of frigid air...would show up at 850 mb as a bunch of isotherms packed tightly together. The leading edge of the colder isotherms would be the Arctic cold front at 850 mb. The front would also extend to the surface (if the 850 mb level is above the surface). When isotherms are packed tightly together and they are being advected into an area, then that area will experience a rapid change in temperature...in the case of an advancing blast of Arctic air, the temperature would plunge as the colder and colder air moves (advects) in.

When warm or cold air is being advected into an area, the stronger the winds are that are associated with the advection, then the faster the warm or cold air will move into an area.

Thus, analyzing for thermal advections is one major use of the 850 mb chart.

(continued)   **PAGE 77**

Analyzing for MOISTURE ADVECTION is another use of the 850 mb chart. The winds transport meteorological properties, and the transport...advection... of moisture is analyzed on 850 and 700 mb charts.

Therefore, it is also important to compare the latest 850 mb chart with one or two previous ones to analyze for the changing 850 mb pattern and determine the changing thermal and moisture advection fields.

Zones of wind speed convergence and divergence, as explained in chapter 10, and their inferences for vertical motions, are also analyzable.

Yet another use of this chart is to analyze for short-wave troughs (see chapter 14), since these are the baroclinic systems that provide much of our "inclement" weather. A well-developed short-wave trough will show up on the 850 mb chart as a CLOSED LOW, i.e., a low center with a height contour surrounding it.

THE CONCEPT OF VERTICAL TILTING OF PRESSURE SYSTEMS:

Due to thermal and other physical rules, weather systems at the surface tilt back toward the cold air as we go aloft. For example, consider a developing low pressure system at the surface. The 850 mb low center or trough axis associated with that low will be displaced usually to the northwest of the surface low by some 100 miles. The 700 mb trough axis lowest height will also be displaced to the northwest of the 850 mb low center by about 100 miles. Thus, the systems tilt towards the cold air as we go aloft, until the surface low occludes (the cold front catches up with the warm front and the warm and cold air advections cease as the air mixes up). The storm is then dying. At this stage, the 500 mb, 700 mb and 850 mb low centers are vertically stacked on top of the surface low, and the whole system moves as a package as it gradually dies.

Thus, the four-dimensionality of weather can be depicted by a time series of surface and upper-level charts.

For the mountainous West, the 850 mb level would be below the ground!...keep in mind that 850 mb averages around 5000 feet in mid-latitudes. The weather data is therefore extrapolated downward for what it would be if there were an 850 mb level at, e.g., Denver or Salt Lake City. For the mountainous regions, meteorologists do not use the 850 mb analysis, but employ the 700 mb chart for the same uses.

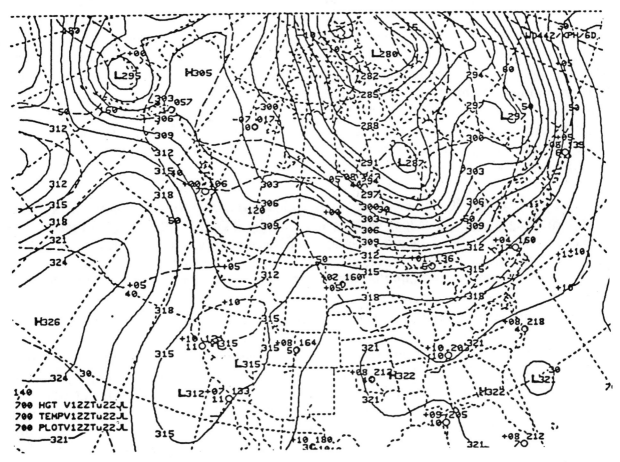

Figure 41. A 700 Mb Chart. The solid lines are height contours; the dashed lines are isotherms in degrees Celsius.

The contour interval on the 700 mb chart is 30 meters and the isotherms are for every 5 Celsius degrees.

The uses of the 700 mb chart include those of the 850 mb chart. In the mountainous West where the surface is above the 850 mb level, the 700 mb weather map is used to find thermal and moisture advections, and to identify short-wave troughs.

The 700 mb flow is used as a steering mechanism for air mass or single-cell thunderstorms, although large areas of organized convection, called mesoscale convective systems, are steered by the thermal wind (thickness pattern) described in chapter 18. Even though the 700 mb flow can be used to predict the movement of single-cell thunderstorms, a severe cell will sometimes split, with one cell usually moving to the right of the path of the original cell. This "right-mover" can be one type of tornadic thunderstorm.

(continued)

As a rule-of-thumb, a 700 mb temperature of 14°C. or higher is too warm to allow thunderstorms to develop. Such a high 700 mb temperature happens in major heat waves and also by subsiding or sinking air diverging in a high pressure system, with the air warming up as it sinks. Thunderstorms are caused by rising bubbles of moist air which keep accelerating upwards as long as they remain warmer than the environment they are rising through. These parcels cool as they rise, but as long as they remain warmer than the surrounding environment, they will keep accelerating upwards or upwards on a slant to produce thunderstorms. When these parcels finally reach a height at which they become cooler than their environment, they decelerate and eventually cease rising, and at that final height we find the tops of the thunderstorm clouds, which can exceed 40,000 feet. Some of the highest thunderstorm tops exceed 60,000 feet.

The short waves on the 700 mb chart and on the other standard-level upper-air charts move through the long waves. Since long waves are essentially BAROTROPIC (the isotherms are parallel to the contours of height, meaning no thermal advections occur except those moving with the wave) and short waves are BAROCLINIC (thermal advections occur which are analyzed as isotherms crossing the contours at some angle), if we cannot readily identify a short wave within a long wave but see warm advection followed by cold advection in a part of the long wave, then a short wave is passing through the long wave pattern.

Because they are smaller than long waves, the short waves move faster. At 700 mb, a short wave typically moves eastward with a northerly or southerly component, at speeds up to 30 knots and occasionally faster. The long waves, which we usually analyze for at 500 mb, well away from most frictional influences of the earth's surface, typically move eastward at speeds of up to 15 knots, but can remain stationary for a while and even back up (RETROGRESS) at up to about 3 knots for up to a few days in extreme cases.

Thus, these upper level charts help us to analyze and predict the weather by depicting the long waves and short waves in the upper-air flow. For example, consider a large amplitude and rather wide (over 75 degrees longitude wide) long wave over North America with the west part of it giving a northwesterly flow from Alaska into the Central Plains. In wintertime this would steer Arctic air deep into the contiguous United States, and the pattern would remain until the long-wave moved on or the pattern slowly evolved into another pattern.

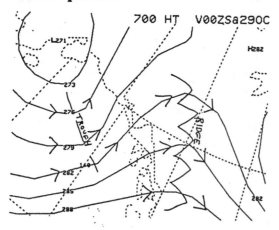

Figure 42. The Ridge and the Trough of an Upper-Level Wave.

Notice how the wind direction aloft changes after a ridge axis or a trough axis passes through the local area. The northwest flow is likely to bring in colder air, while the southwest flow is likely to bring in (to advect) warmer air.

18. THE 500 MILLIBAR (mb) OR HECTOPASCAL (hPa) LEVEL CHART

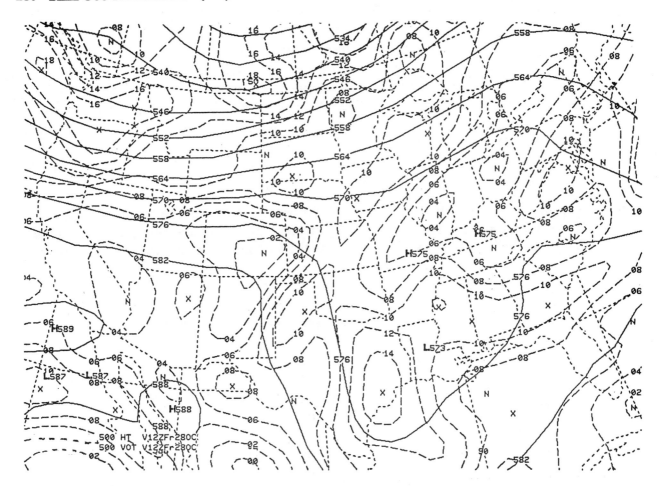

Figure 43. A 500 Mb Chart. **The solid lines are height contours; the dashed lines are isopleths of absolute vorticity.**

The contour interval on the 500 mb chart is 60 meters and the absolute vorticity isolines are usually given for every 2 which represents every 2 times 10 to the minus 5 radians per second.

In lower levels (700 mb, 850 mb and the surface), some of the fields of interest are the thermal and moisture fields. At 500 mb, we are more concerned about flow features and absolute vorticity.

Chapter 8 describes vorticity and why we analyze it.

A center of maximum positive vorticity is referred to as a VORT MAX, and a center of minimum negative vorticity is referred to as a VORT MIN.

(continued)

As described in earlier chapters, positive vorticity advection (PVA) is related to upward vertical motion and negative vorticity advection (NVA) is related to downward vertical motion. Fluid dynamics shows us that in a fluid, increasing PVA with height causes the fluid to spin up, but since vorticity or spin is caused by wind shear and by curvature of the flow, and the wind is usually stronger at 500 mb than in low levels, if we have PVA in low levels, then we probably have stronger PVA in the upper troposphere. The "bottom line" is this: as a rule-of-thumb, if we find PVA at 500 mb, we probably have upward vertical motion from the surface through 500 mb (actually to the tropopause level which is typically between 300 mb and 200 mb in mid-latitudes) caused by the PVA alone. If cold air advection is also occurring, then that would tend to cause air to sink, and we would have to determine the resultant vertical motion caused by competing influences.

The best case scenario for dynamic forcing for upward motion on the synoptic scale is for strong PVA at 500 mb to be accompanied by strong warm air advection from the surface through at least 700 mb. Then we have both the thermal and vorticity advections providing lift.

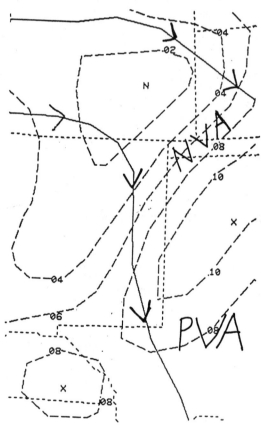

Figure 44. Positive Vorticity Advection (PVA) Areas and Negative Vorticity Advection (NVA) Areas on a 500 Mb Chart.

Notice that a PVA area is ahead of the vort max, and an NVA area is ahead of the vort min.

Vort maxes are typically found in the short-wave trough axis. The PVA in the area contributes to rising air, and lower-level warm air advection also contributes to rising air. Where the two combine, we tend to find the highest upward vertical velocities. For forecasting clouds and subsequent precipitation, we need upward moving air and adequate moisture.

Thus, the component of spin about the vertical axis of a small parcel of air, what we call vorticity, is a major contributor to the synoptic-scale vertical motion field.

(continued)

The reason we use vorticity analyses on the 500 mb chart rather than the 700 or 300 mb charts, e.g., is because of all the standard level charts, the 500 mb chart is closest to the level of nondivergence in the troposphere (see page 60), and we can mathematically show that if there is no divergence of the wind, then the short waves move with their vorticity centers: short-wave troughs move with their PVA centers (vort maxes), and short-wave ridges move with their NVA centers (vort mins).

We have discussed wind speed convergence and wind speed divergence and their relationship to vertical motion. If the winds aloft are fairly light (under about 30 knots), especially at the 500, 300, 250 or 200 mb levels or layers, then we can simply look at the contours showing the air flow. If they are coming together, we have CONFLUENCE, which implies directional convergence. However, confluence is not necessarily convergence. If the lines are spreading apart, we have directional divergence or DIFLUENCE. From our earlier discussion on the level of nondivergence, we know that if we have divergence aloft, then we have convergence in low levels, which means we have rising air through the layer from the surface up through 500 mb. If we have convergence aloft, then we have divergence in lower levels and likely have sinking air through that layer.

This table summarizes features of long waves and short waves.

	LONG WAVES	SHORT WAVES
NUMBER OF WAVES	3 to 7 across hemisphere...usually 4 or 5	numerous...a major short wave is 15 to 40 degrees longitude wide. Short waves move through the long waves.
AMPLITUDE	meridionally, up to 1500 to 1800 miles	meridionally, up to several hundred miles, can exceed 1000 miles
WAVELENGTH	50 to 120 degrees longitude	1 to 40 degrees longitude (between 40 and 50 is a transition "gray" area)
SHOWS UP BEST	300 and 200 mb, where effects of short waves are essentially dampened out	700 mb and 850 mb, with 700 mb usually the better, although short waves can originate anywhere in the troposphere
MOVEMENT	a. generally eastward at up to 15 knots b. stationary for up to a few days in extreme cases c. retrogress at up to 3 or so knots for up to a few days in extreme cases	eastward with a northerly or southerly component, through the long waves and faster than the long waves: up to 30 knots, occasionally faster
ENERGY REGIME	barotropic or equivalent barotropic (see chapter 4) long waves usually increase in intensity with height through the troposphere	baroclinic tilt toward the cold air with increasing height... the horizontal transport of heat by polar-front lows and troughs and their associated short waves is about the same total required to offset the radiative imbalance between low and high latitudes

The fewer the number of long waves, the larger their wavelengths and the slower they move.

19. THE 300, 250 AND 200 MILLIBAR (mb) OR HECTOPASCAL (hPa) LEVEL CHARTS AND THE JET-STREAMS

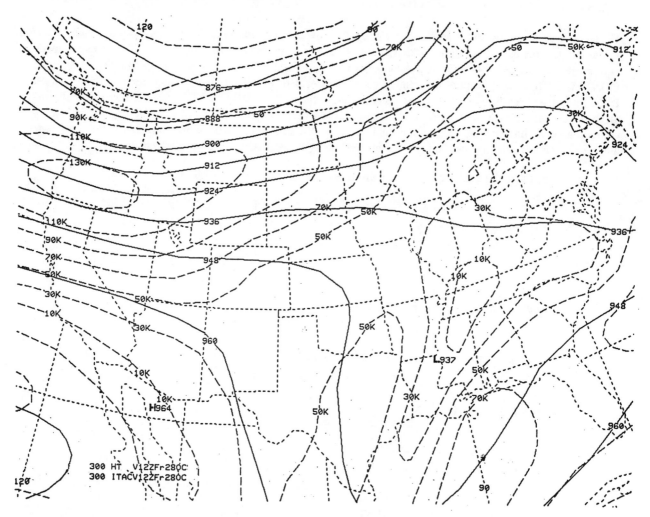

Figure 45. A 300 Mb Chart. The solid lines are height contours; the dashed lines are isotachs (lines of equal wind speed) given in knots.

The contour interval for the 300, 250 and 200 mb charts is 120 meters and the isotachs are for every 20 knots.

The main use of these charts is to analyze for the jet-streams.

THE JET-STREAM AND ITS JET-STREAKS:

The jet-stream is not one continuous band of high winds, but is comprised of discrete segments called **JET-STREAKS** or **JETLETS**. The threshold value for the beginning speed of a jet-streak is 50 knots.

(continued)

PAGE 84

Figure 46. The Polar Jet-stream, and south of it, the Sub-tropical Jet-stream

The polar jet separates colder, polar air from the milder mid-latitude air to its south. The sub-tropical jet separates the mid-latitude air from the tropical air.

Each jet-stream, comprised of individual jet-streaks, can be visualized as a narrow "snake" of air, which can be 10,000 or more feet deep, and moves horizontally and vertically.

Sometimes there is a third jet-stream, called the Arctic jet, which is north of the polar jet, and separates extremely cold Arctic air from the polar air. The Arctic jet can form only when extremely cold air develops in the far north during winter.

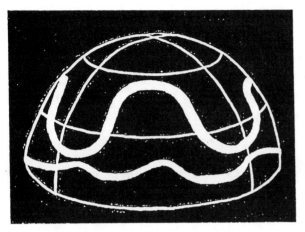

NORTHERN HEMISPHERE

The polar jet-stream is caused by temperature differences between the polar region and lower latitudes. The greater this temperature GRADIENT, the stronger the jet-stream.

Temperature differences cause pressure differences which cause air to move: the wind. Wind is air in motion. Since the thermal gradient is larger in the colder half of the year, the polar jet is stronger during that time.

When a cold polar or Arctic outbreak advances down the globe towards lower latitudes, that part of the jet-stream on the south edge of the cold air also advances towards lower latitudes. Thus, the cold front is at lower levels below the polar jet. Where the warmer mid-latitude air is advancing poleward, that portion of the polar jet is also moving poleward.

CYCLOGENESIS, the development of low pressure systems (cyclones), occurs along the polar front when some warm air tries to move northward and the cold air is moving southward to the west of the warm air advection. Thus, a kink or wave will develop along a portion of the polar front. This wave may be initiated by a short-wave trough aloft, with its areas of positive vorticity advection, but if the wave, the incipient cyclone, is to develop into a major low pressure system, the temperature advections must then begin and intensify.

The polar jet exists so that the low pressure systems that develop on it can transport heat and other properties poleward, and bring cold air southward. Otherwise, the equatorial areas would keep getting hotter and hotter and the polar areas would keep getting colder and colder, and our global climate would be much different from what we have now.
(continued)

PAGE 85

There is more solar radiation coming into the tropics to heat it than there is terrestrial (the earth's) radiation going out into space to cool the air there. In the polar regions, for an annual average, there is a net loss of heat since more radiation is emitted into space in high latitudes than is received from the sun.

In the summertime, when the polar jet is weaker, we find much fewer of these EXTRATROPICAL CYCLONES (what we call the non-tropical storm low-pressure systems) to transport the excess energy poleward. Then, Nature must create something else to do this transporting, so it develops HURRICANES, which are TROPICAL CYCLONES. Thus, if we humans devised a way to destroy hurricanes, then Nature would have to create some other meteorological feature to move much of the excess energy poleward, or else the tropics would become even hotter and the poles even colder.

The transport of heat by polar-front extratropical cyclones and by tropical cyclones poleward and by their associated short-wave troughs aloft, is about the same total required to offset the radiative imbalance between low and high latitudes. Simply put, WE MUST HAVE STORMS!

The Arctic jet is similar to the polar jet, and it happens relatively infrequently. We always have a polar and a sub-tropical jet.

The role of the sub-tropical jet includes thermal transports but also the transport of a quantity known as angular momentum. Angular momentum involves the wind and its transport of mass on a rotating earth. This momentum is generated in low latitudes, and from this source region it is transported poleward to the "sink" region. The thermal gradients across the sub-tropical jet are not as great as across the polar jet; therefore, major cyclogenesis is not as common at the surface beneath the sub-tropical jet.

The jet-streams are lower in elevation in the winter and higher in summer. The 300 millibar chart will catch most of the detail of jet-streaks in the winter, and the 200 millibar chart is used in summer. The 250 millibar chart is a good compromise because it will likely catch the jet-stream winds. Keep in mind that each jet-stream jet-streak undulates and moves forward as it changes its size, including its depth. Thus, we can visualize each jet-streak as a "snake of air" containing very strong winds.

Jet-streaks start at 50 knots, and the core of the maximum winds can easily exceed 100 knots. Sometimes jet-streak maxima even exceed 170 knots, and have been observed to exceed 200 knots (over 230 miles per hour).

Now let us look at the specifics of the jet-stream jet-streaks and the roles they play in our weather.

(continued)

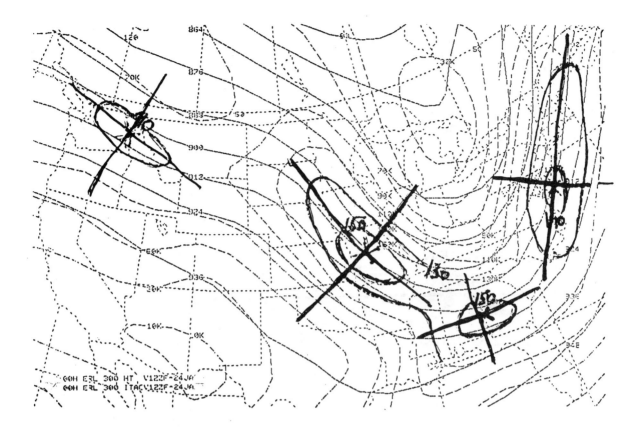

Figure 47. Jet-Streaks within the Polar Jet-Stream.

The figure shows a 300 mb chart which was hand-analyzed to highlight the jet-streaks within the polar jet. Here, the jet cores or maximum winds were highlighted. Note that when the jet-streaks are fairly straight, you can divide each one into four quadrants. The left-front quadrant and right-rear quadrant are regions of upward moving air from the surface through the jet-stream level, and the other quadrants have descending air. The reason why is explained shortly. Thus, in using a jet-stream analysis for forecasting, see if the left-front or right-rear quadrants are headed your way, because if they are, then upward motion will be enhanced. When one of these quadrants passes over a developing low pressure system, we can have rapid cyclogenesis. In the convective time of year, one of these quadrants could condition the environment for thunderstorms that may become severe, even tornadic, especially in the Spring and early Autumn.

The jet-streaks themselves are moving through the flow, typically at 30 to 50 knots, but the air parcels blowing THROUGH the jet-streak are entering it, accelerating to the jet-max speed (e.g., 150 knots), and then exiting the jet-streak. The left-front and right-rear quadrants are named in reference to the jet-streak's movement. In our example in figure 47, a jet-max or jet core is over Missouri, with the jet-streak heading southeast parallel to the 300 mb height contours. The left-front quadrant is over Illinois, Indiana and essentially western parts of Kentucky and Tennessee; the right-rear quadrant is over essentially Kansas and Nebraska. These are the regions where the jet is inducing air to rise. If there is adequate moisture in the air in these regions, then clouds and subsequent precipitation would occur.

(continued)

The left-front quadrant is usually more active than the right-rear quadrant because the thermal gradient, especially aloft, may be greater there.

Now let us analyze an individual jet-streak to see why we have rising air in the left-front and right-rear quadrants of an essentially straight jet-streak.

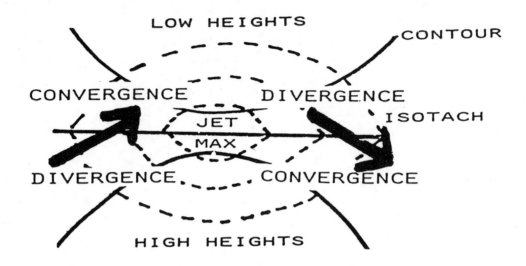

Figure 48. A straight jet-streak, showing the upper-level divergence regions in the left-front and right-rear quadrants, where upward vertical motion is occurring from the surface up through the jet-streak level.

What happens is that the forces that cause the wind are out of balance in the vicinity of jet-streaks, and this leads to compensating vertical motions.

Normally, the air blows roughly parallel to the upper-level height contours, The pressure-gradient force blows the air from high to low heights, and the Coriolis force turns it to the right in the Northern Hemisphere, if there is no friction to prevent it from turning all the way to the right. (See section 2d.) The wind is then called GEOSTROPHIC, which is the balance of the pressure-gradient and Coriolis forces. Near the ground, there is friction, so that the wind is not turned 90 degrees to the right by the Coriolis force due to the earth's rotating, but is turned at an angle somewhat less than 90 degrees. Over the oceans, the frictional component of the wind is less than over the rougher land, so the wind is closer to geostrophic over the oceans than over the land. However, aloft, above the "FRICTION LAYER" (also called the PLANETARY BOUNDARY LAYER), the wind is geostrophic, blowing parallel to the height contours. (The planetary boundary layer is most commonly some 1500 to 2500 feet deep up from the ground, but can get shallower on some nights after the sun sets.)

(continued)

When air parcels approach the jet-streak, they are in geostrophic balance: the pressure-gradient and Coriolis forces balance each other: the wind blows from the high heights to the low heights (the same as from high pressure to low pressure) and the Coriolis force turns it to the right. However, the pressure-gradient force is increasing very rapidly over a relatively short distance as the parcels enter the jet-streak and accelerate towards the jet maximum. The Coriolis force cannot increase fast enough to keep in balance with the pressure-gradient force. Therefore, the parcels are not turned the complete 90 degrees to the right but only partially to the right because the pressure-gradient force in that region is temporarily greater than the Coriolis force.

The air diverges from the entrance region and piles up or converges on the other side. Thus, the right-rear quadrant is a region of upper-level divergence, and the left-rear quadrant is one of convergence. Where the air is diverging..being depleted..aloft, it is being replaced by air from below (see chapter 10), because air cannot be created or destroyed. In the convergence area, air is piling up and sinking (some may be forced upward above that level). We actually set up a circulation across the jet-streak and down to the ground in the rear of the jet-streak.

The forces do become in balance at the jet max, but then as the parcels of air leave the jet max, the wind gets progressively lighter in the jet-streak, meaning that the pressure-gradient force that causes the wind is decreasing very rapidly over a relatively short distance. However, the Coriolis force cannot decrease fast enough to stay in balance with the pressure-gradient force. Consequently, the air blows away from the left-front quadrant (divergence aloft) and toward the right-front quadrant (convergence aloft). Air rises in the left-front quadrant to replace the depleted air, and mostly sinks in the right-front quadrant. A three-dimensional circulation is established here also, from the surface up through the jet-streak.

Although this jet-streak discussion is complicated, especially to someone studying it for the first time, if you take the time to study what is going on with the air parcels entering, blowing through and exiting a jet-streak, a clear picture emerges about the jet-streak dynamics.

The reason there is not a continuous polar jet-stream and sub-tropical jet-stream across the hemisphere is because the vertical circulations would not be easily possible without the breaks between jet-stream segments.

The sub-tropical jet-stream is higher than the polar jet-stream because the tropopause, which separates the troposphere from the stratosphere, is higher as we move equatorward, and the jet-streams occur between overlapping tropopauses. On very infrequent occasions, the left-front quadrant of a sub-tropical jet-streak overlaps the right-rear quadrant of a polar jet-streak. Since these quadrants are regions of upper-level divergence and upward vertical motion, they combine their forcings of air upward, resulting in major air rises.

(continued)

These are extreme events, and when they do happen, the resulting weather can be disastrous. For example, when these two jet-streaks overlapped over the eastern U.S. in March 1993 over a developing low pressure system, the storm "exploded". It intensified (DEEPENED [pressure kept getting lower]) very rapidly, resulting in a "snow hurricane". Winds exceeded 100 mph and parts of the Northeast received over four feet of snow, accompanied by thunder and lightning. Snowfall rates exceeded five inches per hour during the height of the storm. In the late Spring, such overlapping jet-streaks can lead to major tornado outbreaks, with families of tornadoes sweeping across many states.

All of this jet dynamics is true when the air parcels blowing through the jet are moving faster than is the jet-streak itself. Otherwise, the convergence/divergence areas are reversed. This situation would be rare.

A jet-steak is not always fairly straight. When it is curved like a big "U", then the upper divergence area spreads out over most of the northern half of the U and the upper convergence region is over much of the southern half. Then, the upward vertical motion in essentially to the north of the jet-streak axis. The reverse is true when the jet-streak is shaped like an "inverted U" (the upward moving air being south of the jet-streak axis).

Jet-streaks within the general jet-steam flow may be from several hundred to over 2000 miles long and are typically from 100 to 400 miles wide and one to two miles deep.

There are long-term, large-scale general circulation cells in the tropics, mid-latitudes and polar regions. As we ascend to the top of the troposphere, known as the TROPOPAUSE, we find that the temperature stops falling with height. We then enter the stratosphere. (See figure 3 on page 14.) The tropopause is higher in the tropical cell than in the mid-latitude cell, and is higher in the mid-latitude cell than in the polar cell.

Where the higher tropical tropopause overlaps the mid-latitude tropopause, we find the sub-tropical jet-stream, and where the mid-latitude tropopause overlaps the lower polar tropopause, we find the polar jet-stream.

The rest of this chapter is a more technical explanation of some jet-streak dynamics and may be skipped unless you are interesting in exploring this subject in greater detail.

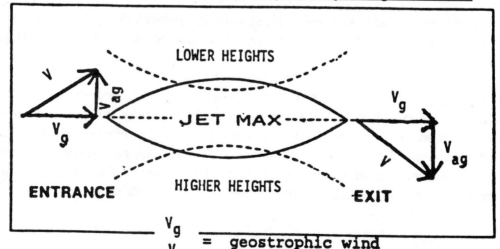

V_g = geostrophic wind
V_{ag} = ageostrophic wind due to the pressure gradient force being out of balance with the Coriolis force
V = actual wind

Thus, in the entrance region of the jet-streak, the wind is blowing across the contours towards lower heights and in the exit region it is blowing across the contours towards higher heights.

Technically, since geostrophic wind is the resultant wind when there is a balance between pressure gradient force and Coriolis force (no friction as in the first 50 or so mb of the troposphere), we must technically be aware that when there is curved flow, centrifugal ("center fleeing") force exists as a response to centripetal ("toward the center") force, giving us gradient wind which is a balance among pressure gradient, Coriolis and centrifugal forces. Thus, in a jet-streak we may have subgradient and supergradient winds in parts of it.

For simplicity, the entrance region of the jet-streak will be considered to be subgeostrophic (pressure gradient force greater than the Coriolis force) and the exit region will be considered to be supergeostrophic (Coriolis force greater than the pressure gradient force). In the entrance region, the air is accelerating. This is because since wind is essentially pressure driven the excess of pressure gradient force (or "pressure gradient force per units mass", i.e., pressure gradient acceleration) speeds the air up.

In the jetstreak, the air is trying to get into the bottleneck to move fast. Air must blow across the contours towards lower heights to accelerate.

The air moving through the jetstreak (jetlet) travels much faster than the movement of the jet pattern itself.

As a jetstreak moves in, more Available Potential Energy is generated for conversion into Kinetic Energy of storm development, especially if the area in question is under the left front flank of the jetlet. Actually, the maximum baroclinicity is found in the vicinity below the jet max because the atmosphere is trying to adjust to the thermal wind relationship.

Jet-streams are caused by thermal contrasts between high and low latitudes and between troposphere and stratosphere, and by the necessity for conservation of angular momentum of the atmosphere. Jetstreaks within the general jet-stream flow may be from several hundred to over 2000 miles long and are typically from 100 to 400 miles wide and one to two miles deep. The polar jet is stronger in winter than summer because the thermal gradient from high to middle latitudes is greater in winter. Simply put, temperature differences cause pressure differences which cause pressure gradients which cause wind.

The question arises, Why do we have upper and lower air divergence and convergence portions of the jetstreaks occurring where depicted on the diagram (next page)?

PAGE 91

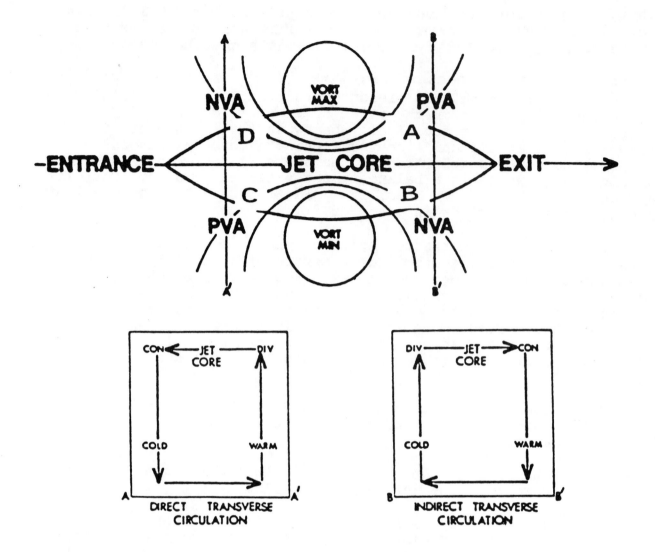

The top diagram shows the zonal jet core, vorticity pattern and vorticity advection, plan view. The lower diagram shows the cross-section through entrance region A-A' and through exit region B-B' from the surface through the jet-stream level. The lower pair of sketches shows what are called DIRECT TRANSVERSE CIRCULATION and INDIRECT TRANSVERSE CIRCULATION associated with the jetlet.

These direct and indirect circulation cells of a jet-streak occur when maximum winds exceed the propagation rate of the jet-streak itself.

The excess pressure gradient force is the ageostrophic wind component in the entrance region aloft because there is where exists a region of lighter winds coming into a region of stronger winds, and the excess Coriolis force is the ageostrophic wind component in the exit region aloft because there is where exists a region of stronger winds entering a region of lighter winds.

When lighter winds enter a region of stronger winds, the pressure gradient force increases and the Coriolis force has not yet increased sufficiently to balance the now-stronger pressure gradient force. When stronger winds enter a region of lighter winds, the pressure gradient force decreases and the Coriolis force has not yet decreased sufficiently to balance the now-weaker pressure gradient force.

In the entrance region, as air parcels accelerate into the core, the ageostrophic components force a transverse circulation with rising motion in the anticyclonic quadrant ("right rear flank"), C and sinking motion in the cyclonic quadrant, D. In the exit region, decelerating parcels force a transverse circulation with rising motion in the cyclonic quadrant ("left front flank"), A and sinking motion in the anticyclonic quadrant, B.

The four-cell vertical motion pattern can be related to vorticity advection as shown on the previous page. The NVA at the jet-streak level in the cyclonic rear and in the anticyclonic forward quadrant coincide with convergence aloft and subsequent sinking motion. The PVA in the anticyclonic rear and cyclonic forward quadrants are related to divergence aloft and subsequent rising motion from below.

The transverse circulations in the entrance and exit regions of a jet-streak are different. In the entrance region, cold air sinks while warm air rises, resulting in a conversion of available potential energy to kinetic energy. Thus, the transverse circulation in the entrance region is a "direct" circulation (warm air rising, cold air sinking). In the exit region, cold air rises and warm air sinks, converting kinetic energy into available potential energy. Thus, the transverse circulation in the exit region is an "indirect" circulation.

The major persistent jet-streams are located between the overlapping tropopauses where the southern end of the polar Hadley cell meets the northern end of the mid-latitude Ferrel cell, and where the southern end of the mid-latitude Ferrel cell meets the northern end of the tropical Hadley cell.

MAJOR CYCLOGENESIS MAY OCCUR WHEN THE LEFT-FRONT QUADRANT, WITH ITS UPWARD MOVING AIR, OF A FAIRLY-STRAIGHT SUBTROPICAL JET-STREAK, OVERLAPS THE RIGHT-REAR QUADRANT, WITH ITS UPWARD-MOVING AIR, OF A FAIRLY-STRAIGHT POLAR JET-STREAK. SOME OF THE GREATEST STORMS OF ALL TIME, E.G., THE MARCH 1993 EAST-COAST SNOW HURRICANE, OCCUR WITH THIS SCENARIO.

Note: Similar upper and lower divergence and convergence areas with associated vertical motion circulations exist in low-level jet-streaks. However, if the jet-streak is moving faster than is the wind blowing through it, then the divergence/convergence field is reversed, which reverses the resulting vertical motions (compared with the usual case of the wind passing through the jet-streak being faster than is the speed of the jet-streak itself).

20. WHAT IS THE PLANETARY BOUNDARY LAYER (PBL)? PBL CHARTS

From the ground up to a certain height, the terrain produces friction as the moving air tries to pass over it. This frictional layer is referred to as the PLANETARY BOUNDARY LAYER, and typically extends from the surface up to about 1500 to 2500 feet during the daytime, and after sunset over fairly level terrain, can shrink to as little as several hundred feet deep. During the daytime, especially under clear skies, the sunlight heats the ground which in turn warms the PBL. Solar heating results in conduction, reradiation and convection of heat, causing mixing of the air in that layer.

Moreover, another reason we have a PBL or friction layer along the earth's surface is because, as inferred by the first sentence, the wind is resisted some by terrain and objects this air is trying to pass over. This frictional resistance slows down the wind speed by about 20% and makes the wind somewhat less than geostrophic in direction.

At night, without that component of the mixing due to the sun's radiative effects, the depth of the layer decreases, and if there exist higher winds above the PBL, these higher winds can come down to a lower level, and help to transport moisture into or out of your area.

Some weather maps are generated for the planetary boundary layer to be used as guidance products for wind forecasting, fog forecasting, ocean wave heights forecasting based on projected PBL winds, agricultural forecasting (how much relative humidity does the layer have or is forecasted to have by a certain time?...with clear skies and light PBL winds, will we have dew overnight?), for some examples.

Forecasts of wind direction and speed for locations under the PBL are done for the mid-point of the PBL. If the PBL over your area tonight is expected to be 1000 feet deep, then a wind forecast done by a computer forecast model would be for about 500 feet off the ground.

A PBL forecast graphic of average relative humidity for the layer, or for the relative humidity in the middle of the layer, is another type of PBL chart.

Aviation interests are users of PBL charts for take-offs and landings, mostly for the wind data.

On the next page are examples of common PBL charts.

(continued)

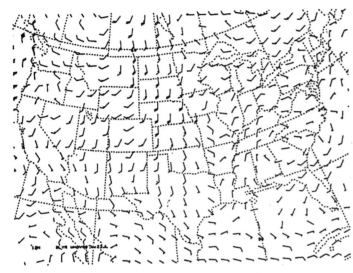

Figure 49. Example of a Wind Forecast for the Midpoint of the Planetary Boundary Layer, from one of the Computer Forecast Models.

The wind barbs are plotted according to the standard notation, pointing in the direction from which the wind is coming. The barb by itself means a wind of 2 knots or less, a half-line on the barb is for 5 knots, a whole line on the barb is for every 10 knots, and a triangle on the barb is for 50 knots.

Example: the above is for a northeast wind at 75 knots.

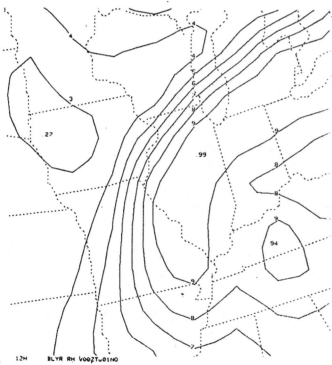

Figure 50. A Zoomed-in Portion of a Computer Forecast Model's Map of the Relative Humidity in the Planetary Boundary Layer for a Specific Time.

The relative humidity is given to the nearest 10%. Thus, a contour labelled 7 means 70%. The maxima and minima centers are given to the nearest percent.

The chart shows if significant very low-level moisture is forecast to be available. In warm weather, the air can hold more moisture than when the air is cold; thus, a relative humidity of 90% in warm air contains much more moisture than does bitterly cold Arctic air with a 90% relative humidity.

21. SURFACE-TO-500-MILLIBAR MEAN RELATIVE HUMIDITY CHART

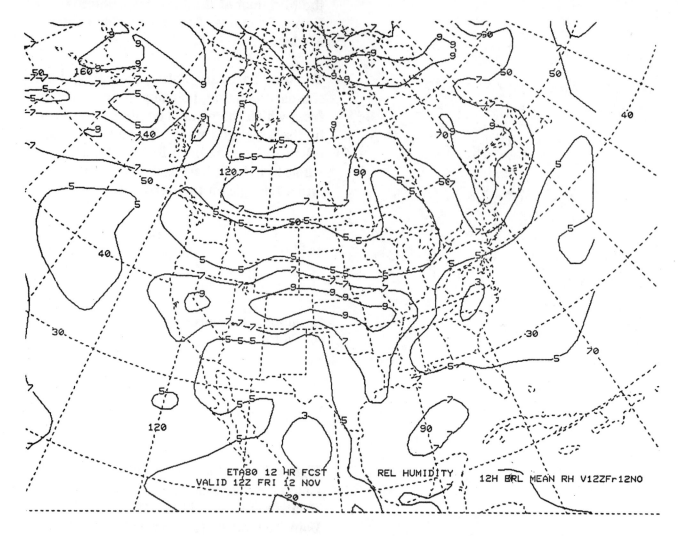

Figure 51. Surface-to-500-Mb Mean Relative Humidity (RH) Chart.

This chart is the latest analysis or a forecast from one of the computer models. The forecast valid time is given on the bottom of a forecast chart. Multiply the labelled contours by ten to get the RH; e.g,, a 7 means 70% relative humidity.

If the RH is about 70% or greater through this deep layer (500 mb averages about 18,000 feet high in mid-latitudes), and the vertical velocity there is upward, expect considerable cloudiness. When the mean surface-to-500 mb RH is 90% or greater and the vertical velocity at 700 mb (about 10,000 feet up) is upward, precipitation is likely. A study by this author shows that a RH from this analysis of 90% or greater with a 700 mb vertical velocity of +3 microbars/second or higher yield a high probability of precipitation. Thus, use this chart in combination with the 700 mb vertical velocity prognostication for the same time.

22. 700 MILLIBAR (700 MB) VERTICAL VELOCITY CHART

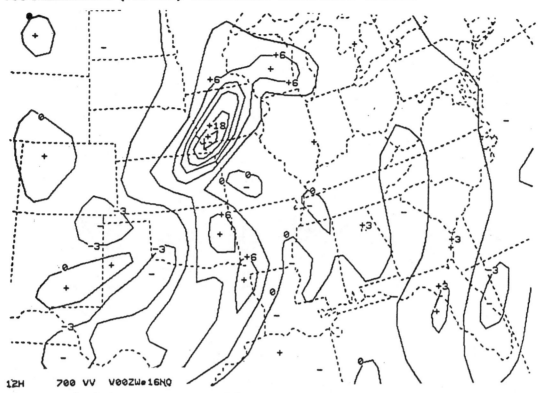

Figure 52. A zoomed-in portion of a 700 mb Vertical Velocity (vv) Chart, showing 700 mb vv in increments of 3 microbars/second.

At 700 mb, 1 microbar/second of vv = approximately 1.12 cm/sec. This chart is depicting broad-scale synoptic vertical motion.

A significant value for upward vv is +3 to +6 (or higher) microbars/sec. A threshold value for significant sinking motion would be -3 microbars/sec. When high 700 mb upward vvs are coupled with average relative humidities from the surface to 500 mb of 90% or greater, the probability of precipitation is near 100%. Proportionally lower values of vv and RH yield lower precip. chances.

Isolines of vv are given for every 3 microbars/sec. with centers of maxima and minima given by a + an - respectively.

$$1 \text{ bar} = 10^6 \text{ dynes/cm}^2 \qquad 1 \text{ millibar (mb)} = 10^{-3} \text{ bar} = 10^3 \text{ dynes/cm}^2$$

$$1 \text{ microbar} = 10^{-6} \text{ bar} = 10^0 = 1 \text{ dyne/cm}^2$$

Units of vv could be given in cm/sec, but computer forecast models solve directly for vertical motion in terms of the pressure change as the parcel rises or sinks; thus, we use microbars/second rather than cm/second.

23. 1000-to-500 MILLIBAR (1000-TO-500 MB) THICKNESS CHART

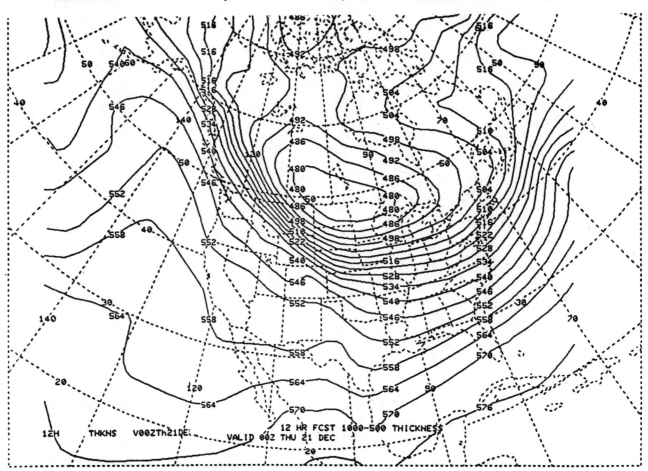

Figure 53. A 1000-to-500 Millibar Thickness Chart. The thickness lines interval is 60 meters of height. Thickness values are in meters, with the last digit, a zero, left off.

The concept of thickness is rather interesting and has proven useful in analysis and forecasting. THICKNESS is the vertical depth of a layer between two pressure levels. Thus, if over your location the 1000-to-500 mb thickness is reported to be 5640 meters, that means that the vertical distance between the 1000 mb level and the 500 mb level over your location is 5640 meters.

When the air gets warmer, it stretches, and the vertical distance between those same pressure levels would increase, say to 5700 meters. Values over 5800 meters are typically associated with surface temperatures of 90 degrees F. or higher, and values over 5900 meters are typical of surface high temperatures of 100 degrees or more.

Meteorologists east of the Rocky Mountains have found the 5400-to-5460 meter band to be the rain/snow transition zone much of the time, except for freezing rain/sleet environments.

(continued)

PAGE 98

Thickness values below 5200 are typical of surface temperatures of zero degrees Fahrenheit or below. Values below 5000 occur in bitter Arctic air, below 20° below zero F. Conversely, thickness values approaching 6000 meters are associated with extreme heat in the column, with surface temperatures of about 110 degrees or higher. Desert areas can get as hot without thicknesses quite that high because of the intense heating of the lighter-colored soil which then heats the air above it.

Consider the wintertime in the Arctic. Over several successive days with a net loss of heat to space in that region, the cold air will get progressively colder. It is also getting denser, especially near the ground and especially in the (planetary) boundary layer. Its thickness values will decrease. Eventually, all or some of this "blob" of heavy, frigid air starts to slide down the globe towards lower latitudes. On a thickness chart, the leading edge of colder air, the cold front, shows up as the leading edge of lower values of thickness advancing towards and into warmer air.

If strong warm air advection is occurring into a region, we would expect the thickness values to rise. If they hardly rise or do not rise at all, then that warm air advection is going into producing rising of the air, which, when combined with sufficient moisture, leads to cloudiness and subsequent precipitation.

Another use of the 1000-to-500 mb thickness pattern is for forecasting the movement of organized convection known as mesoscale convective systems (MCSs). An MCS is a very large area of thunderstorms that forms in warm, moist air, and may persist for many hours, often for over 12 hours. They tend to stay in the same thermal field in which they originated, so they move parallel to the thickness lines. This is unlike most air mass or single-cell thunderstorms which tend to move with the average 1000-to-500 mb flow or 700 mb flow as a good first approximation. The only exception to the MCS thickness rule is when thickness lines ahead of the MCS spread apart. This is known as DIFLUENT THICKNESS. For reasons not yet entirely clear, when difluent thickness occurs MCSs then propagate BACKWARDS away from the difluent thickness and to where the thickness gradient is tighter.

Besides the 1000-to-500 mb thickness chart, there are charts for other thicknesses, such as 850-to-300 mb thickness. That chart would be useful from the Rockies westward where the 850 mb level is at or below the surface, and 1000 mb would be useless.

24. THICKNESS AND THE THERMAL WIND

The thickness of a layer is the height difference between two pressure levels. The colder the air is in a layer, the lower the layer's thickness; the warmer the layer, the higher the thickness value. Numerous studies have been done relating thickness values to precipitation types and to other aspects of forecasting. East of the Rockies, the 1000 to 500 mb thickness is commonly used. For example, the thickness ribbon of 5400 to 5460 meters is usually the transition zone between rain and snow, unless it is too warm near the surface.

The advection of lower thicknesses implies cold air advection, whereas the advection of higher thicknesses implies warm air advection. However, if an 850 mb chart shows strong warm air advection into your area yet the 1000 to 500 mb thicknesses are not rising, then that warm air advection is going even more strongly into upward vertical motion.

The thermal wind is the difference between the geostrophic wind at two different levels. Thus, it is a vector.

Thickness advection, for warm and cold air advection, can be shown using the thermal wind.

$$V_{ug} = \text{upper-level geostrophic wind}$$

$$V_{lg} = \text{lower-level geostrophic wind}$$

$$V_{th} = \text{thermal wind} = V_{ug} - V_{lg}$$

WARM AIR ADVECTION

$$V_{ug} = 220° \text{ at } 25kt$$

$$V_{lg} = 160° \text{ at } 25kt$$

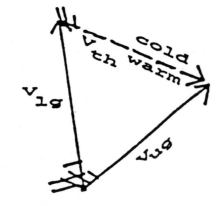

Therefore, veering (clockwise in direction) winds with height imply warm air advection.

COLD AIR ADVECTION

$$V_{ug} = 160° \text{ at } 25kt$$

$$V_{lg} = 220° \text{ at } 25kt$$

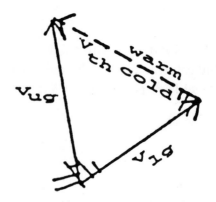

Therefore, backing (counter-clockwise in direction) winds with height imply cold air advection.

THE ABOVE APPLIES ABOVE THE PLANETARY BOUNDARY LAYER.

The lower-level geostrophic wind is, of course, above the planetary boundary (friction) layer.

If there is no change of geostrophic wind direction with height in a layer, then this implies neutral temperature advection and the thermal wind is parallel to that same wind direction in the layer.

The thermal wind exists mathematically and is used to explain some atmospheric activity; the thermal "wind" itself is not a physical reality.

From our elementary meteorological dynamics texts, we learn how to derive an equation which is a very good approximation relating thickness to the average temperature of the layer:

The hydrostatic equation is $dP = -\rho g\, dz$.

Because $P = \rho RT$, if we divide the hydrostatic equation by P on both sides and rearrange terms, we get:

$$\frac{1}{P}\frac{dP}{dz} = -\frac{g}{RT}$$

. Now we integrate between two isobaric surfaces, P_1 and P_2, from z_1 to z_2, to obtain:

$$\ln\frac{P_1}{P_2} = \frac{g}{R}\int_{z_1}^{z_2}\frac{dz}{T}$$

.

Thickness, then, is:

$$z_2 - z_1 = \left(\frac{R}{g}\ln\frac{P_1}{P_2}\right)\overline{T} = -\left(\frac{R}{g}\ln\frac{P_2}{P_1}\right)\overline{T}$$

The texts show how the thermal wind is related to the thickness:

$$\vec{V}_{th} = \Delta\vec{V}_g = \frac{-g}{f}\nabla_P(\Delta z)\times\hat{k} = \frac{g}{f}\hat{k}\times\nabla_P(\Delta z)$$

For the nonmeteorological reader of this booklet,

P = pressure T = temperature

ρ = density g = acceleration of gravity

z = height R = specific gas constant for dry air

The introduction of moisture needs to be accounted for in the density of the air and by the temperature; this is accomplished by applying the correction for the effects of water vapor to the temperature term by using the virtual temperature. The virtual temperature is the temperature that the dry air would have if its density were equal to the density of moist air at the same pressure.

25. PRECIPITABLE WATER (PW) CHART

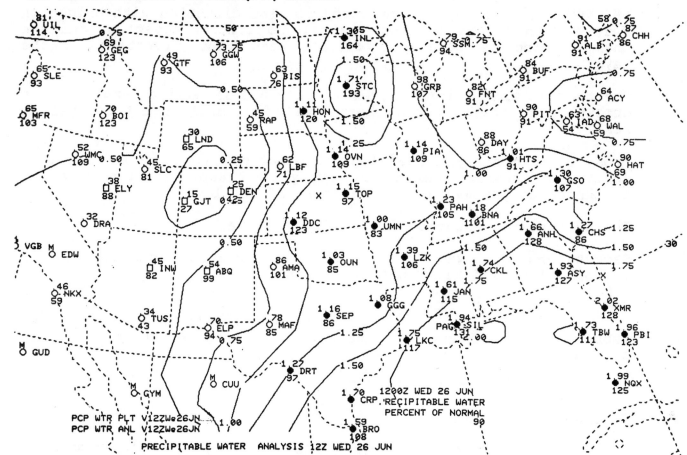

Figure 54. A Precipitable Water (PW) Chart. The top value for each station is the PW in hundredths of an inch, and the bottom number is the percent of normal of PW for that time of year. The contours are in 0.25" increments of PW.

Precipitable water is the amount of water vapor in a column of air from the surface to 500 millibars.

From the soundings from weather balloons, the temperature and dewpoint are recorded as the balloons ascend. From the dewpoint, the actual amount of water vapor in the air is known, which is given as grams of moisture. This water vapor parameter is called the **MIXING RATIO**, which is the parts of water vapor per thousand parts of air, i.e., parts per thousand. At the surface, mixing ratio values range from a trace to 2 to 3 parts per thousand, up to a maximum even higher, depending on the temperature. The warmer the air, the more moisture it can hold (the higher the dewpoint it can have).

What is the purpose of this chart?

(continued)

PAGE 102

To find the PW value, we integrate (sum up) all the moisture from the surface to 500 mb (around 18,000 feet up for a mid-latitude average). There is not much moisture usually found above 500 mb except for deep moisture raised by strong convection. The precipitable water value represents the amount of precipitation that would fall over that location if all the moisture were suddenly condensed out as precipitation.

However, a PW value of, e.g., 1.25" does not mean that the most it can rain over that locale is 1.25". During a synoptic storm or a mesoscale (smaller-scale such as thunderstorm scale) storm, the converging air that is required for lift will advect or bring in more moisture from the surrounding area, so that a PW of 1.25" could represent a potential of 4 or 5 inches of rainfall.

For example, a forecaster's rule-of-thumb for thunderstorms is that with slow-moving (moving at less than 20 mph) organized storms, the maximum rainfall is typically up to five times (sometimes more) the PW value. Thus, PW is useful for heavy rain/flash flood forecasting.

If the 1.25" value is normal for that location for that month, then it is 100% of normal. Values of 150% or more of normal are considered excessive, and could yield heavy amounts of precip. for that time of year if precipitation were to occur. The percent-of-normal figure is not as important as the actual precipitable water value, however, because the PW value itself gives an indication of the potential rainfall.

For snowfall potential from major winter storms, an inch of water would give an average of about one foot of snow for surface temperatures a few Fahrenheit degrees below freezing. But a PW of 1" might yield much more than one foot of snow because of additional low- and mid-level moisture transported in towards the low pressure system's center by converging winds.

Again, it is important to remember this point about using the precipitable water chart for rainfall/snowfall amount guidance: In using PW, keep in mind that the winds will transport more moisture into a precipitating area, so that the PW value is not the upper limit of the amount of water that will precipitate out in that area.

26. LIFTED INDEX CHART

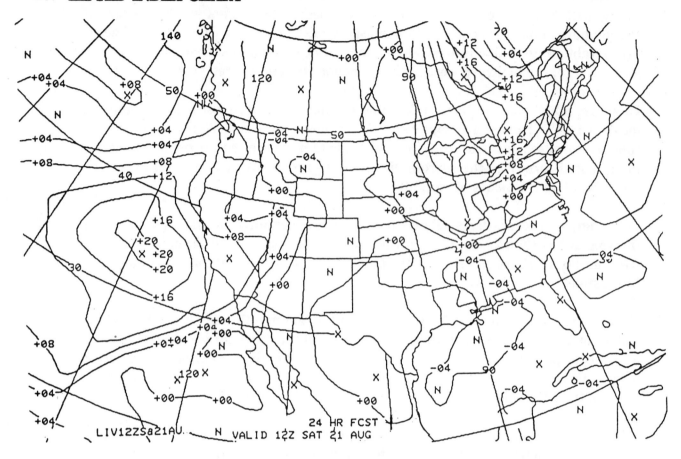

Figure 55. A Lifted Index (LI) Chart (above, a 24-hour forecasted lifted index, from a computer forecast model). Areas with unstable air have negative values, and with stable air have positive values.

The lifted index is a tool used in thunderstorm forecasting. Thunderstorms require three conditions, occurring simultaneously: a lifting mechanism in the low or mid levels, low and/or mid-level moisture and an unstable environment. Furthermore, there should not be a warm pocket aloft around 700 mb. This is a temperature inversion caused by sinking, diverging air in a high pressure system, which warms as it descends...it is called a SUBSIDENCE INVERSION. It would then be too warm in mid-levels for air to keep rising to form thunderstorms.

An unstable atmosphere is one in which air parcels, once forced upward by a lifting mechanism (e.g., by a cold front or some other boundary or mechanism), will remain warmer than their environment and will therefore keep rising because they are positively buoyant. Thus, we want a temperature sounding that cools off with height faster than the air parcel is cooling as it ascends. The bubbles of rising air need to expend energy if they are rising on their own; thus, they cool as they rise.
(continued)

As unsaturated air rises, it cools at the DRY ADIABATIC LAPSE RATE, which is approximately 10° Celsius per kilometer (specifically, 9.76° C/km).

ADIABATIC means there is no heat added to or withdrawn from the parcel and environment. Since the dewpoint is conservative, the air keeps the almost the same dewpoint as it rises until it cools off to that dewpoint temperature. (Actually, there is a slight drop in dewpoint with height, due to a vapor and environmental pressure effect.) Then the air is said to be saturated (the temperature and dewpoint temperature are the same...the air is holding as much moisture as it possibly can at that pressure. Then, as air rises, it still cools but has to condense out some of the moisture as it rises, since cooler parcels cannot hold as much water vapor. The HEAT OF CONDENSATION, or the energy required to condense the vapor into cloud or water droplets (or ice if cold enough) is released, so that once the parcels of air have reached condensation yet keeps rising, they do not cool at as fast a rate as when unsaturated. The MOIST ADIABATIC LAPSE RATE at which the parcel cools is about 6° C/km as an average, but varies from about 9.2° C/km near sea-level in very cold air, to only about 3° C/km in the higher troposphere. The process is still called adiabatic because no external heat is being added to or taken away from the system, with only the heat of condensation being generated by the local parcel/environment system itself.

The air parcel will continue rising as long as it remains warmer than the environment. That is why the most severe thunderstorms have the strongest updrafts which can take the air parcels into the lower stratosphere. The parcels themselves are accelerating until their temperatures are the same as the environmental sounding at which point they start decelerating. Then the parcels are slowing down as they rise and eventually cease going any higher. Also, the parcels are not necessarily rising purely vertically; they can rise at some angle, depending on the wind shear.

The lifted index follows these parcels as they rise, and at an arbitrary level, 500 mb, looks at the temperature of the sounding and the temperature of the parcel.

The Lifted Index (LI) = the sounding's (environmental) temperature MINUS the parcel's temperature

If the parcel is warmer than the environment it is rising through, then the LI is a negative number, which refers to an unstable environment.

If the parcel were to be forced up to 500 mb but is colder than the environment, then we have a positive number, which refers to a stable environment. In a stable environment, the parcel will be negatively buoyant; therefore, it would sink, not rise.

A stable sounding can become unstable by making ITS lapse rate increase. This can be done by warming the environment in the low-levels of the troposphere and/or cooling it aloft, also by adding moisture in the lower levels and/or drying it aloft.

(continued)

Thus, a +2 LI, which is minimally stable, could change to, e.g., a -2 LI in say 6 to 12 hours. An example is a sunny day with a morning +2 LI becoming a mid-afternoon -2 because solar heating has warmed the ground which in turn warms the lower layer of the troposphere. This is assuming no significant low-level warm or cold air advection which would also contribute in a destabilizing or stabilizing way, respectively, to the environmental sounding.

Thus, by warming in low-levels by heating of the day, for example, or by warm air advection, and/or by cooling aloft, the slope of the temperature sounding steepens. The temperature drops off faster with height. This makes the sounding less stable. Keep in mind that the rising parcels of air can cool at only the dry adiabatic lapse rate, and when saturated, at the moist adiabatic lapse rate. These rates do not change. However, the environmental lapse rate does change. This is how destabilization and stabilization occur.

Reviewing, then, what the lifted index process is: we raise air from or near the surface to 500 mb and compare the rising parcel's temperature there with the 500 mb temperature. If the parcel is warmer than the 500 mb environmental temparature, then we have instability and a negative lifted index value; if the parcel is colder than the 500 mb environmental temperature, then we have stability and a positive lifted index value. The lifted index is the 500 mb temperature minus the temperature the parcel would have if lifted to 500 mb. The air parcel cools as it rises, at the dry adiabatic lapse rate if the parcel is initially unsaturated, and at the moist adiabatic lapse rate once the parcel cools to its dewpoint temperature, becoming saturated, or if the parcel is initally saturated when it starts rising.

The rising or lifting is caused by some lifting mechanism. Examples of lifting mechanisms are:
- solar heating during the daytime if the sky is clear of at least most non-thin clouds;
- an advancing cold front which lifts the warmer air ahead of it;
- an OUTFLOW BOUNDARY from a thunderstorm or remnant of a thunderstorm or thunderstorm complex;
- other advancing boundaries such as a sea-breeze front;
- air flowing up a rising terrain, such as UPSLOPE or, for up mountains, OROGRAPHIC LIFTING;
- intersection of boundaries...e.g, if two thundersorms approach each other, their intersecting outflows result in major mass (of air) convergenge and new lift which forces new convective development.

If there are no big temperature inversion layers below 500 mb, then the following lifted index values are used as a guide:

LIFTED INDEX	CONDITION
+6 or higher	quite stable
+3 to +5	stable
0 to +2	weakly stable
less than 0	unstable
-6 or less	quite unstable; greatest tornado potential

27. K-INDEX CHART

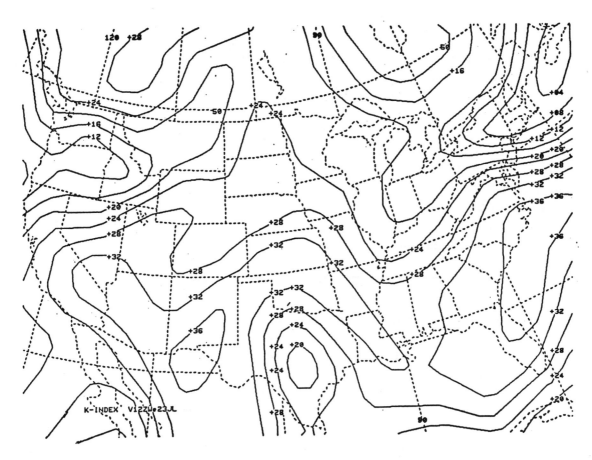

Figure 56. A K-Index (KI) Chart, in intervals of 4 units.

The K-Index (KI) (the "K" does not stand for anything) is an invention used to predict thunderstorm potential and heavy rain/flash flood potential.

The K-Index = (850 TEMP - 500 TEMP) + 850 DEWPT - 700 DEPRESSION

TEMP is the temperature, dewpt is the dewpoint, and depression is the difference between the temperature and the dewpoint; 850 is 850 mb, 700 is 700 mb and 500 is 500 mb; all of these temperatures are in degrees Celsius.

The first term of the KI formula tells how steep the environmental lapse rate is between 850 and 500 millibars. The greater the temperature drop through that layer, the lower the stability. A good value for an unstable environment is 30 or more.

The second term is the 850 mb dewpoint temperature. If we are looking for heavy rain, we want as high an 850 mb dewpoint as possible. A warm season value of 10 or more would be high.

(continued)   **PAGE 107**

For flash flooding, we need slow-moving organized convection with deep moisture. The third term is the 700 mb temperature/dewpoint depression or spread, i.e., the difference between the temp. and the dewpoint at 700 mb. For heavy rain, we need copious amounts of moisture..water vapor..through a deep layer. Thus, the dewpoint should be high from the planetary boundary layer up through about 500 mb. Therefore, at 700 mb, the closer the temperature and dewpoint are to each other, the better for heavy rain potential when the first two terms of the K-Index are also high. Zero, then, is the ideal value for the third term.

Consider our example of 30 for term 1 and 10 for term 2. If zero is the value for term 3, then our KI is 30+10-0=40. If the air were very dry at 700 mb, e.g., if the depression there were 20, then the KI would be 30+10-20=20. The higher the KI, the greater the threat of thunderstorms.

Values used in operational forecasting are:

WHEN THERE IS ADEQUATE LIFTING OF THE PARCELS:

K-Index	Relationship to Convection
<28	thunderstorms not likely
28 to 32	chance of thunderstorms
33 to 35	good chance/likely to have thunderstorms
36 or above	expect thunderstorms
38 or above	heavy rain/flash flood potential

A KI of 40 or above is considered "extremely juicy". It would be accompanied by rather high precipitable water (PW) values (see chapter 25). PWs well in excess of one inch would likely accompany a KI of 40 or more. PWs can reach 2" or more with a very moist dewpoint sounding.

CAVEAT: Sometimes a high KI can be misleading. Since we are looking at values at only three levels, 850, 700 and 500 mb, sometimes there can be dry slots between these levels. If we were to take these into account, there would not be deep, continuous high moisture content.

To check to make sure that the dewpoints do not dry out between these levels, it is necessary to look at the weather balloon sounding of temperature and dewpoint in the vertical, or to look at the radiosonde weather report itself to read these values and assure that the atmosphere is indeed moist. With dry slots aloft there may still be thunderstorms, but they would likely not be heavy rain producers and flash flood threats. Moreover, dry intrusions aloft around 700 mb actually contribute to making the thunderstorms more severe, since the temp. and dewpoint lapse rate may be greater which allows the rising parcels to accelerate faster and higher, leading to more violent updrafts. What separates a severe thunderstorm from a routine one is the strength of the updrafts. (See the comments on convective-scale vertical motion, in chapter 3.)

PAGE 108

28. CONVECTIVE OUTLOOK FOR DAY 1 CHART

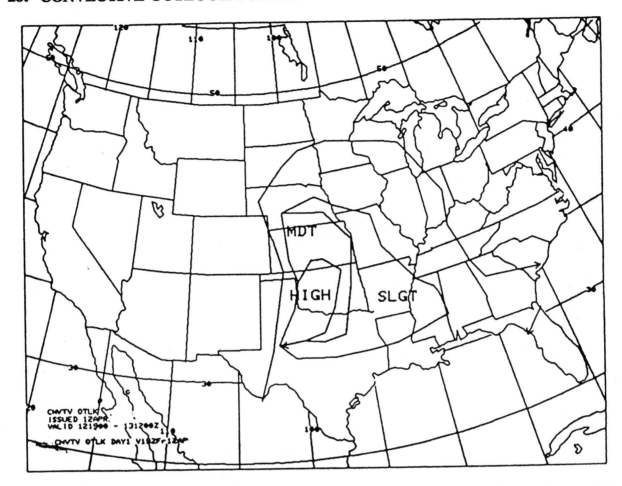

Figure 57. A Convective Outlook for Day 1 Chart. Day 1 is from 15Z today to 12Z tomorrow morning; for day 2, see next page.

(Note: this chart may undergo changes, but the information given on it should be essentially the same.)

This chart is issued early in the day and may be updated. It gives the thunderstorm outlook and severe thunderstorm outlook for 15Z today through 12Z tomorrow morning.

General thunderstorms are possible to the right of the solid unlabeled line, and areas of slight, moderate and high risk for severe thunderstorms, which may include tornadoes, are within their respective enclosed areas. A slight risk of severe thunderstorms is 2 to 5% areal coverage, a moderate risk is 6 to 10% and a high risk is for greater than 10% of the area receiving severe thunderstorms within that time period. Each category is per 100,000 square nautical miles.

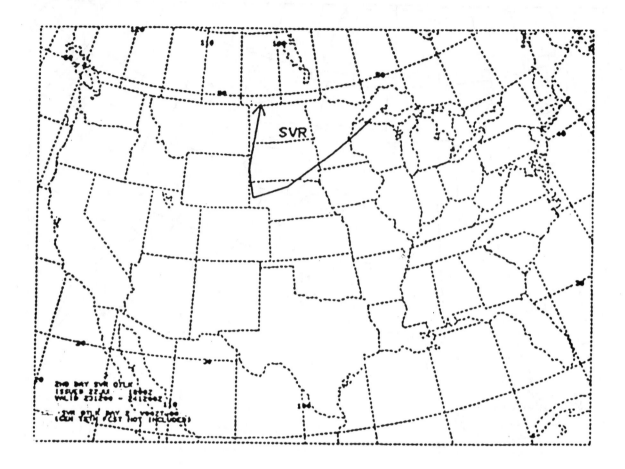

Figure 58. A Severe Weather Outlook for Day 2 Chart. Day 2 is from 12Z tomorrow morning through 12Z the following morning.

(Note: this chart may undergo changes, but the information given on it should be essentially the same.)

This chart is issued early in the day and may be updated. It shows areas where potentially severe thunderstorms may occur during that time period. A severe thunderstorm is a thunderstorm with winds of 50 knots (58 mph) or more and/or hailstones of 3/4 inch diameter or more and/or a tornado.

The area to the right of the line is the area (or areas) in which the conditions are expected to be ideal for severe thunderstorm potential. General (non-severe) thunderstorms may occur elsewhere in the lower 48 states; this chart gives only those areas where severe thunderstorm conditions may exist.

30. QUANTITATIVE PRECIPITATION FORECAST (QPF) CHARTS

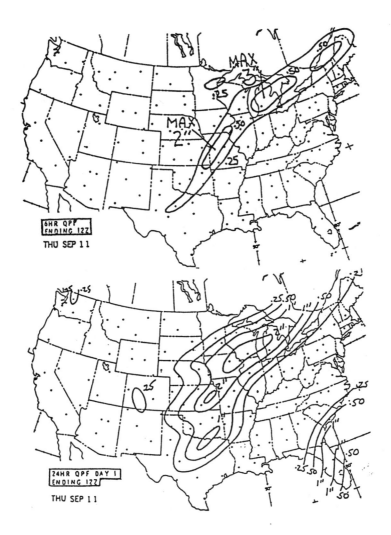

Figures 59a. and 59b. A 6-Hour Quantitative Precipitation (QPF) Forecast (a.), and a 24-hour QPF (b.).

A team of National Weather Service forecasters specializes in heavy rain and heavy snow forecasting. Several times a day they issue 6-hour QPFs. Other QPFs are issued by the computer forecast models.

The time-period of the forecast is typically given on the bottom of the chart. For example, fig. 59a is a forecast for rainfall for the 6-hour period ending at 12Z. The first contour is for 0.25", the next for 0.50", the next for 1", then 2", then 3" and then greater than 3". The 24-hour forecast as in fig. 59b is for the same amounts. If snow is forecasted, then a dashed line would be drawn indicating the rain/snow line. (The mid-latitudes rule-of-thumb is that one inch of rain would be about one foot of snow in most storms.)

31. EXCESSIVE RAINFALL POTENTIAL CHART

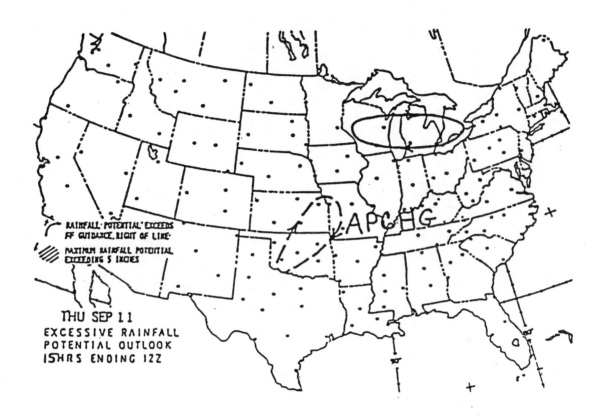

Figure 60. An Excessive Rainfall Potential Outlook.

This chart is issued as national guidance from the National Weather Service, for the time period given typically on the bottom of the chart, and is for areas that will approach, or that will meet or exceed flash flood criteria.

A hydrologic computer model determines the amount of rain needed in x number of hours (usually under 6 hours and frequently within 3 hours) to produce flash flooding, based on soil moisture and other hydrologic conditions before the rain begins for this time period. This threshold rainfall amount is called the FLASH FLOOD GUIDANCE. If the QPF is expected to approach, or to equal or exceed the flash flood guidance, then that area or those areas are delineated on this chart [the equal or exceed area(s) and the approaching flash flood guidance area(s)].

32. HEAVY SNOW QPF CHART

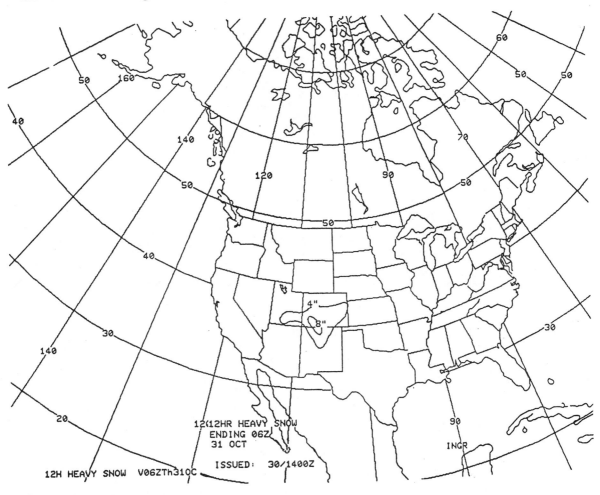

Figure 61. A 12-Hour Snow Forecast issued by the National Weather Service

Above is a snow QPF issued as national forecast guidance by the National Weather Service. This may be issued up to several times a day, updated based on latest information. Amounts are in inches, but could also specify "greater than 6 inches", or "greater than 12 inches", e.g., for that 12-hour period only.

33. SATELLITE INTERPRETATION CHART

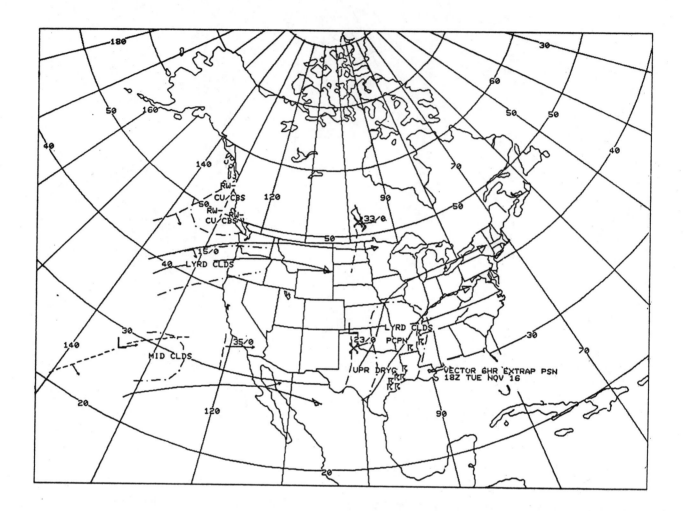

Figure 62. A Satellite Interpretation Chart, depicting weather features that the weather satellites are showing.

The purpose of this chart is to identify what you are looking at when you look at visible, infrared and water vapor imagery from our weather satellites.

Especially for someone new to satellite interpretation, this chart is useful for identifying features depicted on weather maps; i.e., the satellite signatures of these features are identified. Examples: cu (cumulus clouds), cb (cumulonimbus clouds), trough axis, vort max (see chapter 13), lyrd clds (layered clouds), mid-level (bases of 6500 to 20,000 feet) clouds, upr dryg (upper drying, i.e., drying out in upper troposphere), etc.

The future of this chart may change. For in-depth satellite documentation and interpretation information, contact the government's weather satellite meteorologists at the World Weather Building at Camp Springs, Maryland.

34. FREEZING LEVEL PLOT CHART

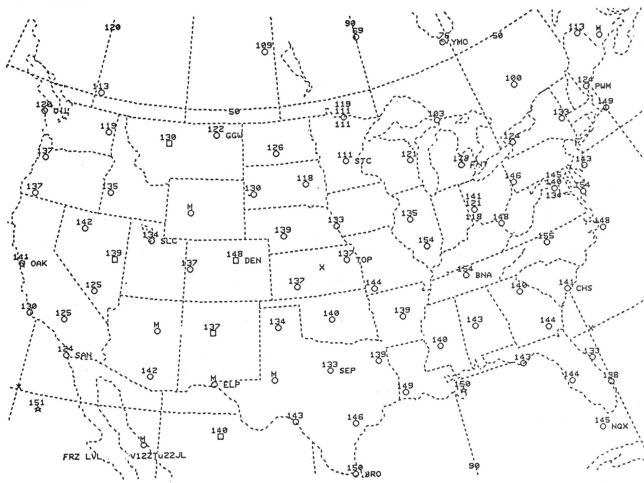

Figure 63. The Freezing-Level Chart, useful for aviation briefings and for forecasting precipitation types: liquid, freezing, solid.

Heights are in hundreds of feet above mean sea-level. If the surface is at or below freezing, then BLO is plotted. If 3 or more values appear above each other for the same station, then there are more than one freezing level. For example, 120 over 70 over 50 means the initial freezing level is at 5000 feet but the temperature goes above freezing at 7000 feet and then back below freezing at 12,000 feet.

In moist air, ice can form on aircraft; therefore, pilots need to know the locations of freezing levels.

For forecasting, a freezing level above about 2000 feet means that all or most snow will melt into rain before hitting the ground. As the freezing level descends, the snow level descends.

(continued)

Sleet and freezing rain can be inferred from a freezing level depiction, if the air is saturated and precipitation is occurring or expected.

If the air at the surface is below freezing, but at about 1000 feet up the air is ABOVE freezing, and is not below freezing again until several thousand feet higher, then all precipitation becomes rain in the above-freezing layer, but will freeze on contact with objects at or below freezing when the rain falls into the thin sub-freezing layer hugging the surface.

If the surface-based sub-freezing layer is 2000 or more feet deep with a deep layer (several thousand feet deep) of above freezing air above it, then the rain falls into the below-freezing layer and still has 2000 or more feet to fall before hitting the surface. This sub-freezing layer is sufficiently deep to freeze the rain or partially-melted snow into balls of ice which we call SLEET.

This, whether we have freezing rain or sleet depends upon how deep is the surface-based freezing layer that lies below the above-freezing, warmer inversion layer above it. A thin below-freezing layer gives us freezing precipitation whereas if the layer is about 2000 feet deep or deeper, we receive sleet.

Sleet can exist at temperatures somewhat above freezing right near the surface. In such a case we know that we have a thin layer above freezing based on the surface, above which is a sub-freezing layer about 2000 feet or more deep, above which is a layer above freezing that is deep enough to melt snow falling into it from above. Sometimes, some of the snowflakes do not melt or melt completely, and combinations of rain, snow and sleet occur and vary with time.

Sometimes, with air or layers of air around the freezing point near the surface, snowflakes can start to melt but then fuse with other snowflakes and refreeze, yielding flakes of two to three inches in diameter...heavy "wet" snow. "Wet snow" is snow with a high water content when it is melted into water.

Thus, snow, rain, sleet, freezing rain, drizzle and freezing drizzle combinations occur based on the vertical velocities, moisture content and vertical and horizontal thermal structure of the low- and mid-troposphere.

35. FREEZING-LEVEL AND LOW-LEVEL TURBULENCE PROG.

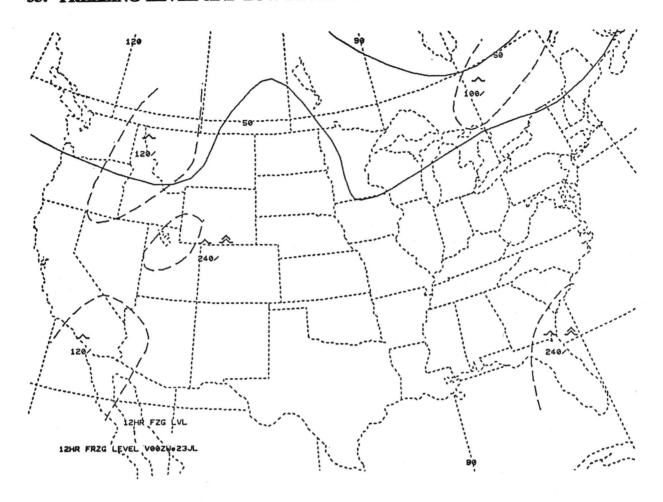

Figure 64. A prognostication (prog) of Freezing Level and Low-level Turbulence, used by pilots

A description of the uses of the freezing level is in the previous chapter.

This chart is for weather briefings for pilots and for forecasters who compose aviation forecasts.

The chart depicts the prediction of moderate and severe turbulence for up through 24,000 feet MSL (above mean sea-level). Bases of the expected turbulence are to the right of the solidus and tops to the left, in hundreds of feet MSL, for moderate turbulence, depicted as ⌃, and for severe turbulence, ⌃ .

Freezing-level contours are solid lines labeled in hundreds of feet MSL in intervals of 4000 feet (thus, 120 means 12,000 feet), and turbulence areas are outlined in hundreds of feet MSL by dashed contours.

36. 500 MILLIBAR WAVE-5 CHART

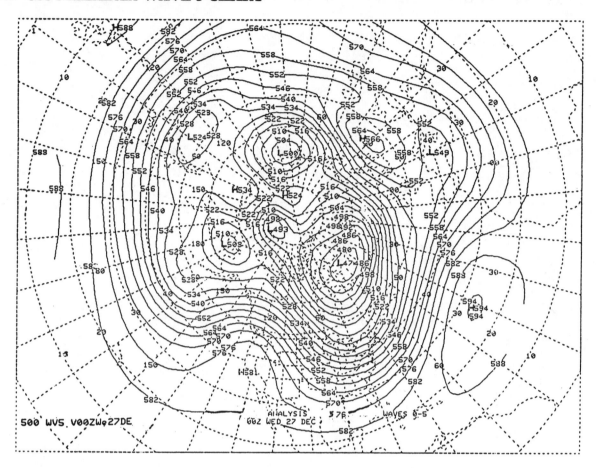

Figure 65. A Wave-5 Chart for 500 mb, showing the five longest waves across the northern hemisphere at 500 MB.

This chart is the result of mathematically subtracting out all the shorter wavelengths in the 500 mb hemispheric flow greater than 5, so that only the five longest waves are depicted.

The philosophy for the existence of this chart is that a meteorologist could start his/her analysis of the weather by first looking at the large-scale flow pattern and then coming down in scale to the local region. By damping out the shorter waves, the general flow pattern, which changes more slowly than do the shorter waves that move through it, can be analyzed. The short waves generally move through the larger flow pattern.

Thus, you can compare this chart with the actual 500 mb chart for the same time which shows all the long waves and the short waves passing through them, to see how the short waves, especially the baroclinic short-wave troughs, will move through the more-slowly changing and moving long-wave pattern. (See chapters 18 and 17 for discussions on long and short waves of the atmospheric flow pattern.)

(continued)

Interplay between the large and smaller scales is the concept behind following migratory short waves moving through the more stationary long waves. A tool for observing this interplay is an animated time-series loop of the 500 mb flow for several days (the actual 500 mb, not prognostications), and the same time-series of the wave-5 500 mb chart. The interaction of the planetary- and synoptic-scale waves can usually be observed.

Here are some examples of the usefulness of this approach.

1. Suppose we have a quasi-stationary long-wave pattern. Short-wave troughs deepen as they move into long-wave trough positions, subsequently weakening and seeming to disappear as they move over the downstream long-wave ridge. Often, they can be observed to appear again and deepen as they move into the next long-wave trough.

2. When the long-waves are in transition, either progressing or retrogressing (going backward), the short-wave troughs are typically the mechanism which realigns the long-waves. An example of this is discontinuous retrogression, which is when a short-wave translates over a long-wave ridge and then propagates southeastward, cutting a path farther west than did the prior short-wave, causing the long-wave to retrogress westward.

3. Consider a quasi-stationary long-wave trough, e.g., a wintertime long-wave trough off the West Coast of the U.S. It can appear to keep ejecting short-wave troughs (storms). Such patterns can be observed through time-lapses on a computer display of weather charts.

Thus, the 500 millibar wave-five chart embodies the philosophy of starting with the big picture and then working down to the synoptic scale and then the mesoscale to the fine mesoscale, looking at the interplay of scales of motion.

37. SURFACE MOISTURE-FLUX CONVERGENCE CHART

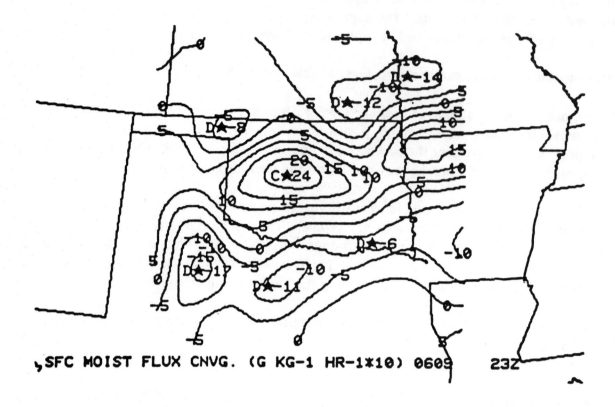

Figure 66. An hourly regional Surface Moisture-Flux Convergence Chart, showing areas where moisture and air parcels are converging (piling up and rising), C, and areas from where moisture and air parcels are diverging, D, replaced by sinking air.

There are hourly national and regional analyses of surface moisture-flux convergence and progs (prognostications, i.e., forecasts) of it.

Units are in grams per kilograms multiplied by ten, per hour. Thus a 20 means 2.0 grams of air and moisture per hour. If a plus, there has been an increase of 2.0 and if minus, a decrease. Thus, a positive value represents surface moisture-flux convergence and a negative value represents surface moisture-flux divergence.

Surface moisture-flux convergence is comprised of mass (air) convergence and moisture advection. Thus, a positive value means that there has been an increase of air and moisture (higher dewpoints) in the past hour, brought in by converging winds. Convergence also implies lift. To get clouds and subsequent precipitation, we need moist air to be lifted.

(continued)

One particularly good use of this chart is to locate bullseyes of moisture-flux convergence when the atmosphere is unstable or becoming unstable. Surface moisture-flux convergence bullseyes of 20 (i.e, 2 gm/kg/hr) or more typically locate where the first convection will fire within about two to three hours.

Thus, e.g., suppose we are following this analysis hour to hour, and for this hour a bullseye of 20 (2.0) appears. Then next hour, the bullseye is 45 (4.5). If the vertical sounding information for that area shows that the atmosphere is unstable without a strong cap inversion (such as a subsidence inversion) aloft (see chapter 20), then expect thunderstorms to form within about 3 hours after the first bullseye or within about two hours after the next hour's bullseye in the same general area.

What is happening is that the surface winds are transporting more air and water vapor into a locale, forcing the air to rise. If the environment there is unstable without a strong cap inversion aloft, then expect thunderstorms soon. The 20 (i.e, 2.0) value works well as a minimum or threshold value for convection.

An area of surface moisture-flux divergence is one of drying air (lowering dewpoints) and sinking, diverging air. Fair or clearing weather would be likely in these regions.

The surface moisture-flux convergence chart does not describe what is happening aloft, and can be misleading if used alone, especially for nocturnal convection. Lifting mechanisms just off the surface or above a thin surface inversion layer can also generate convection.

When a strong bullseye of positive values (a value of 40 or more [4.0 or more]) is next to, i.e., coupled with, a strong bullseye of negative values (a value of minus 40 or less [-4.0 or less]), severe thunderstorms are possible within the positive bullseye region. On a surface weather map mesoscale analysis, we would typically see a pressure drop in the convergence area next to a pressure rise in the divergence area: this is a fall-rise pressure-change couplet, that is typically found with severe thunderstorms.

When surface moisture-flux convergence is increasing, this means that one or more of the following is occurring:
   a. the wind convergence is increasing;
   b. the moisture is increasing;
   c. the moisture advection is increasing.

Thus, it may be possible to have a mass increase of air without an increase of water vapor. This is checked by observing the dewpoint change in that area. If the dewpoint is also rising, then the moisture is increasing through surface moisture-flux convergence.

USES OF SURFACE MOISTURE-FLUX CONVERGENCE

1.   Surface moisture-flux convergence is comprised of mass convergence and moisture advection. (The mass convergence is the wind convergence multiplied by the mixing ratio.)

2.   Typically, in an unstable atmosphere, it takes a few hours for surface moisture-flux convergence (SMC) to initiate convection. It is therefore helpful to locate areas of pre-existing or sustained SMC.

3.   SMC does not always reflect what is occurring aloft, especially for nocturnal convection.

4.   Errors creep in along the boundaries of the SMC analysis, and the analysis itself is susceptible to noise in the wind field and occasionally in the moisture field. An inaccurate surface observation, if used in the analysis, can create a wrong bullseye of moisture convergence or divergence.

5.   No actual number threshold is established for convective initialization. The number varies from case to case. Conditions aloft vary from case to case.

6.   The change of SMC is often more significant than the value of the SMC.

7.   Storms can develop in an area in which the gradient of SMC is large --where the SMC increases rapidly over a given distance. Development tends to occur on the moist side of the SMC axis.

8.   Storm severity appears to be greater when a strong surface moisture-flux convergence center is coupled with a strong surface moisture-flux divergence center with the highest mixing ratios (highest dewpoints) between the two centers.

9.   Analyze soundings for a cap inversion aloft, which is a subsidence inversion typically found around 700 mb. If the cap is greater than 2 Celsius degrees and deeper than 100 mb, it may be impossible to break the cap in the next several hours. Therefore, convection will not occur beyond the cap height.

10.   The SMC analysis is scale-dependent. Even though it is mesoscale, it is high mesoscale. We would need a much denser network of surface observations to identify more localized concentrations of SMC and other parameters. Thus, the fueling of individual storms cannot be determined, although an area where convection is likely to develop can be identified. It is recommended to use this analysis with low-level (usually 850 mb east of the Rockies and 700 mb in the mountain west) theta-e analysis (equivalent potential temperature analysis) as good supplementary analyses in convective forecasting. 850 mb theta-e analysis is discussed in chapter 45.

11.   Changes in SMC appear to reflect actual important changes underway, such as a shifting of the axis for convective development.

12. Areas of increasing SMC are important when other indications show the possibility of significant thunderstorms.

13. When surface moisture-flux convergence is increasing, this means that one or more of the following is occurring:
   a. the wind convergence is increasing
   b. the moisture is increasing
   c. the moisture advection is increasing.

An increase in the wind convergence implies more low-level forcing (air parcels are "piling up" and forced to rise). A moisture increase also destabilizes the low levels. An increase in moisture advection further fuels the storms. Thus, any of these three conditions can lead to convection.

14. There are two types of SMC centers. The first is a convergent center by itself, without a divergent center. The second type has the convergent center coupled with the divergent center. This type appears to be more associated with severe thunderstorms. Research on why is underway. These severe storms tend to form in the gradient of SMC, on the moist side of the SMC axis.

15. Centers of SMC that remain quasi-stationary for hours, can be areas of excessive rainfall and/or severe weather.

16. When the pattern shows a small quasi-circular bullseye and the data is accurate, a single thunderstorm complex or a supercell may develop.

17. A more-or-less west-to-east axis of SMC can lead to a squall line. With a low-level southerly moist flow, cells in the line can be supplied with moisture. If the SMC is not shifting with time, with the cells successively moving over the same areas, then flash flooding may result. This is the train effect scenario.

18. A squall line can form from a more-or-less north-to-south, or northeast-to-southwest axis of SMC. The storms may initially form in the SMC gradient area closest to the maximum of convergence, subsequently building along the axis of convergence (northward and/or southward along the axis). In this case, as contrasted with the quasi west-to-east line, the likelihood for severe cells is greater. The cells more likely to be severe are the initial cells. In a quasi north-to-south or northeast-to-southwest line, certain cells have preferential access to available moisture, as contrasted with cells in the quasi west-to-east line with a steady moist southerly flow in the low-levels feeding the cells.

19. Obviously, SMC alone should not be used to forecast convection. When used with the other analyses, it promises to improve the accuracy of forecasting convection.

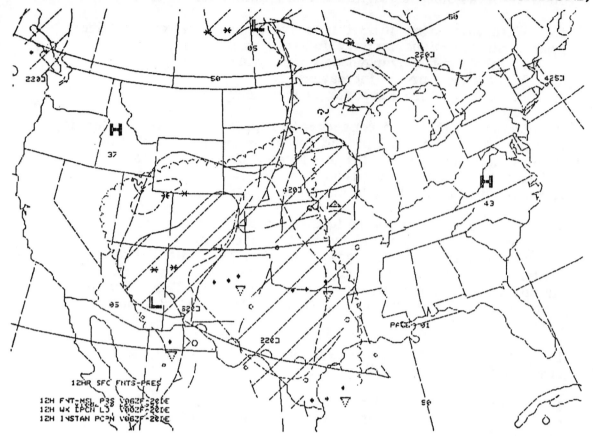

Figure 67. A 12-hour Surface Weather Map Prog (Forecast), valid for the Z-time (UTC Time) given on the chart.

This set of forecasts is for weather features that are expected to occur 12, 24, 36 and 48 hours from the initial time. The valid time, in Z-time (UTC), and date, for the forecast is given on the chart.

The 12-hour and 24-hour forecasts give the locations of high and low pressure centers and fronts. Ridges of high pressure and troughs of low pressure are also depicted. Isobars are drawn for every 4 or 8 mb.

Some of the surface progs also include information of interest to the aviation community: areas of low clouds and low visibilities. For example, IFR conditions ("instrument flight rules": ceilings [cloud bases] below 1000 feet above the ground and/or visibilities below 3 miles) are enclosed within a solid line. MVFR conditions ("marginal visibility flight rules": ceilings from 1000 feet to 3000 feet and/or visibilities from 3 to 5 miles) are enclosed within a scalloped line. The rest of the area is expected to be in VFR conditions ("visibility flight rules": ceilings above 3000 feet and visibilities above 5 miles).

(continued)

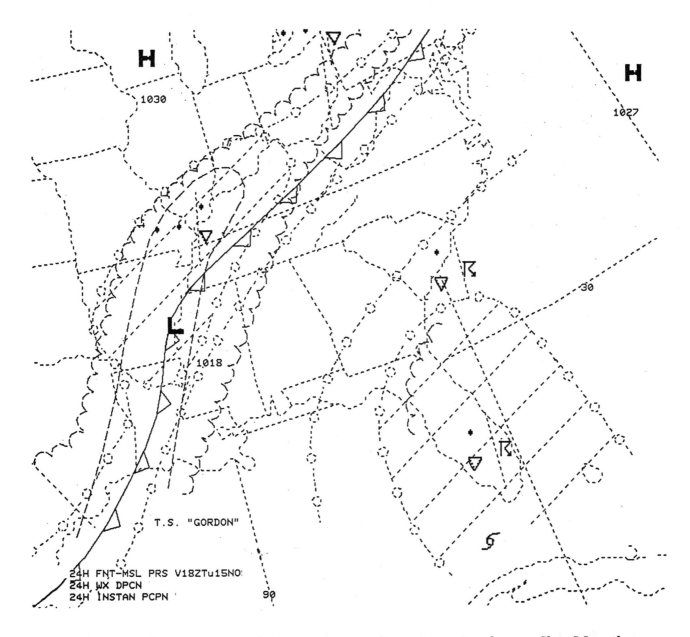

Figure 67a. A zoomed-in section of a 24-hour surface prog, showing predicted locations of high and low pressure centers, fronts, clouds and weather. Standard weather symbols (as given in chapter 2) are used for precipitation types, thunderstorms and hurricanes. The "T.S. Gordon" refers to the predicted location for 18Z for Tropical Storm Gordon, located in the vicinity of the Florida keys.

(continued)

Areas of scattered precipitation are within dashed or dotted lines, and areas of broken (6 to 9 tenths coverage) to solid precipitation are within a solid line. The type of precipitation is plotted, using standard weather symbols given in chapter 2.

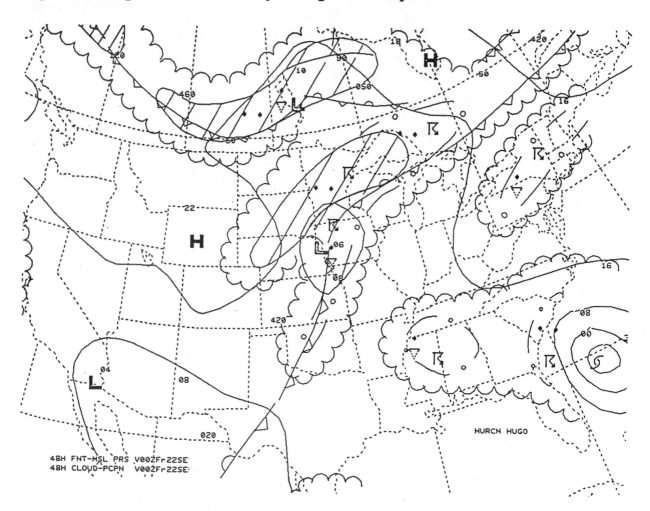

Figure 68. A 48-hour Surface Prog. The 36- and 48-hour progs are not as detailed as the 12- and 24-hour forecasts in that a general cloud forecast is depicted.

On the 36- and 48-hour progs, generally cloudy or mostly cloudy skies are scalloped in, for low and/or middle clouds and for thick high clouds.

Low clouds have bases of 6500 feet or less, above the ground, such as cumulus, stratus and stratocumulus clouds. Cumulus clouds that grow into cumulonimbus are the showers that become thunderstorms. Stratus clouds are low, straight-based clouds that yield very small water droplets called drizzle. When stratus clouds are based on the ground, we call them fog. Stratocumulus clouds and nimbo-stratus clouds can give steady precipitation, such as steady rain or snow.

(continued)

Middle clouds are clouds with bases above 6500 feet high to 20,000 feet high. Examples are cumulus and stratus clouds with bases that high, which are then called altocumulus and altostratus. Although it is possible to receive some precipitation from clouds with such high bases (mid-level based precip.), the precipitation would likely evaporate before reaching the ground, which phenomenon is called VIRGA.

High clouds are clouds with bases above 20,000 feet. This clouds are high enough so that they form in temperatures below freezing; because of this, they are comprised of ice crystals. Examples are cirrus clouds, which look like feathers in the sky, and stratus and cumulus clouds that occur that high up, and are therefore called cirrostratus and cirrocumulus.

These are not all the cloud forms, but do define the broad classifications. These heights are for mid-latitudes. In the tropics, the low, middle and high categories would have somewhat higher base limits, and in the high latitudes the upper limit height of each category would be lower (for example, middle clouds in the Arctic would start nor at about 6500 feet above the ground, but more like 4500 feet).

On all of these surface progs, areas of more widespread precipitation may also be stippled-in.

The various suppliers of weather data may opt to modify these charts with varied presentations, but they all will include locations of fronts and pressure centers, and should include areas of cloudiness and precipitation.

39. CLIMATOLOGICAL CHARTS: TEMPERATURES, RAINFALL, SNOWFALL

Within about an hour after 00Z (00 hours UTC), a map of the daytime high temperatures up until 00Z is available from the National Weather Service. Within about an hour after 12Z, a map of the overnight low temperatures up until 12Z is available. Any new temperature records established for any of the reporting stations are also given.

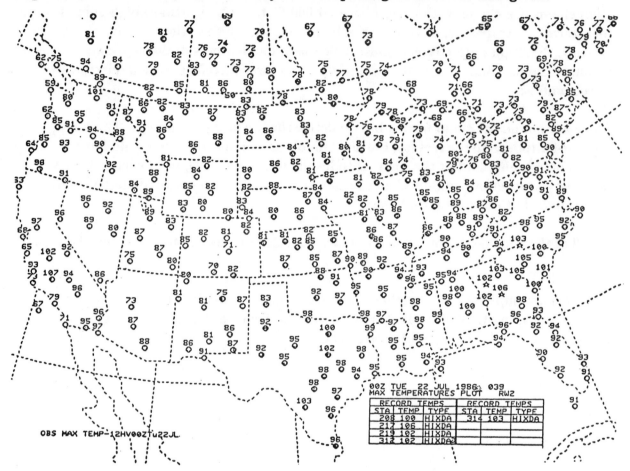

Figure 69. A Maximum 12-Hour Temperature Chart for high temperatures at each reporting station for the 12 hours ending at 00Z.

A similar chart is issued for the 12-hour minimum temperature through 12Z.

Any additional reports not plotted are listed with their station identifiers to the side of the map.

If any records are tied or set, both the Maximum Temperature Chart and the Minimum Temperature Chart lists them next to their station identification numbers, using the code on the following page

(continued)

Coding for record high and low temperatures set or tied:

HIEDA & LOEDA = Highest (Lowest) Equalled for Date
HIXDA & LOXDA = Highest (Lowest) Exceeded for Date
HIESE & LOESE = Highest (Lowest) Equalled for So Early in Season
HIXSE & LOXSE = Highest (Lowest) Exceeded for So Early in Season
HIEFM & LOEFM = Highest (Lowest) Equalled for the Month
HIXFM & LOXFM = Highest (Lowest) Exceeded for the Month
HIESL & LOESL = Highest (Lowest) Equalled for So Late in the Season
HIXSL & LOXSL = Highest (Lowest) Exceeded for So Late in the Season
HIEAT & LOEAT = Highest (Lowest) Equalled for All Time
HIXAT & LOXAT = Highest (Lowest) Exceeded for All Time

If a station circle is replaced by a star, this indicates a new or tied record for that location.

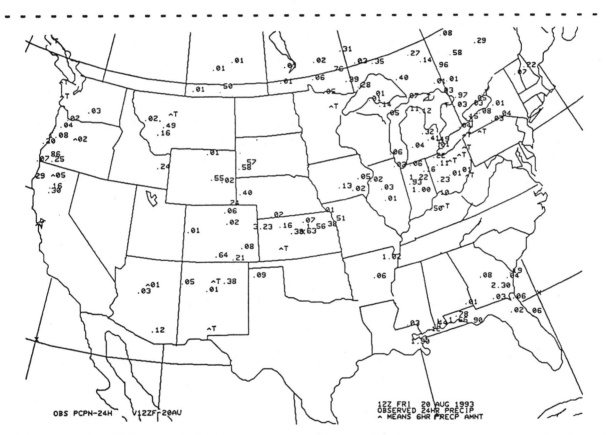

Figure 70. A 24-Hour Rainfall Chart, which is issued for the water equivalent of rain and melted solid precipitation that falls within 24 hours ending at 12Z.

Amounts are to the nearest 0.01"; a trace (under 0.01") is reported as T. If a station reports no 24 hour total but has a total for the 6 hours ending at 12Z, a carat, ∧ , is plotted next to the value.

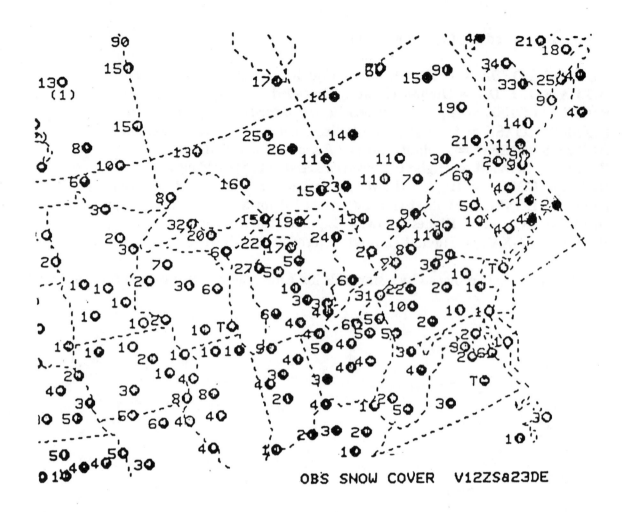

Figure 71. A zoomed-in portion of a Snowcover Chart, issued daily for snow depth on the ground reported at the 12Z surface observation to the nearest inch. If there were snowfall in the past 6 hours ending at 12Z, then that snowfall amount is plotted in parentheses, next to the observed snowdepth which is plotted if different from that six-hour snowfall.

Low-level winds blowing from the direction of a heavy snowcover are likely to hold temperatures down downstream. Therefore, this chart has some forecasting applicability besides being of climatological interest.

40. COMPUTER FORECAST MODELS
...and their Prognostications

History:

Around the year 1900, weather researcher Vilhelm Bjerknes in Europe stated that the future weather could be predicted by taking the mathematical equations of motions that define atmospheric behavior, and inserting for data the initial conditions describing the atmosphere, and then solving the equations out in time to generate weather maps showing forecasted conditions at the surface and aloft that could be used as guidance in weather forecasting.

We know much about atmospheric processes. Meteorologists know the equations of motion for the atmosphere and relevant related equations dealing with such things as parameterizing friction, radiation and moisture transport. Thus, if we have the means to collect a plethora of data at the surface and aloft and insert it as the initial conditions into these equations and then calculate the results, we can generate forecast weather maps (prognostications or "progs").

In Bjerknes time, there were no computers to grind out solutions for these integrated equations, so the concept remained a wish item.

Then, during the World War I period of 1914-1918, a British researcher, Lewis F. Richardson, while on duty in France as a medical corpsman, wrote a manuscript describing a scheme for using current weather observations of surface and upper-air parameters, with the basic (called "primitive") equations of motion of the atmosphere, to forecast "by the numbers" (called "NUMERICAL FORECASTING").

Richardson's manuscript on numerical modeling was later lost in a coal bin. It was recovered several months later, refined, and published in 1922 as "Weather Prediction by Numerical Process". Richardson determined that with the use of mechanical hand calculators, it would require some 6000 persons, all working at the same time, to do the necessary computations to generate a 12- to 24-hour set of forecast maps! Computers were not even a viable concept at that time.

Eventually, in 1948, John von Neumann, a Hungarian mathematician, working at Princeton University, used one of the very first computers to successfully generate a numerical forecast. The first computer forecast model was born.

The first model took up to a few hours to create an analysis, and 12-, 24- and 36-hour forecasts of the 500 millibar height and vorticity fields. Eventually, more sophisticated models were developed, leading to forecasts of much of the weather maps included in this book. Thus, there are now computer forecasts, from several weather forecasting models, of the maps of surface and upper-air conditions, including forecast maps showing the distribution of moisture and predicting derived fields such as the vertical velocity field.

(continued)

This is a complex topic, but anyone who enjoys meteorology would likely find it fascinating how these forecast models are set up and how they work. This chapter describes the fundamentals of "numerical forecasting".

The Four Steps of Numerical Weather Prediction by Computer Models:

1. ANALYSIS - objectively analyze the data

2. INITIALIZATION - adjust the analysis so that the model can be run with it

3. PREDICTION - run the computer model

4. POST-PROCESS - generate products such as forecasted weather maps, from the computer-model output, and clean up any erroneous lines or data

STEP 1. ANALYSIS
The technique called "objective analysis" of the data puts these observations into the computer. The computer program then reads these numbers at data points called grid points. Thus, an analysis grid can to be created. This can be the same grid as the final result in the forecast grid.

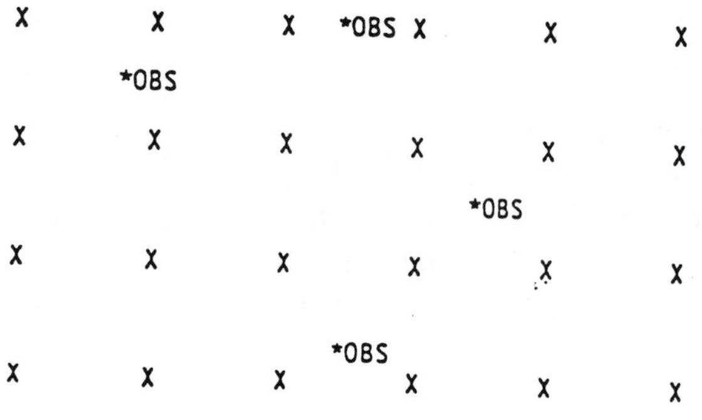

```
X       X       X  *OBS X       X        X
    *OBS

X       X       X       X       X        X

                            *OBS

X       X       X       X       X         X

            *OBS
X       X       X       X       X         X
```

Figure 72. A Small Section of an Analysis Grid. The X's are the analysis grid points. "OBS" represents the actual sites where the observations at the surface and aloft are made. The objective analysis scheme uses these randomly-spaced observations to determine what their values would be at the analysis grid points. There are different interpolation schemes employed to assign the values of such meteorological parameters as temperature, moisture, pressure, wind, etc. to each grid point. One type of scheme is a "distance-weighted" scheme in which the computer program assigns more "weight" to the data closest to the grid points. If there are no observation sites near a grid point, the analysis uses a forecast made a few hours earlier from a computer forecast model, for those points, as a "first guess" for the weather conditiions there.

(continued)

STEP 2. INITIALIZATION

A computer forecast model is set up using equations to solve for the state of the atmosphere at future times. The analysis done in step 1 is therefore then rewritten, redescribed, so that it is compatible with being input to these equations used by the forecast model.

STEP 3. PREDICTION

There are many equations used to describe the atmosphere and atmospheric processes. The first set of these is called the PRIMITIVE EQUATIONS, because they are the set of basic equations that define the conditions.

The primitive equations are the following. The wind is defined by its components: the westerly (west-to-east) component, the southerly component and the vertical component. Then, the equations used are for the accelerations of the components of the wind. There is an equation called the EQUATION OF CONTINUITY, which is used because air cannot be created or destroyed; each parcel of air must be accounted for as it moves about. Another primitive equation is called the HYDROSTATIC EQUATION, which relates the change in pressure to the change in height. It is derived from the equation for the acceleration of the vertical component of the wind. Another equation, called POISSON'S EQUATION, relates the temperature and pressure and a quantity called POTENTIAL TEMPERATURE which is what the temperature of a parcel of air would be if brought down or up to 1000 millibars. The potential temperature of a parcel of air is a CONSERVATIVE PROPERTY of that air parcel. In meteorology, the term "conservative" means it changes relatively slowly and can therefore be used to trace or follow the air parcel. Another example of a conservative property is the dewpoint. Poisson's equation is based on the First Law of Thermodynamics which defines the change of heat energy per unit mass by the parcel's temperature change, density, pressure and specific heat capacity. Another primitive equation is for SPECIFIC HUMIDITY or MIXING RATIO, so that moisture can be parameterized. The mixing ratio is the ratio or parts of water vapor in a sample of air, per 1000 parts of that sample. It defines the amount of water vapor in the air.

In the three equations for the accelerations of the westerly, southerly and vertical components of the wind, respectively, are included terms to describe the local time rate of change of that wind component, the two horizontal advection components and the vertical advection component. These terms we want to solve for from the following: the Coriolis term, the pressure-gradient term and the friction term. These are factors that determine what the wind will be.

Beyond the primitive equations are equations for derived fields such as divergence and vorticity of the wind. The model also must use a coordinate system: for example, is it easier to solve these equations in isobaric coordinates than in some other coordinate system?

This part of designing a forecast model is quite complicated and quite difficult. If you are, or plan to become, reasonably versatile in calculus, then you would likely enjoy reading the mathematical/physical equations/definings for the state of the atmosphere and atmospheric processes in a good college text on DYNAMIC METEOROLOGY. (continued)

If we want a forecast set of weather maps for the surface and aloft and for such weather variables as moisture, and if we also want cross-sections of such features as vertical velocity and moisture mixing ratio, and we want that set of numerical data and their derived weather maps to be for 3 hours for now and for every three hours out to, say, 72 hours, the computer model does not jump from the current conditions to the first 3-hour prognostication. Instead, the model solves in short TIME-STEPS.

The model starts with the initial conditions and solves for the conditions minutes later. Suppose the time step is 5 minutes. If the initial time is 00Z, then the first forecast or projection is for 5 minutes after 00Z, and the next forecast is for 10 minutes after 00Z. The first set of products issued would be for 03Z. The next set would be for 06Z, and so on for every 3 hours out to 72 hours.

If the model is run again at 03Z, then a new set of 3-hourly progs out to 72 hours would be generated using 5-minute time steps.

The grid spacing and time steps give rise to a serious modeling problem known as COMPUTATIONAL INSTABILITY. If d is the grid spacing, Δt is the time step and c is the speed of the fastest waves or disturbances in the solution, then d > or = c Δt.

Thus, the smaller the grid spacing, d, the smaller the time-step possible. Also, a problem arises because there are other waves in the atmosphere besides meteorological long and short waves. Examples are sound waves and gravity waves. These such waves need to be filtered out or otherwise compensated for, or else they provide "noise" (they distort) the forecasts. For example, nonmeteorological waves can distort height lines on a forecasted upper-air chart.

To add to the already complex problem of numerical forecasting, the effects of radiation from the sun and from the earth, and the effects of friction, need to be parameterized. Sometimes, "fudge factors" are thrown in to compensate for such effects.

Thus, you can see how difficult and fascinating it is to attempt to create a computer program, a meteorological model, to forecast weather conditions.

STEP 4. POST-PROCESS

After the model makes its set of forecasts, the output is interpolated from the model coordinates to the display coordinates. The data and maps are also "cleaned up", i.e., filtered, for cosmetic purposes. The results are the model forecast weather maps and numerical data from the models.

Grid-point data from the models are also used by contemporary software to generate weather graphics. Thus, you can create your own weather maps from the output of various forecast models.

(continued)   PAGE 134

Some Model Problems:

When you create a computer program which is a model of the atmosphere, and start with initial conditions, solve the equations, and receive a set of forecasts for conditions for out to 72 hours or longer, you must expect significant problems to arise because of the complexity of the undertaking.

Following are examples of the most serious problems in using computer models to obtain forecast guidance.

1. Relatively small amount of observational data

In the better models, the analysis grid points may be less than 50 km (less than about 30 miles) apart, but upper air observations and sometimes surface observations may be over 100 miles apart. Assuming that the observations are accurate, we can say that the more inaccurate the initial analysis is, the greater is the likelihood that forecast charts will contain inaccuracies, especially as we go further out in time since errors keep amplifying. Thus, observational errors and inadequate spacing of observation sites contribute to inaccurate analyses.

2. Boundary errors

The best models would be global models so that errors creeping in through the boundaries would be minimized. For example, suppose we are using a forecast model whose domain is essentially North America. Weather also moves in from off Asia and the Western Pacific. The model would not see and treat this activity beyond its western limits. Therefore, the accuracy of that model diminishes more rapidly with time than would the accuracy of a global model of similar sophistication, A good operational rule is that if the current weather charts look very close like what the model forecasted 12 hours ago for the current time, then the model likely has a good "handle" on the atmospheric behavior, and its forecasts for out to 36 and maybe 48 hours can be used as guidance.

3. Loss of most mesoscale features

The grid-spacing of some models precludes detection and prediction of some sub-synoptic scale features (smaller-scale features such as individual thunderstorms, for example). As the models improve over the years and the grid-spacing gets closer, these "mesoscale" or smaller-scale features will be easier to account for in the initial analysis and will be easier for the models to forecast. Also, there are many short-waves in the low and middle troposphere that are only a few degrees or less longitude wide. Since each is baroclinic, each has its own areas of upward vertical motion and downward vertical motion. For example, showers may be initiated or enhanced by the moving in of an undetected short-wave trough, but the model would be unable to forecast its occurrence.

(continued)

4. Parameterizing physical processes

Processes such as solar radiation, terrestrial (from the earth outward) radiation (including radiation reflected and rereflected by cloud tops and bases, etc.), evaporation from below clouds, precipitation and other physical processes must be explicitly or implicitly accounted for in order to have the model give a realistic simulation of the atmosphere. Here is an example of a wrong solution: a model would continue to warm the atmosphere in lower latitudes if radiative effects on the earth, its oceans, cryosphere (snow- and ice-covered regions) and its atmosphere were improperly accounted for.

Clouds and precipitation are some of the most important physical processes that a model must predict. These models can be structured such that the average relative humidity in a vertical layer of the atmosphere, or the relative humidity at the midpoint of each such layer, must be at or above a certain threshold before cloudiness will be predicted, and at or above a higher threshold value before precipitation will be forecasted. Upward vertical motion must also be present. However, this binary-type yes-no approach may yield a wrong forecast when actual initial conditions are borderline.

It is also important to know how the layers in the models are structured because that may infer where some biases could arise.

5. Parameterizing convection

Early forecast models were incapable of analyzing and then forecasting on the small scale of the thunderstorm. Contemporary models are getting better at it because of smaller grid-spacing and time-steps, more observations from the surface and aloft, and more computer power. However, sometimes when a major thunderstorm is occurring at the time of a sounding and this data becomes part of the analysis and initialization of the model, the model could "blow the storm up" in time into a hurricane-like storm or at least into a copious rainmaker far above what is realistic. This problem is known as CONVECTIVE FEEDBACK. Moreover, mesoscale features that create convection may be difficult for the model to detect and forecast. For example, a model may not handle a mesoscale convective system well because there is no real accounting for downdrafts and rainfall amounts in that particular model. The bottom line is this: be careful of quantitative precipitation forecast amounts generated by forecast models, especially when it involves convection.

A SUMMARY: WHY DO COMPUTER FORECAST MODELS GENERATE ERRORS AND WHY DO ERRORS GROW?

The initial analysis contains errors because of observational errors and too few observations. There are phenomena on scales that are sub-grid. There are some approximations in using the governing equations. The physics are crudely incorporated. Most of the governing equations are nonlinear, which causes initial errors to grow in time. If most of the equations were linear, then probably most of the errors would be advected around but not grow. Thus, forecasting the state of the atmosphere via a computer program/model is rather difficult, but newer models keep making progress in this fascinating aspect of meteorology.

(continued)

Figure 73. **Examples of 3 Forecast Models, Showing their Vertical Layers in Millibars.** Keep in mind that the vertical difference between each millibar is much greater the higher we go; thus, this diagram is not drawn to scale. Notice that there are more and thinner layers near the ground, since this is where most of the varied weather occurs.

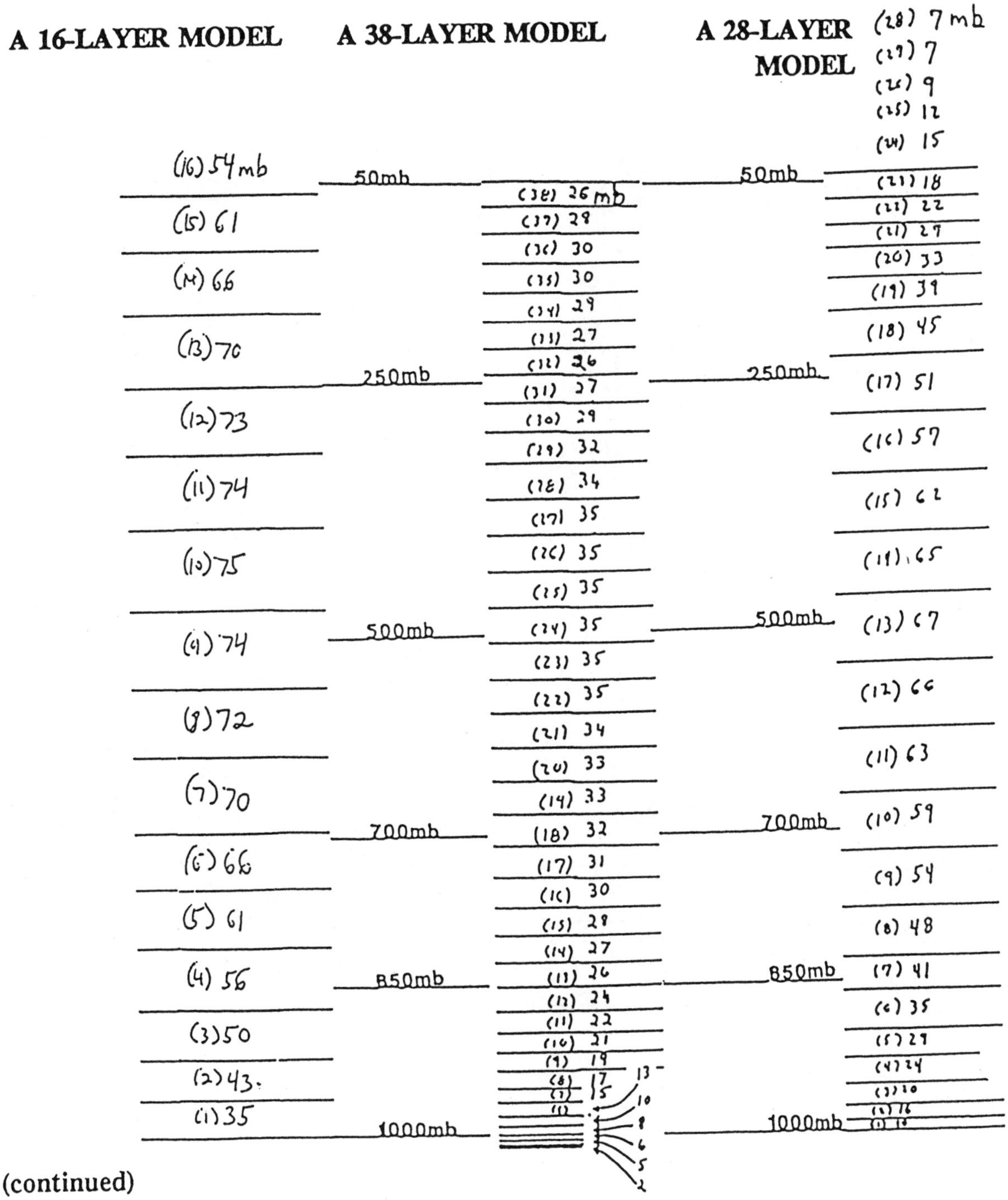

A 16-LAYER MODEL   A 38-LAYER MODEL   A 28-LAYER MODEL

A 16-LAYER MODEL:
(16) 54mb
(15) 61
(14) 66
(13) 70
(12) 73
(11) 74
(10) 75
(9) 74
(8) 72
(7) 70
(6) 66
(5) 61
(4) 56
(3) 50
(2) 43.
(1) 35

A 38-LAYER MODEL (reference lines 50mb, 250mb, 500mb, 700mb, 850mb, 1000mb):
(38) 26mb
(37) 29
(36) 30
(35) 30
(34) 29
(33) 27
(32) 26
(31) 27
(30) 29
(29) 32
(28) 34
(27) 35
(26) 35
(25) 35
(24) 35
(23) 35
(22) 35
(21) 34
(20) 33
(19) 33
(18) 32
(17) 31
(16) 30
(15) 28
(14) 27
(13) 26
(12) 24
(11) 22
(10) 21
(9) 19
(8) 17
(7) 15
...

A 28-LAYER MODEL:
(28) 7mb
(27) 7
(26) 9
(25) 12
(24) 15
(23) 18
(22) 22
(21) 27
(20) 33
(19) 39
(18) 45
(17) 51
(16) 57
(15) 62
(14) 65
(13) 67
(12) 66
(11) 63
(10) 59
(9) 54
(8) 48
(7) 41
(6) 35
(5) 29
(4) 24
(3) 20
(2) 16
(1) 14

(continued)

The analysis grid may or may not be the same as the forecast grid. You can design these computer model programs to your own specifications after justifying to yourself which way to do them. For example, suppose the analysis grid and the forecast grid are the same. Here, then, is an example of a map of the grid-spacing.

Figure 74. A map showing the horizontal grid-points (in this case, 92 by 141) for a computer forecast model whose domain is essentially North America and some of the surrounding region.

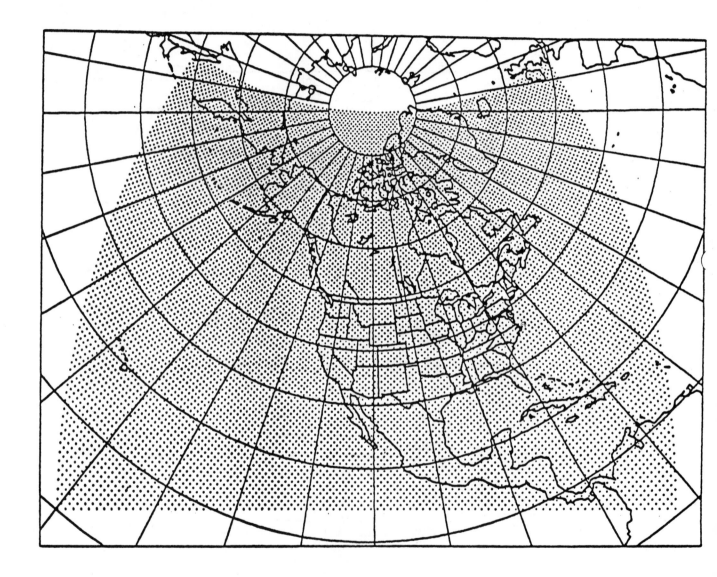

(continued)

In figure 74, the horizontal resolution is approximately 49 miles (80 km). This means that the distance between a mass point and the next mass point is about 49 miles. Each row is along a parallel of latitude and each column is along a meridian of longitude. In this type of model grid, the grid is oriented as if the earth's latitude/longitude lines are rotated by taking the point where the equator crosses the prime meridian and shifting it to the center of the region over which the model is making its forecasts.

The central point on this particular grid is at 52 degrees N latitude and 111 degrees W longitude. This central point is located at the intersection of the rotated equator and the rotated prime meridian. By positioning the new equator across the center of the forecast domain, the CONVERGENCE OF MERIDIANS effect is minimized. This effect arises because the longitude lines converge at the poles, and that would conflict with our grid spacing.

Note in figure 73 that our 38-layer model example has layers that are under 30 millibars thick around 250 mb. This is where the polar jet-stream is typically found. The better resolution at these levels allows for a better definition of conditions/features in the jet-streaks and vicinity, just as the better definition through more and less-deep layers near the ground allows for better detail of the weather in the region where people live.

The models must also consider the topography of the surface. Features such as mountains, large bodies of water, and vegetative cover also affect the air flow and rest of the weather.

Returning to our discussion on the forecast grid, it is better to have a global grid so that errors along the boundaries do not "creep inward" with time, distorting the forecasts. When these and any other errors are introduced into the models, they ruin the forecasts the farther out in time we run the projections.

We can also design a model that covers more than the Northern Hemispheric domain but less than the entire planet. An example is a Northern Hemispheric model in which the initials conditions south of the equator are given as a mirror of what is occurring north, or else a "wall" at the equator ends the analysis.

An interesting approach to computer modeling of the weather is a NESTED GRID MODEL. This type of model has a grid within a grid, with the forecast area of interest being the innermost grid. That way, the outer grid's conditions affect the weather for the area for which we want the forecast...the area inside the inner grid...and keeps out many boundary errors and for a longer time, since these errors work inward through the grids.

Also, a model can be designed to have THREE grids: a grid within a grid within a grid, to protect the innermost forecast grid from boundary errors.

(continued)

Figure 75. An example of the forecast grid for a Nested Grid Model.
The forecast grid is the inner grid, but conditions/weather systems in the outer grid that eventually move into and otherwise affect the conditions within the forecast grid (inner grid) are accounted for. This minimizes boundary errors that would arise because there would be no other data beyond the boundaries of the forecast grid. A nested grid model is unnecessary with a global grid, since a global model has no terrestrial boundaries or limits.

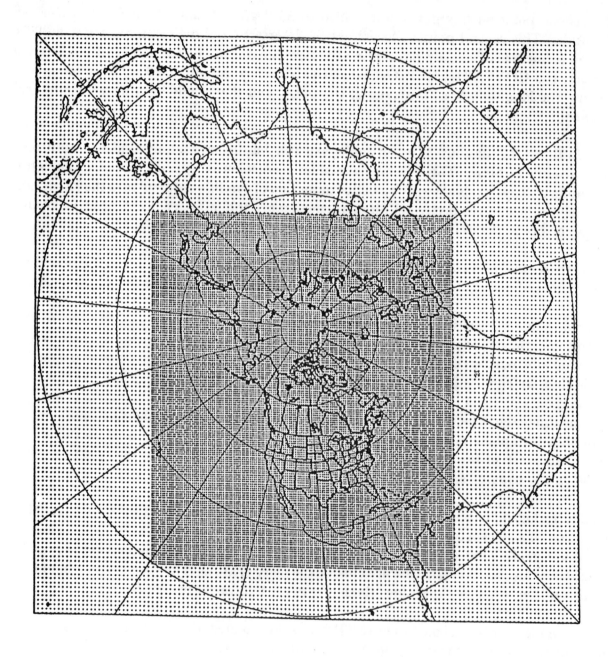

(continued)

Another type of model is one for which the model is centered on a storm. This is a movable grid, also called a movable mesh. The value of this is that if the domain is somewhat smaller than North America, the weather system of great importance, e.g.: a major winter storm or a hurricane, can be placed in the middle of the model's domain and the model can be run to make forecasts for out to 60 or 72 hours in an attempt to forecast how that major storm is likely to move. Errors creeping in from the boundaries would increase the inaccuracies of the forecast with time, but the model may be quite useful for the first 12 to 24 or even out to 36 hours in forecasting the development and movement of the storm. Most of the influences of the storm would come from its ambient environment, which would be about the center of the grid.

For long-term forecasting for over ten days out, and for climatological forecasting for months or years out, a global model is needed. This type of forecasting from a computer model/program is general in nature: that is to say, its strength is in showing basic long-wave patterns that infer where temperatures will be above, about and below normal for specific time periods, and hopefully similar guidance for precipitation.

How the Forecast Model Programs Solve the Mathematical Equations

The complex meteorological equations of calculus mathematics are solved by using either of two schemes: FINITE DIFFERENCING or SPECTRAL ANALYSIS.

Finite differencing uses discrete distances to solve many of the equations. As an example, consider a part of an equation that solves for a simple local change in the west-to-east component of the wind. In meteorology, the wind is separated into its west-to-east, south-to-north and vertical components. An southeast wind, then, (wind coming from the southeast) has a positive south-to-north component and a negative west-to-east component.

In the meteorological calculus, the west-to-east wind component is called u. The west-to-east distance is x (the south-to-north distance is y and the vertical distance is z, when using cartesian coordinates).

So, if we want to use the finite differencing method to solve for the local change in the u-component (west-to-east component) of the wind, we are solving for $\frac{\partial u}{\partial x}$.

Now let us see how to use the finite differencing method to solve for this, and to solve for some slightly more complicated weather parameters: relative vorticity and horizontal divergence of the wind.

(continued)

Figure 76. Using finite differencing to solve for the local change in the west-to-east (u) component of the wind. What is the change at point zero, 0, if we know u at points 1 and 2?

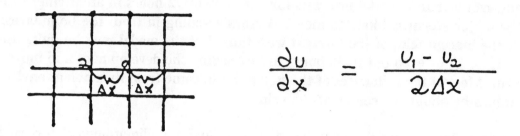

$$\frac{\partial u}{\partial x} = \frac{u_1 - u_2}{2 \Delta x}$$

Figure 77. If we want to solve for relative vorticity, ζ, at point 0, then, since

$$\zeta = \frac{\partial v}{\partial x} - \frac{\partial u}{\partial y} \quad , \text{ then:}$$

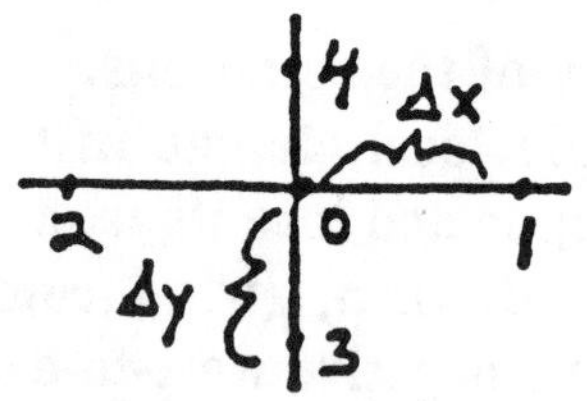

$$\zeta = \frac{\partial v}{\partial x} - \frac{\partial u}{\partial y} =$$

$$\frac{v_1 - v_2}{2 \Delta x} - \frac{(u_4 - u_3)}{2 \Delta y}$$

Figure 78. For horizontal divergence at point zero, δ_0, we have:

$$\delta_0 = \left(\frac{\partial u}{\partial x}\right)_0 + \left(\frac{\partial v}{\partial y}\right)_0 = \frac{u_1 - u_2}{2 \Delta x} + \frac{(v_4 - v_3)}{2 \Delta y}$$

(continued)

When we use this finite differencing method to solve the calculus equations in mathematical weather forecast computer models, we are using grid points of the same distance apart in the x-direction, and in the y-direction the grid points are equally spaced but the y-spacing need not be the same as the x-spacing. Then through the objective analysis technique described earlier, data values are interpolated for the grid points. We cannot use an unequal grid: a grid with the grid points being where the data sites are. If we did, then a proportional-type grid spacing would need to be devised.

Another technique for solving the model's equations is called SPECTRAL ANALYSIS, which essentially converts the equations to wave forms and then solves wave equations, afterwhich the solutions are transformed back into forecasts of the various variables such as heights, temperatures, pressures, moisture, etc.

A model using this spectral technique is called a SPECTRAL MODEL, just as a model employing finite differencing to solve the equations is called a FINITE DIFFERENCING MODEL.

In a spectral model, atmospheric fields such as temperature, pressure and density are represented by waves around the hemisphere. Suppose, for example, that we devise a 160-wave global spectral model. With 360 degrees of longitude around the hemisphere, 160 waves translates into a wave "grid-spacing" of 2.25 degrees.

The wave number is the number of oscillations over the hemisphere. What this means is that wave number 1 has one ridge and one trough, with the ridge and trough being 180 degrees of longitude apart; wave number 2 has two oscillations, i.e., 2 ridges and 2 troughs across the hemisphere, 90 degrees longitude apart. Thus, this spectral model's 160 waves define the data sets in terms of 160 ridges and 160 troughs (160 oscillations) across the hemisphere, with each wave having a length (wavelength) of 2.25 degrees longitude. A mathematical technique known as Fourier analysis is then used to determine the actual conditions which are combinations of the various wave numbers, with the combinations varying across the hemisphere.

Therefore, a spectral-type of forecast model assumes that all the meteorological fields of interest in the atmosphere can be described in a Fourier-type series of eaves (e.g., sines and cosines) over a sphere. Thus, data are described by waves.

As we approach the poles, the wave numbers need to be truncated, which is similar to the situation in a grid-point model wherein there are fewer grid points as we approach the poles.

Thus, we can appreciate the ingenious methodologies being used to attempt to forecast atmospheric conditions which require the solutions of complex equations.

(continued)

Sigma and Eta Surfaces

Sigma is the Greek letter σ. Some numerical weather prediction models use pressure, p, for the vertical coordinate, and some use sigma surfaces. Solving the primitive equations in an x-y-p coordinate system is difficult because the lower boundary, the earth's surface, is not an isobaric surface. The problem is worsened because the modeling needs to be done over large variations of terrain elevation, and isobaric surfaces intersect the terrain at sometimes steep angles. Keep in mind that the models are divided into layers of the atmosphere. The top and bottom of each layer is a pressure surface.

Therefore, it is challenging to specify the lowest boundary conditions for the model variables.

The problem is solved by transforming the vertical coordinate, pressure, into the sigma, σ, coordinate.

$$\sigma(x,y) \equiv \frac{p}{P_S(x,y)} \qquad P_S = \text{surface pressure}$$

Sigma coordinates are determined by the following:

$$\frac{(P) - (P \text{ at top})}{(P \text{ at bottom}) - (P \text{ at top})}$$

Thus, when using sigma, σ, as the vertical coordinate rather than using height, z, or pressure, p, the value (of sigma) is 1 at the "surface" and 0 at the top of the model's domain.

By creating the sigma vertical coordinate as the pressure at any level "normalized" by the surface pressure, the ground also becomes a coordinate surface. Then, the effects of the variable terrain are better parameterized by the forecast model.

A variation of the sigma coordinate is the ETA, η, coordinate, where the mean sea-level rather than the ground becomes a coordinate surface.

One benefit of using eta surfaces is that the computer model can do a rather good job of computing the pressure-gradient force in areas of steeply-sloping terrain, which had been a problem in previous models. This is because eta surfaces do not slope steeply as the ground does, and as do the sigma surfaces at low levels. Sigma surfaces follow the terrain.

(continued)

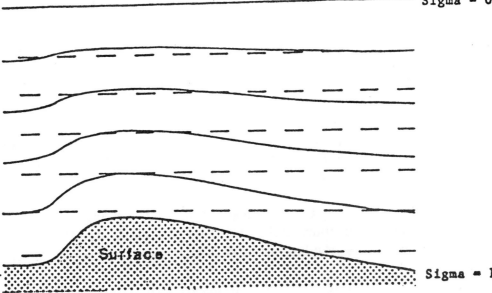

Sigma = 0

Surface

Sigma = 1

Figure 79. This diagram illustrates how sigma surfaces, the solid lines, typically compare with pressure surfaces, the dashed lines. Notice that in the lower atmosphere the lines of constant sigma more-or-less follow the terrain.

Both sigma and eta surfaces are fairly horizontal over flat terrain and over the oceans; however, in the areas where there are significant elevation changes of the ground surface over relatively short distances, the horizontal variation of the sea-level pressure is much less than that of the surface pressure, so that the sea-level-pressure-based eta surfaces do not slope as much as the surface-pressure-based sigma surfaces, near the earth's surface.

With the more-horizontal nature of eta, modelers typically design an eta model's topography in the form of steps for mountainous areas.

Looking at figure 79 for sigma surfaces, notice that sigma varies from 1 at the model's ground surface to zero at the top of the model's atmospheric domain. The eta vertical coordinate varies from 1 at mean sea-level to zero at the top of the model's atmospheric domain. Ideally, we would want a model that has the top of the atmosphere, zero millibars, as the top of its atmospheric domain, but the models can stop at say 50 mb.

Sigma is normalized with respect to the surface pressure, and eta is normalized with respect to the mean sea-level pressure.

Thus, referring again to figure 79, sigma is the pressure at any particular level, "normalized" by the surface pressure. It is a nondimensional coordinate variable. Eta is similar, but "normalized" by the mean sea-level pressure.

(continued)

Weather Maps from Forecast Models

Most of the types of weather maps in this book are also produced by the various forecast models. In the United States, teams of National Weather Service modelers and forecasters in the issues these maps from the World Weather Building in Camp Springs, Maryland.

For example, you can obtain from several models, sets of 6-, 12-, 18-, 24-, 36- and 48-hour prognostications ("progs") (and progs for other times from various models) of these maps: the surface, 850 mb, 700 mb, 500 mb, 300 mb, 250 mb, 200 mb, 100 mb, average relative humidity from the surface to 500 mb, 700 mb vertical velocities, and many more.

All models are given names. (When the models are wrong, they sometimes are given other, unofficial names!) The name or abbreviation of the specific model and the valid time and date of each prog are printed at the bottom of each chart.

For example, a 12-hour 700 mb temperature (isotherms) prog issued from the model run of the "ETA MODEL" at 12Z on Tuesday, February 14th would say something such as:

12H ETA 700 TEMP V00ZWe15FExx
(where xx is for the year)

This 700 mb isotherm prog from the ETA Model came out at 12Z on Tuesday and is a 12-hour prog valid at 00Z Wednesday the 15th of February.

Each weather map must be labelled to identify it and give the time for which it is valid. A current, latest conditions map is 00H (00 hour), and the Z time gives the time of the chart. All maps are issued in Z time, also called Universale Temps Coordinee (Universal Coordinated Time) (UTC), which is also called Greenwich (in England) Mean Time. This is the time there on the zero degree longitude meridian, which is the international time standard.

Thus, to convert from Z time to Eastern Standard Time, subtract 5 hours; to convert from Z to Eastern Daylight Saving Time, subtract 4 hours. Subtract an additional hour for central, another hour for mountain and another hour for Pacific time zones.

For example, a 36-hour prog would say 36H, and would also give the valid time in UTC (Z) time.

WHAT IS TELECONNECTIONS?

Teleconnections is a statistical, climatological comparison of weather features over one part of the globe having a usual connection in time and space with the weather features over another section of the globe.

For example, a 500 mb positive height anomaly over a certain portion of the North Pacific may mean that it is usually coupled with a strong long-wave trough and very cold 500 mb cutoff low for that time of year, over a certain portion of east-central North America.

Thus, if one situation is developing in one region, it typically is coupled with and expected situation elsewhere.

WHAT IS ENSEMBLE PREDICTION (OR ENSEMBLE FORECASTING)?

Ensemble prediction refers to multiple runs of a computer forecast model for the same forecast period, which each run starts with a different set of "perturbed conditions".

The differences among the sets of model forecasts tell us about the range and likelihood of possible solutions. On average, the ensemble mean forecast should beat the best single forecast from the model/

The objective of ensemble forecasting is to improve the accuracy of that model's forecasts.

An example of a more complex differential equation solved by the method of finite differencing (see pages 141-142):

Find $\dfrac{\partial^2 z}{\partial x^2} = \dfrac{\partial}{\partial x}\left(\dfrac{\partial z}{\partial x}\right)$

$$\dfrac{\left(\frac{z_2 - z_0}{\Delta x}\right) - \left(\frac{z_0 - z_1}{\Delta x}\right)}{\Delta x}$$

Thus, $\dfrac{\partial^2 z}{\partial x^2} = \dfrac{z_2 - 2z_0 + z_1}{(\Delta x)^2}$.

Similarly,

$\dfrac{\partial^2 z}{\partial y^2} = \dfrac{z_3 - 2z_0 + z_4}{(\Delta y)^2}$ Let $\Delta x = \Delta y = H$ (the grid-length) and we have

$$\dfrac{\partial^2 z}{\partial x^2} + \dfrac{\partial^2 z}{\partial y^2} = \dfrac{z_1 + z_2 + z_3 + z_4 - 4z_0}{H^2}$$, call it $\dfrac{\varepsilon}{H^2}$ (this is $\nabla^2 z$).

This is a way to solve for absolute vorticity, η, since $\eta = \dfrac{g}{F}\left(\dfrac{\varepsilon}{H^2}\right) + f$

where F = the Coriolis parameter.

THE PRIMITIVE EQUATIONS IN CARTESIAN COORDINATES

The equations of motion:

(Eq. 1)
$$\frac{\partial u}{\partial t} + u\frac{\partial u}{\partial x} + v\frac{\partial u}{\partial y} + w\frac{\partial u}{\partial z} = 2\Omega\left(v\sin\phi - w\cos\phi\right) - \frac{1}{\rho}\frac{\partial p}{\partial x} + \frac{1}{m}F_x$$

(Eq. 2)
$$\frac{\partial v}{\partial t} + u\frac{\partial v}{\partial x} + v\frac{\partial v}{\partial y} + w\frac{\partial v}{\partial z} = -2\Omega u\sin\phi - \frac{1}{\rho}\frac{\partial p}{\partial y} + \frac{1}{m}F_y$$

(Eq. 3)
$$\frac{\partial w}{\partial t} + u\frac{\partial w}{\partial x} + v\frac{\partial w}{\partial y} + w\frac{\partial w}{\partial z} = 2\Omega u\cos\phi - \frac{1}{\rho}\frac{\partial p}{\partial z} - g + \frac{1}{m}F_z$$

The equation of continuity:

(Eq. 4)
$$\frac{\partial \rho}{\partial t} + u\frac{\partial \rho}{\partial x} + v\frac{\partial \rho}{\partial y} + w\frac{\partial \rho}{\partial z} = -\rho\left(\frac{\partial u}{\partial x} + \frac{\partial v}{\partial y} + \frac{\partial w}{\partial z}\right)$$

The hydrostatic equation:

(Eq. 5) $$dp = -\rho g dz$$ (This is derived from eq. 3.)

Poisson's equation:

(Eq. 6) $$\frac{T}{\theta} = \left(\frac{p}{1000}\right)^{\alpha}$$

which is based on the 1st Law of Thermodynamics: $dh = c_p dT - \alpha dp$

When dh (change of heat per unit mass) = 0, the motion is adiabatic and the density of each parcel is determined solely by the pressure. Thus, we can use Poisson's Eq.

For the reader who is not a meteorologist and who is not familiar with these equations, here is a simple very general explanation of the terms:

Equations 1 through 3 are, respectively, the accelerations of the westerly (u), southerly (v) and vertical (w) components of the wind. The left-hand terms are, in order, the local time rate of change, the two horizontal advection components and the vertical advection. All of these terms become the total time derivatives for the parcels of air. To the right are, in order, the Coriolis term, the pressure-gradient term and the friction term. The equation of continuity shows that air is continuous; i.e., it cannot be created or destroyed in Newtonian physics. The hydrostatic equation relates the change in pressure to the change in height. Poisson's equation relates the temperature, potential temperature and pressure. The potential temperature is a characteristic property of a parcel of air; it does not change during adiabatic processes. Thus, it is a conservative property and is used to label a parcel of air which can be followed and identified by its potential temperature. Another primitive equation is one for specific humidity or mixing ratio, so that moisture can be parameterized. Again, refer to basic meteorology dynamics texts for derivations and explanations of these equations. Many other equations (vorticity, for example) are derived from the primitive eqs.

In isobaric coordinates, pressure is the vertical coordinate and in isentropic coordinates, the potential temperature is the vertical coordinate. Since in adiabatic situations air tends to move along isentropic surfaces rather than along isobaric surfaces, one would suspect that a model run in isentropic coordinates may be the preferred system; however, this author has discussed this with modelers and finds that there are arguments pro and con for isentropic models. What can be said is that a display of isentropic prediction charts would be another forecast tool.

A FOOTNOTE ON METEOROLOGICAL COMPUTER MODELLING:

The primitive equations cannot be easily solved in the analytical form because they are coupled, nonlinear partial differential equations. Analytical solutions exist for only a few greatly simplified types of models which have very little application to operational weather prediction. Therefore, for forecasting, we solve the primitive equations by first rewriting them in a form on which we can apply numerical computational techniques (such as finite differencing schemes or spectral techniques) on a computer. The continuum of space and time is broken down into finite, discrete intervals. This is known as "discretizing the equations". This transforms the analytical continuous equations into a set of algebraic equations which then are solved after given the initial conditions. All this is easier said than done! Meteorological modelling remains a tough challenge!

41. MODEL OUTPUT STATISTICS (MOS) AND MOS CHARTS

Model Output Statistics or MOS started out as a game. If a computer forecast model is giving us numerical and graphical output, why not try to use some of the numerical output to see if we can develop forecast guidance "by the numbers"?

For illustration, suppose we want to forecast the overnight low temperature for Happytown. If we have a forecast model that gives us analyses and predictions of various weather parameters for Happytown, we can look at what items would logically affect the overnight low temperature at Happytown and improve on any model forecast of temperatures alone. For example, the 1000-to-500 mb thickness would be related to the overnight low. So might the model projections of the 850 mb temperature and dewpoint, as well as the wind direction and speed. What about the observed data also, besides the model's numerical output? Also, the temperature of the soil surface and perhaps the latest surface dewpoint temperature should also be considered.

After we have determined the most logical model "predictors" and observed "predictors" that would be involved in developing a MOS equation to predict the overnight low temperature, we compare thousands of overnight lows with the values of the predictors to develop correlations. The value of each predictor is multiplied by a fraction or decimal. These decimals are therefore coefficients that are multiplied by the value of the predictor such as wind direction or thickness. All of these sets of coefficients multiplied by predictor values are then added together to predict the minimum temperature (or are related to another correlation coefficient for the low temperature). If the forecasted MOS temperature is too high or low consistently, then one or more of the coefficients needs to be changed to make the prediction equation more accurate.

We would keep about ten or twelve of the greatest contributors (most significant predictors) and drop the rest which contribute relatively very little to the value of the predicted element.

We would also have some predictors that are used some of the tim--only when they affect the overnight low temperature at Happytown. Snowcover is an example. Suppose two inches or more is needed to lower the temperature forecast, based on past observation. Then, snowcover is a "binary predictor"; that is, it is turned on (used) only when the snowcover is two inches or greater.

From here, the equations become more involved as we discuss other aspects of MOS development, such as simultaneous development of temperature and dewpoint prediction equations so that the dewpoint is not forecasted to be higher than the temperature. Also, sometimes the same equations could also be used for some of the surrounding locations. When this is possible, we have a regional set of prediction equations for one or more weather element(s) we want to try to predict using MOS. Equations could be changed seasonally, so that we have a warm set and a cold set, or that we have four sets for the year.
(continued)

Figure 80. **Two examples of a MOS maximum temperature prediction, showing the MOS predictors at the right, and the coefficients at the left.** The top MOS equation is for Topeka, Kansas and the bottom one is for Moline, Illinois. (COS DOY is cosine of the day, related to radiation from the sun.) For Topeka there are 12 predictors, with 7 of them coming from a forecast model called the NGM (Nested Grid Model) and 5 coming from actual observed data. For Moline, there are also 12 predictors, 8 from the model output and 4 from observed data. For Topeka, the binary snow-depth used is 3" or greater, but for Moline it is 1" or greater. Why?: because it works!

MAX TEMP FOR TOPEKA, KS

COEFF	MODEL	PREDICTOR
0.231130	NGM	850-1000 MB THICKNESS
-0.039539		DEW POINT
0.255040	NGM	1000 MB TEMP
-0.304150	NGM	850 MB DEW POINT TEMPERATURE
0.028751	NGM	1000 MB DEW POINT TEMPERATURE
-0.039963		TEMPERATURE
3.825400		SNOW DEPTH
-2.777900		COS DOY
0.104020	NGM	1000 MB GEOSTROPHIC WIND SPEED
0.681280		SURFACE TEMP
0.023091	NGM	700 MB U COMPONENT
0.100310	NGM	1000 MB GEOSTROPHIC V COMPONENT

CORRELATION COEF=   0.943

MAX TEMP FOR MOLINE, IL

COEFF	MODEL	PREDICTOR
0.577120	NGM	1000 MB TEMP
0.165650	NGM	850-1000 MB THICKNESS
0.093182	NGM	850 MB DEW POINT TEMPERATURE
-0.263760		DEW POINT
0.443580		TEMPERATURE
0.042164	NGM	850 MB TEMPERATURE ADVECTION (GRID WINDS)
-0.227270	NGM	850 MB DEW POINT TEMPERATURE
0.175140	NGM	1000 MB GEOSTROPHIC WIND SPEED
2.202900		SNOW DEPTH
-3.519300		COS DOY
0.035525	NGM	700 MB U COMPONENT
-0.011126	NGM	850 MB TEMPERATURE ADVECTION (GRID WINDS)

CORRELATION COEF=   0.950

(continued)

MOS equations are of the form:

$$P = (a_0) + (a_1)(X_1) + (a_2)(X_2) + (a_3)(X_3) + \ldots + (a_N)(X_N).$$

A "linear screening regression technique" is used to develop these equations. P is what we are trying to predict. If we are trying to predict the maximum temperature, then the X's represent those factors from the model and from observed and climatological data that relate to temperature. The X's are the predictors. The a's are the multiple regression coefficients.

Because most of the MOS predictors are from one of the forecast models, this means that the model cannot be changed. If we did change the model, the MOS equations based on the model output would be rendered unusable, and new equations would need to be developed. MOS equations can come from more than one model, with the guidances for each model being compared daily in operational forecasting. Thus, if one model's MOS equations show temperatures consistently too cold compared to more accurate MOS output based on another forecast model, then a known bias is acknowledged in the first model. The forecaster choosing to use the first model's guidance can know to lower the forecasted temperature by x degrees or can hope that the MOS developers change that model's MOS equation for that predicted element.

MOS guidance tends to be fairly reliable in routine weather situations, but falls apart in unusual or extreme events. This is because the non-model predictors...the observed data...from many past events are used to develop the coefficients; therefore, as the MOS equations go farther out in time, they tend to predict towards climatological means, not extremes.

When MOS is in error, it usually means that the forecast model is in error, but not always. Again, the observed data predictors have their coefficients that have been tweaked so that they work for routine weather events; therefore, the statistical relationships and their weighted importances in predicting a weather element may be in error at times.

MOS works well in routine weather but it has a greater chance of failing in extrem events such as record heat or a blast of record-breaking Arctic cold.

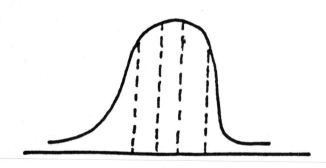

The bell curve at left illustrates the reliability of MOS. Routine weather, including storms of moderate intensity, occur within the great middle bulge of the curve. The rare events occur in the wings (these are the "outlayer" events).

SUPPLEMENTAL COMMENTS ON MOS

1. Most numerical guidance is developed by using a linear regression technique. Non-linear effects are included in the equations by virtue of some of the predictors used. For example, each binary predictor operates in a non-linear mode with respect to the original meteorological variable from which it was defined.

2. Single-station equations for probability of precipitation (POP) were not developed because of the lack of sufficient data. Thus, POP equations are regionalized.

3. MOS typically fails in unusual weather events. If MOS equations were to be developed for major unusual events such as a record-breaking Arctic cold wave or a record-breaking heat wave, they would have to be developed based on many past events, and they theoretically would improve the skill of numerical guidances when used during these episodes.

4. If the forecast model on which MOS is based were changed in any way, then the MOS equations based on that model would also need modification.

5. MOS predictions tend toward the climatological mean of the predictand at longer forecast projections.

6. Observations are also used as predictors in MOS.

7. Regionalized equations are in the same geographical and climatic area. Thus, some regions contain more stations than others.

8. Regionalized equations are developed for a particular weather element if there are insufficient data to develop single station equations.

9. Simultaneous equation development (e.g., so that a dewpoint forecast is not higher than a temperature forecast for the same time) is done to maintain meteorological consistency among the various forecasted items.

10. Examples of equations developed simultaneously are: MOS equations for the 6-hour POPs, for the 12-hour POPs, for the max/min temperatures, for the 3-hour temperature forecasts and for the 3-hour dewpoint forecasts. Separate sets of simultaneous equations are developed for different projections.

11. Consider the regression curves (lines) below.

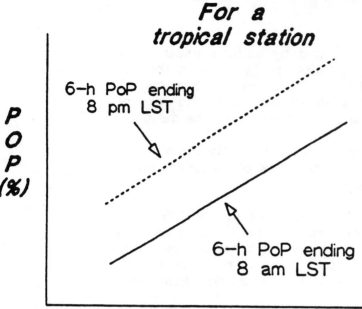

For a tropical station

P O P (%)

6-h PoP ending 8 pm LST

6-h PoP ending 8 am LST

MEAN RH (%)

Diurnal, local and climatic effects are incorporated into the numerical guidance equations. This pair of regressions lines shows that, given a constant mean RH at a tropical station, it is more likely to rain during the late afternoon than during the early morning.

Normally snowless location has a substantial snow cover

M I N   T E M P   (°F)

Forecast

Observed

1000-500 mb THICKNESS (m)

Since this station rarely if ever has a snowcover, this fact is built into the min temperature equation. Thus, if a snowcover should occur, the equation would not account for the greater radiational cooling due to a deep snowcover.

12.   Since MOS does not work for unusual, extreme or rare synoptic events (also for extreme mesoscale events at the station), we might consider the development of equations for these events. One problem is that a large number of these events would be needed to develop the statistics et cetera upon which the MOS equations would be based. Even if these equations were developed, if would be a major challenge to determine for each unusual event, which set would be applied on a given day.

13. For demonstration purposes, use the following equation to predict the max temperature during a relatively mild winter day at a Northern Plains station.

The following MOS equation bears little resemblance to the an actual MOS equation because it is very simplified in order to give you the general idea.

MAX T = 1.3 (observed 12Z surface temperature) + 5 (12Z snowcover)

with the snowcover being a binary predictor having a 4" cutoff.
To compute how the temperature forecast would change from DAY 1 to DAY 2, if the 12Z temperature is 40 degrees F on each day and the observed snowcover melts from 5" on DAY 1 to 2" on DAY 2, we would do the following:

The binary predictor is set to 1 when the value of that predictor is equal to or less than the binary limit; it is 0 if it is greater. Thus,

$$\text{DAY 1 MAX} = 1.3 \ (40) + 5 \ (0) = 52 \text{ degrees F}$$

$$\text{DAY 2 MAX} = 1.3 \ (40) + 5 \ (1) = 57 \text{ degrees F}$$

This simplified equation is not applicable when the observed surface temperature falls below 0 degrees F because if the 12Z temperature is below zero with a snowcover of greater than 4", this equation would forecast the max temperature to be much lower than the 12z temperature! In reality, the actual MOS equation for this station would include a regression constant and additonal terms which would cause the result to behave more reasonably.

14. Systematic biases appear. A systematic bias is one which occurs routinely in the model, such as the model being too cold after 36 hours, for example. Some systematic biases occur only with certain synoptic conditions. Thus, if you can quantify the bias, you can use MOS more effectively.

15. As a supplement to item 14 above, random errors or biases cannot be accounted for by the MOS approach to numerical forecasting.

16. Numerical/statistical forecasting (forecasting "by the numbers") generally tends towards the climatic mean of the predictand (at least to some extent), as we go out in time. This is because the equations were developed by comparing predictors to actual observed data. This, climatology in inherently included.

The next few pages give examples of the most commonly used MOS guidance graphics that weather forecasters use.

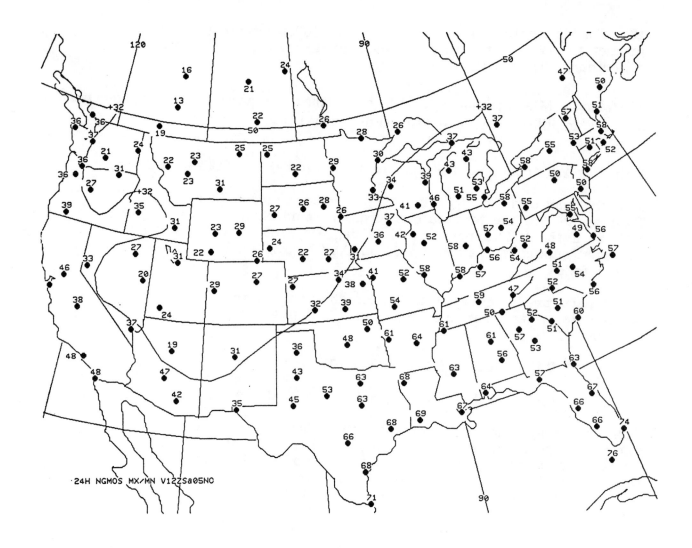

Figure 81. MOS MAXIMUM/MINIMUM TEMPERATURE FORECAST MAPS
Twice daily, from the 00Z and 12Z model runs, MOS charts are generated which predict
for the various MOS forecast locations the maximum/minimum temperatures. The
forecasts are not just for today but go out in time for several days. The legend at the
bottom of the chart shows the valid time of the prog, and whether it is a 24-hour, 60-hour,
etc. prog. The max temperature MOS progs are valid for up to 00Z of a particular day,
and the minimum temperature MOS progs are valid for up to 12Z of a particular day.

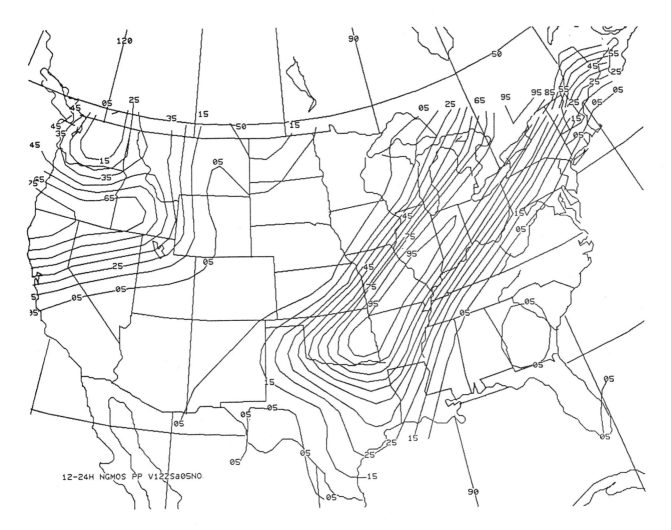

12-24H NGMOS PP V12ZSa05NO.

Figure 82. MOS PRECIPITATION PROBABILITY CHARTS

MOS charts are generated to give guidance to the forecaster on the likelihood of measurable rainfall (or the water equivalent of melted solid precipitation) for various time periods. Measurable rainfall is defined as 0.01" or greater, since rainfall is measured to the nearest 0.01". The MOS equations that predict this probability would be based primarily on parameters that involve moisture, vertical velocity and temperature.

The legend is given on the bottom of the chart. The example below is a 12-hour MOS precipitation probability based on output from one of the forecast models and the observed and climatological data that also comprise the predictors in the MOS equations. For this chart, the values are for the 12-hour period ending at map time, with the isolines in increments of 10%, ranging from 5% through 95%.

PRECIPITATION PROBABILITY is defined as the likelihood of occurrence, expressed as a percent, of a precipitation event at any given point in the forecast area.

This definition is from the National Weather Service Operations Manual. Thus, if a forecast says, "a 40% chance of rain this afternoon in Clay County", this means that anywhere you are standing in Clay County, you have a 4 in 10 chance of receiving measurable precipitation this afternoon.

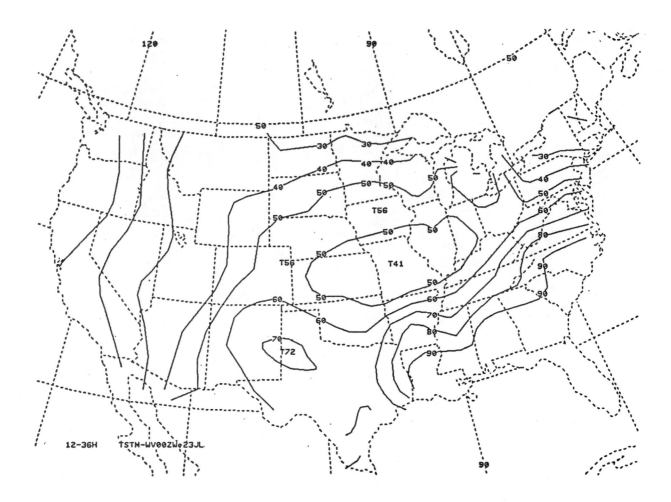

Figure 83. MOS THUNDERSTORM PROBABILITY CHART. This chart gives the MOS probability of thunderstorms during a 24-hour period centered at 24 hours after initial time; i.e., the time-period for the forecast is from 12 to 36 hours after initial time. Other MOS time period charts are likely to be developed for thunderstorm probability guidance.

The contours of thunderstorm probability are labelled in percent. A "T" is plotted for the greatest threats, with those respective probabilities given to the nearest whole %.

There is also a MOS chart that gives the probability that if thunderstorms occur, they will be severe. This is a conditional severe thunderstorm probability chart.

The MOS equations for thunderstorms address the conditions required for thunderstorms: a lifting mechanism, instability, moisture, and whether and how strong are any cap inversions (see chapter 20).

42. TRAJECTORY CHARTS

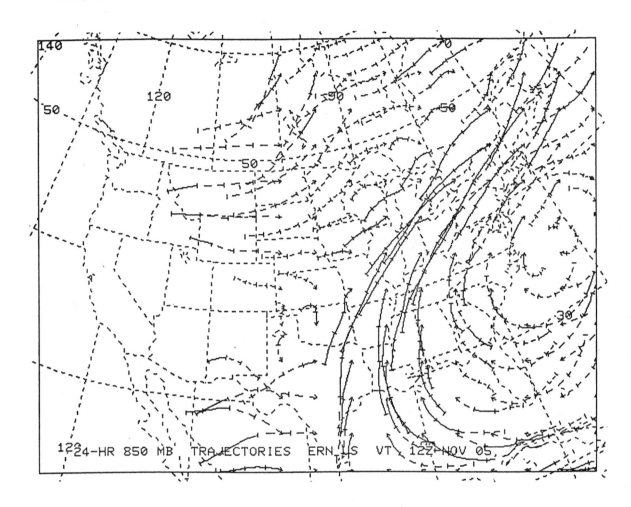

Figure 84. An Example of a 24-Hour 850 Millibar Trajectory Chart, Eastern Part.
There is a series of air trajectory charts for air that will be at 850 mb in 24 hours, ending
at the valid time printed on the chart. There is also the same series for 700 mb.

This chart shows the paths of the air parcels during that 24 hour period, with the hatch
marks at 6-hour intervals, working backwards from the 24-hour forecast time. Solid lines
or sections of lines indicate rising air and dashed lines or sections of lines show sinking air.
Thus, you can see when for the next 24 hours the air will be rising or sinking to arrive at
850 mb (or to arrive at 700 mb for the 700 version).

Since forecasting for clouds and subsequent precipitation requires moisture and rising air,
we would use this chart to see if air is rising to be at 850 mb and also if it is rising at
higher levels, to be at 700 mb. The chart also shows us from where the air is coming. Is
it a cold northwest trajectory, or is the air coming from a warm source to the southeast,
for example.

(continued)   **PAGE 159**

An excellent meteorological dynamics question is this: why is not the synoptic-scale vertical motion much much stronger than it is, because the pressure-gradient force that causes air to move (that causes most wind) is far greater in the vertical than in the horizontal? To go from 1000 mb of pressure to 500 mb in the vertical, we have to rise typically only about 18,000 feet…about 3 and 1/2 miles. In the horizontal at the surface, we can travel 100 miles and rarely find a pressure change of 10 millibars within that distance.

The reason we do not have extreme vertical velocities is because the pressure-gradient force is about exactly balanced by the force of gravity which exerts in the opposite direction to the pressure-gradient force. The pressure-gradient force is upward, from high to lower pressure, while the gravitational force is downward. This situation in the atmosphere is known as HYDROSTATIC EQUILIBRIUM.

These forces can be also viewed as accelerations, since an acceleration is a force per unit mass. In hydrostatic equilibrium, the accelerations are balanced, which means air that is moving upward or downward is not accelerating at that time, but is moving. There are, therefore, vertical velocities with hydrostatic equilibrium, and changes in these vertical velocities (positive or negative accelerations) occur when the local atmosphere goes into hydrostatic inequilibrium.

The trajectory chart vertical motions would be used with forecast charts of moisture from the surface through 700 mb, and even through 500 mb, since a good lift at 700 mb typically implies lift from the surface through at lest 500 mb. Thus, for adequate moisture with the lift, look at sets of 6- through 24-hour progs of average relative humidity (RH) from the surface through 500 mb. When the average RH is 70% or better with rising air, then cloudy or at lest mostly cloudy conditions are likely; when the average surface-to-500 mb RH is 90% or greater with lift, then precipitation is likely.

Other moisture indicators include dewpoints 5 Celsius degrees or less than the temperatures at the surface, 850 mb and 700 mb.

When forecasting, you therefore have information from numerous excellent weather maps to massage and then come to a solution (your forecast).

43. THE 700 MILLIBAR NET VERTICAL DISPLACEMENT CHART

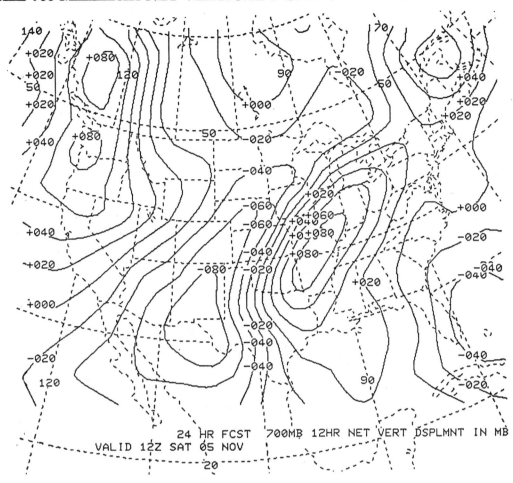

Figure 85. A 700 Millibar 12-Hour Net Vertical Displacement Chart.
This chart shows how much air parcels that will be at 700 mb during the 12 hours ending 24 hours from initial time, have risen or fallen, or if they remained around 700 mb for that 12 hours. The valid time on the chart shows the time at the end of the 12-hour period. There are charts valid for 12-hour periods ending 24, 36 and 48 hours from initial time.

Contours of equal values of rising (+) or sinking (-) air are labelled in whole millibars in intervals of 20 mb.

In the warmer part of the year, a significant lift is equal to or greater than 20 mb/12 hrs, and in the colder part of the year, a significant lift is equal to or greater than 40 mb/12 hrs. This is synoptic-scale vertical displacement, not convective scale.

A point stressed several times in this text is that forecasting precipitation vs. nonprecipitation depends ultimately on two factors: vertical motion and moisture availability. The net vertical displacement chart is yet another type of graphic to give information on the synoptic-scale vertical motion.

PAGE 161

44. THE "MAGIC CHART" FOR SNOW FORECASTING

The next three pages are reprinted from the National Weather Digest, published by the National Weather Association. The article describes the Magic Chart for forecasting not only where the heaviest snow is likely to fall from a synoptic-scale low pressure system, but approximately HOW MUCH. The technique is widely used for guidance in snow forecasting.

Since the article was written for National Weather Service and other forecasters, some terminology used in the article needs to be explained before you read it.

7WG and 82T: you can replace these, which represent call-up codes for weather maps in National Weather Service equipment, with what these charts are:

7WG = 700 mb net vertical displacement chart (see previous chapter) for the 12-hour
    period ending 24 hours after initial time; and
82T = 850 mb isotherm prog valid 12 hours from now.

The third chart which must be used in the technique is the 12-hour prog of average relative humidity from the surface through 500 mb. This must be 90% or greater where the bullseye of greatest net vertical displacement occurs.

AFOS = an acronym for the old telecommunications system used by the National Weather
    Service; AFOS is Automation of Field Operations and Services.

LFM = Limited Area Fine-Mesh Model, now an obsolete forecast model.

NGM = Nested-Grid Model.

NMC = the name for the weather service office responsible at that time for generating the
    weather maps; it stood for National Meteorological Center; these maps are now
    generated by a branch of NCEP, the National Centers for Environmental Prediction.

GMT = Greenwich Mean Time, now known as UTC, Universale Temps Coordinee
    (Universal Coordinated Time), commonly referred to as Z-time.

The technique, as described in the article, is the same. Only some of the acronyms have changed, and computer forecast models keep changing.

If you have access to weather maps but cannot obtain 700 mb 12-hour net vertical displacement chart, substitute the 12-hour 700 mb height-change chart and look for the bullseye of greatest height falls, rather than the bullseye of greatest net upward displacement.

(continued)

FORECASTING

THE MAGIC CHART FOR FORECASTING SNOW AMOUNTS

Peter R. Chaston (1)
National Weather Service Training Center
Kansas City, MO 64124

ABSTRACT

One of the major challenges for meteorologists is accurately predicting the amount of snowfall, especially for a major storm. A form of the magic chart was initially experimented with at the NWS Forecast Office at Milwaukee to attempt to pinpoint where the heaviest snowfalls would occur during synoptic-scale storms. During the 1987–88 snow season, a modified form of this chart was used at the NWS Training Center to forecast not only where the heaviest snowfall would occur, but also the amounts during 12-hr periods. The appropriate moisture supply must be expected before the chart is useable. The magic chart is a combination of a 12-hr period 700-mb net vertical displacement (NVD) prog by NMC's Trajectory Model, and a 12-hr prog of the 850-mb temperature field by the NGM. The initial results from one snow season were surprisingly accurate. The physical reasoning behind this approach is also given.

1. INTRODUCTION

During the past several decades, weather forecasters have been struggling with the problem of predicting as accurately as possible the amounts of snowfall from major synoptic systems. More recently, as NMC forecast models improved, some of their output have been applied to this challenge, employing unique approaches. Essentially, the best techniques locate approximately where the heaviest snowfalls would likely occur. Development of a method that predicted actual amounts of heavy snow remained elusive.

It is obvious that a reliable technique for forecasting actual snowfall amounts with a high degree of accuracy, would benefit society. This paper presents the results of a technique known as THE MAGIC CHART for forecasting snow amounts, so-named because it is easy to use and works "like magic." Initially, the chart was a modification of the approach tried at the NWS forecast office at Milwaukee (2) for identifying the areas of heaviest snow. Partially by accident, it was discovered that the modified approach did more than locate heavy snow areas; this forecasting scheme actually succeeded in predicting the actual amounts of heavy snow with surprising accuracy.

2. METHODOLOGY

Any weather forecasting scheme must be based on sound physical reasoning. Therefore, a forecasting scheme for snow amounts must be logically developed, based on physical principles.

The magic chart is based on the following assumptions:

1. This approach does not apply to mesoscale snowstorms such as topographical/frictional convergence types and lake-effect snowstorms;

2. Adequate moisture must first be available or forecast to be available,

3. The LFM and its subset, the Trajectory Model, are accepted as being reasonably reliable for the first 24-hr projection, and the NGM for the first 12 hr.

The Steps of the MAGIC CHART Procedure

1. Call up AFOS chart 7WG, which is the 12-hr net vertical displacement, in millibars, for air that will arrive at the 700 mb level 24 hr after initial time. (This displacement is for the 12 to 24 hr time-period after initial time.)

2. Overlay AFOS chart 82T, which is the 12-hr 850-mb temperature prog from the NGM.

3. Where the greatest net vertical displacement (NVD) overlays the temperature region between −3°C and −5°C is where the heaviest snowfall is likely to occur using the following guidance for the time-period 12 to 24 hr after initial time:

NET 12-HOUR VERTICAL DISPLACEMENT	12-HOUR SNOWFALL
20 mb to 40 mb	2" to 4"
40 mb	4"
60 mb	6"
80 mb	8"
100 mb	10"
120 mb	12"
140 mb	14"
>140 mb	>14"

4. The above procedure works with a mature or developing synoptic low-pressure system but only after determining that adequate moisture will be available for 12 to 24 hr after initial time for that region where the NVD overlays the −3°C to −5° C area. Adequate moisture means temperature-dew point spreads of no more than a few degrees at 850 mb and 700 mb, or a 1000-500 RH of about 90% or greater.

3. EXPLANATION OF FIGURES 1 AND 2:

The presentations overlay AFOS charts 7WG and 82T. Where the −3°C to −5°C temperature band overlays the highest NVD band, is where the heaviest snowfall is predicted for that 12-hr period.

In Figure 1, the −3° to −5°C temperature zone that lies within the +040 isoline of NVD is the area where about 4 in. of snowfall can be expected in the 12-hr period from 0000 to 1200 GMT Wednesday, February 10, 1988. Warmer temperatures lead to a snow/rain transition zone and then to rain; therefore, −3°C is the warmest allowable temperature in this forecasting scheme. Colder temperatures than −5°C lower the amount of moisture (saturation mixing ratio) the air can hold; therefore, the same NVD would yield a lower snowfall

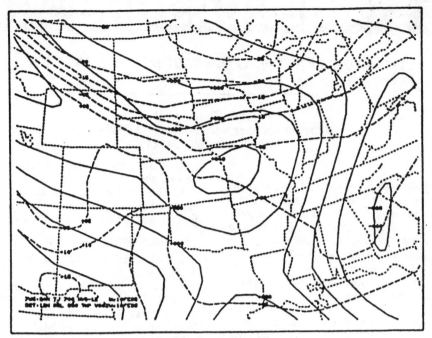

Fig. 1. Two to four in. snowfall forecast for northern Missouri.

amount. In this case, 4 in. was the representative snowfall over northern Missouri during this time period.

In Figure 2, the $-3°$ to $-5°C$ temperature band overlays an essentially $+120$ to $+140$ mb 12-hr net vertical displacement for air that will be at 700 mb 24 hr after the initial time. In this case, 12 in. to 14 in. of snowfall can be predicted for central Illinois during the 12-hr period of 0000 to 1200 GMT Tuesday, December 15, 1987. The actual snowfall during this period for the region was about 13 in. This particular storm was followed from the Plains to the Northeast, employing the magic chart technique. For example, in the prior 12-hr period, the $-3°$ to $-5°C$ area coincided with a $+120$ area over northern Missouri. Thus, 12 in. of snowfall was predicted. The observed snow amounts that fell were from 11 in. to 13 in.

Eight major synoptic storms were followed, using the magic chart to forecast snow amounts. There were several forecasts during the life-cycle of each of these storms. The magic chart was successful in 100% of these cases. This author believes that some of this was due to nothing more than luck. When the magic chart fails, which it undoubtedly will in some cases, the reasons why must be determined. In all of the storms in 1987–88 for which the magic chart approach was used, the LFM and NGM were reliable for the 12- and 24-hr forecasts.

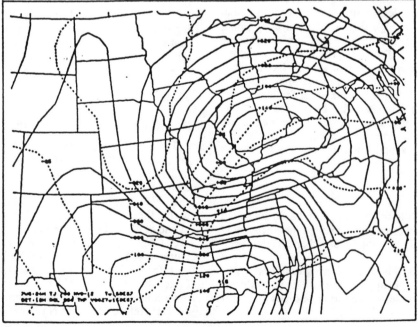

Fig. 2. Twelve to fourteen in. snowfall forecast for central Illinois.

If a model does not have an acceptable diagnosis and prognosis of the weather, then obviously the magic chart cannot be used. The forecaster needs to determine the level of competence of the models' forecasts—sometimes not an easy task.

The meteorological rationale for the magic chart approach needs to be explained, because the technique appears to work exceptionally well, even though it has been applied in this way for only one snow season.

4. METEOROLOGICAL REASONING

This can best be described by a question and answer format:

Question: This method is questionable. Isn't it just another rule-of-thumb scheme?

Response: Try it for a couple of winters to assess it yourself. It works for the area between the Rockies and the East Coast. For the Western Region, a 700-mb temperature threshold seems appropriate and more research and case studies are needed to determine appropriate values. As with all rules-of-thumb, understand the physical reasoning behind it so that you know when to use it and when to suspect it. Also, this approach was presented in a recent talk in Fairbanks, Alaska, suggesting that the technique is not limited to the lower 48 states.

Question: What is the physical rationale for this procedure?

Response: For the heaviest snowfall in a developing or mature synoptic low-pressure system, we are looking for the highest available moisture amounts occurring simultaneously with the greatest synoptic-scale lifting, in a region where the temperature regime is sufficiently cold for snow.

The higher the temperature, the higher the saturation mixing ratio, at the same pressure. Therefore, we are analyzing for the highest moisture content occurring with the highest possible temperatures that are still cold enough for snow. Thus, the 850-mb temperature ribbon of $-3°C$ to $-5°C$ is the choice temperature zone because, if saturated through a deep layer, it would contain the highest volume of moisture (compared with lower temperatures in saturated air). The $-3°$ to $-5°C$ zone also is normally cold enough for snow.

We also want that area to coincide with the strongest synoptic-scale lifting; lifting implies low-level convergence. A strong lift implies strong low-level moisture convergence. If the air being lifted is moist, then the stronger the lift the greater the likelihood of higher amounts of precipitation.

Keep in mind that the temperature-dew point spread must be no more than a few degrees at both 850 and 700 mb before this procedure is useable.

Question: How did you equate the 700-mb NVD values with the snowfall amounts?

Response: This project began as an experiment with meteorological interns doing daily forecasting exercises in the Forecaster Development Course at the weather service's in-house training academy. We noticed that within the $-3°C$ to $-5°C$ band, the heaviest snowfall amounts occurred with the strongest NVDs. During the 1987–88 snow-season, we followed eight major synoptic storms that fit the conditions described earlier for using this method. In each of these storms, two to four 12-hr periods were followed and forecasts made. To our amazement, the technique worked in every forecast episode, for forecasting where the heaviest snow would fall in that 12-hr period as well as accurate amounts. It is a rather nice coincidence that the snowfall amounts

correspond to the NVD amounts (e.g., 60 mb relates to 6 in. of snowfall, 80 mb relates to 8 in. etc). For NVDs above 120 mb, it is preferable to forecast "in excess of 12 in." rather than try to pinpoint the value precisely.

Question: The magic chart as herein proposed uses output from the trajectory model but the temperature prognostication from the NGM. Is it not inconsistent to use the NGM rather than the LFM, because the trajectory model is essentially a 3-layer subset of the LFM?

Response: At first impression, it would seem logical to overlay the trajectory model's NVD with the LFM temperature prog. However, in doing this, we found that the forecast snow amounts were slightly displaced, whereas the NGM's temperature forecast had greater accuracy. In dealing with a 12-hr 850-mb temperature forecast, it is true that most of the time the LFM and NGM forecasts should be essentially identical. However, with a large-scale low-pressure system typically undergoing major development, the 12-hr NGM apparently does a better job at delineating the thermal field in the area of that system, compared with the LFM's performance.

Question: What caveats should be kept in mind when using the magic chart?

Response: The magic chart works only when the moisture in the area of concern is forecast to be deep; thus, temperature-dew point depressions through 700 mb should ideally be no more than about 3°C. Moreover, the magic chart is used only for large-scale low-pressure systems and does not include local effects such as orographic, frictional convergence, and lake effect.

Keep in mind, also, that the NGM is still being modified and tweeked, whereas the LFM is not being changed because the MOS equations are based on the LFM. However, it is inconceivable that any good modification of the NGM would harm the 12-hour 850-mb temperature prog.

Finally, the magic chart works only when the 12–24 hr 700-mb NVD prog from the trajectory model is accurate and when the 12-hour NGM 850-mb temperature prog is accurate. If you suspect a forecast problem with either model, do not use the magic chart.

5. RECOMMENDATIONS

Try the magic chart for forecasting the area of greatest snowfall potential, and experiment with forecasting the amounts. It would be prudent not to base official snowfall projections on this procedure unless the magic chart works for your area and the staff knows when to use it.

More seasons of verification are necessary to uphold or dispute the conclusions of the original findings. Moreover, Western mountainous areas would need a scheme developed based on 700-mb temperature forecasts, rather than on 850 mb. Therefore, we need many more case studies to fully substantiate this approach.

NOTES AND REFERENCES

1. Peter R. Chaston is in charge of the Meteorology Program at the NWS Training Center in Kansas City. Previously he was the Meteorologist-in-Charge at the NWS Office at Rochester, NY, and has been stationed at various other NWS offices in the Eastern Region. Chaston received his M.S. in Meteorology from the University of Wisconsin while on a NOAA Fellowship. He is current President of the Kansas City Chapter of the AMS.

2. Sangster, W., and E. Jagler, 1985: NWS Central Region Technical Attachment 85-1, January.

NOTE: In 1990, chart 7WG became an NGM-based trajectory product.

45. THETA-E AND THETA-E CHARTS

Figure 86. The Symbol for Theta-e, the Equivalent Potential Temperature.

One of the most significant breakthroughs in analysis and forecasting has been the evolution of the understanding of how to use the weather parameter known as the equivalent potential temperature, commonly referred to in meteorology as THETA-E.

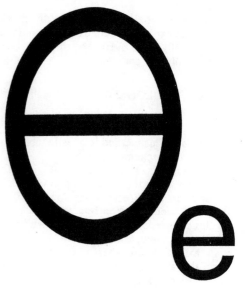

Theta-e is a method of combining the temperature and moisture content, using the dewpoint for the measure of moisture, into one value, and then plotting these theta-e values on a map, analyzing them in order to find areas of concentrated high values of theta-e, and then using that information to forecast such things as flash flood potential, thundersnow and hurricane movements. Thus, correctly using the analyses and forecasts of the theta-e field are one of the biggest forecast advancements of our era.

Using what forecasters call thermodynamic analysis, parcels of air which originate at a specified level...typically 850 millibars east of the Rocky Mountains and 700 mb from the Rockies westward...are raised until all the moisture is condensed out, and then these parcels are brought back down dry adiabatically to 1000 millibars which is called the potential temperature reference level. Inotherwords, on a thermodynamic diagram or via a computer program, we take the current sounding data from a location, and go through the process of raising air from, say 850 mb, up to a level so high that by then all the moisture is "squeezed out of it" (typically around 200 mb in common computer programs), and then descending the parcel down to 1000 mb. At that point, at 1000 mb, we read the temperature of the parcel. The value it has is its 850 mb theta-e value.

In effect, we are combining the temperature of the parcel with the heat of condensation released as the air becomes saturated and then releases its moisture, and then descending the parcel past its origination point, 850 mb, down to 1000 mb.

The convention is to express the theta-e value in degrees Kelvin rather than degrees Celsius; therefore, add 273 to the Celsius value to get the degrees K value.

Now, the next logical series of questions is, "So what? What good is it? How do we use it?"

(continued)

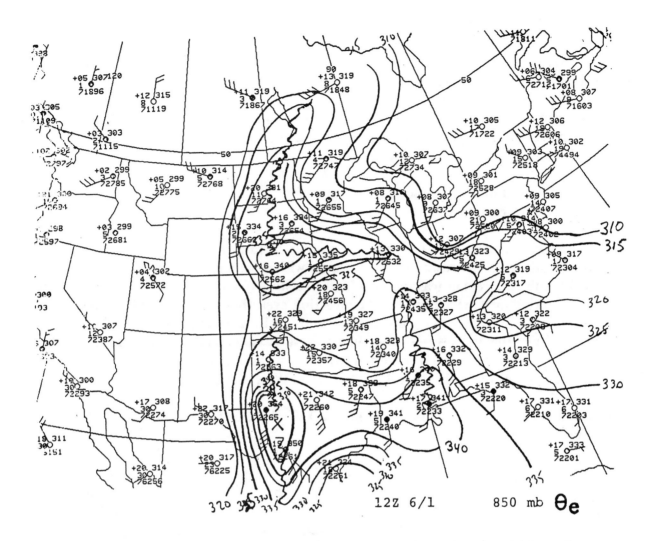

Figure 87. An 850 mb Theta-e Analysis. This is an 850 mb chart in which each location's 850 mb height value, in the upper right of each station plot, is replaced by the 850 mb equivalent potential temperature (850 mb theta-e) in degrees Kelvin (°K). For example, the 850 mb theta-e value for Topeka, Kansas is 323 degrees K.

This analysis was done by hand, drawing lines of equal 850 mb theta-e for every 5 K degrees.

850 mb theta-e ridges exist from Nebraska through the Dakotas, from Nebraska through Iowa, in west Texas, in the central Gulf states and a smaller one is observed in Kentucky-West Virginia.

All these ridges were inactive or "wasted theta-e ridges" at this time except for the one extending from the theta-e max in Nebraska east-southeastward through Iowa. In that ridge, some 6 hours later, thunderstorms formed. The surface moisture-flux convergence chart showed some one to two hours ahead of the convective onset where the first cells would likely form.

(continued)

These cells merged into clusters (with severe weather at some of the merging locales), and the thunderstorm clusters, continuing to feed on high-value theta-e air (which is a concentration of warm, moist air) then merged into a MESOSCALE CONVECTIVE SYSTEM (MCS) by 00Z, about the size of the state of Iowa. An MCS is a large area of organized convection, typically about the size of the state of Iowa, and persisting for 12 hours or more. The MCS that formed on this date produced a flash flood for eastern Nebraska and central and southern Iowa.

This case is typical of how to use theta-e ridges for forecasting organized convection (not single-cell type of convection).

Organized convection did not develop in the other theta-e ridges at this time because: the ridge north from Nebraska was in a region with a strong widespread cap inversion around 700 mb (the region was under a high pressure system with subsidence, i.e, with diverging sinking air), which inhibited convection even though the conditions for convective development existed (low- and/or mid-level lifting mechanism[s], moisture and instability); the air was too stable in the west Texas ridge; the ridge north of the Gulf coast was slightly active in barely unstable air; and there was no lifting mechanism nor instability in the ridge going over West Virginia.

Figure 88. Note the theta-e changes from the 12Z chart in figure 87 to the 00Z chart twelve hours later, below.

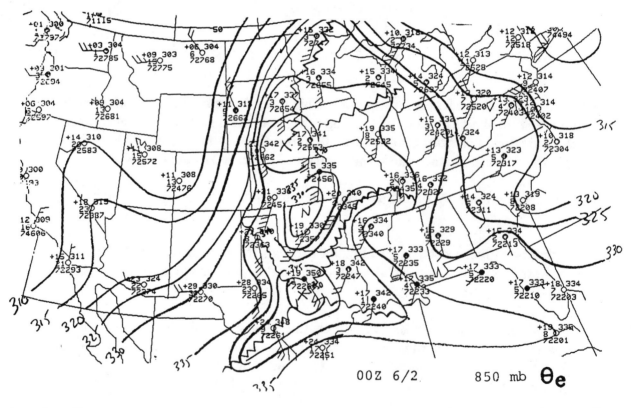

(continued)

Notice how the theta-e patterns evolve and shift during the 12 hours between the 12Z and the 00Z charts. These changes are gradual. Therefore, because of the conservativeness of theta-e, it can be used to trace the warm moist air it signifies, from chart to chart.

At 00Z, organized convection was underway in Iowa and the theta-e ridge that was over the Dakotas 12 hours earlier had shifted into Minnesota into unstable air without a subsidence inversion aloft, and organized convection began forming within a few hours later over Minnesota in the theta-e ridge.

THE IMPORTANCE OF 850 MB THETA-E RIDGES IN CONVECTIVE FORECASTING: When thunderstorms form in a theta-e ridge, these are the storms that merge and feed off the warm, moist energy supply which is high-value theta-e air (theta-e ridges are concentrations of warm, moist air). These thunderstorms therefore grow into a huge organized mass of thunderstorms and rain known as a mesoscale convective system (MCS). The crucial point about MCSes is that most very heavy rain events (3 inches or more within several hours) are caused by MCSes, so that most flash floods are caused by MCSes.

We now have an analysis and forecasting tool that can be used to anticipate most of the flash floods! This is a major breakthrough in weather forecasting.

A theta-e ridge, when acted upon by a lifting mechanism (e.g., a short-wave trough in the low- and mid-troposphere moving into the theta-e ridge) can be thought of as an axis of available potential energy that can be converted into kinetic energy of the subsequent convection.

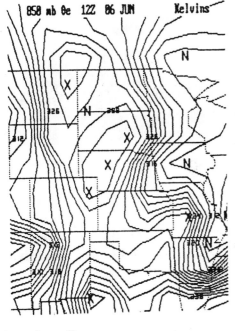

Figure 89. An 850 mb theta-e chart showing theta-e analyzed for every 2 degrees.

An analysis in 2-degree increments rather than in 5-degree increments (°K) permits a more detailed look at the theta-e field and helps to find side-lobes of theta-e, or side-ridges. Sometimes even subtle ridges or side-lobe ridges off a main ridge can become the focus for the start of organized convection when the conditions for convection exist within the side-ridge.

An example of a subtle side-ridge in the eastward-poking theta-e ridge into eastern South Dakota.

(continued)

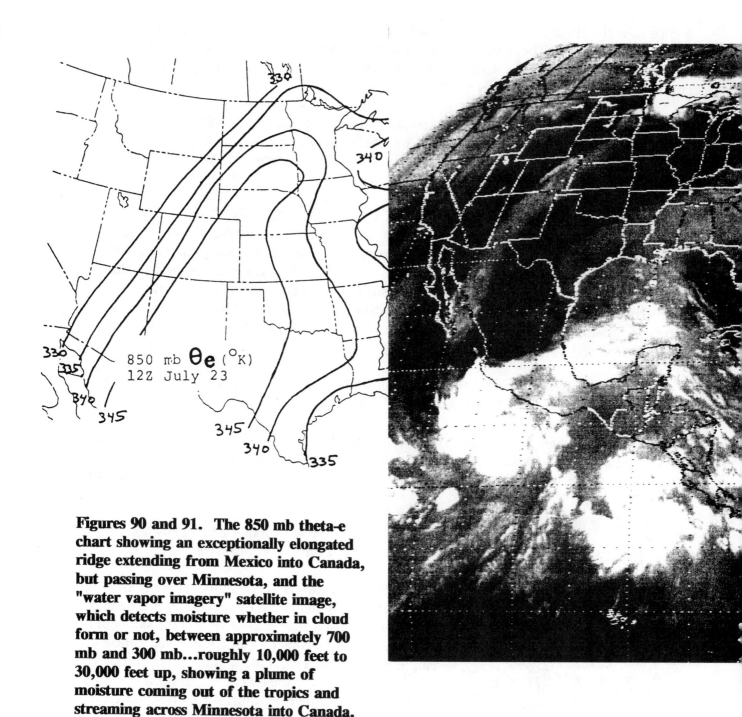

Figures 90 and 91. The 850 mb theta-e chart showing an exceptionally elongated ridge extending from Mexico into Canada, but passing over Minnesota, and the "water vapor imagery" satellite image, which detects moisture whether in cloud form or not, between approximately 700 mb and 300 mb...roughly 10,000 feet to 30,000 feet up, showing a plume of moisture coming out of the tropics and streaming across Minnesota into Canada.

This plume of moisture is called a TROPICAL CONNECTION. When thunderstorms form in a theta-e ridge, we know that we are likely to experience a mesoscale convective system, which is a very heavy rain producer...over 3" and frequently over 5" of rain...and therefore a flash flood threat, especially if the antecedent local soil conditions are already wet. The flash flood threat is enhanced when a tropical connection exists, with the tropical moisture streaming into the developing MCS.

(continued)

There will be little moisture added above 500 mb in the troposphere, since the air is too cold to hold copious amounts there, but much moisture will be added from 700 mb to 500 mb, into the developing convection. Moreover, a tropical connection is a continuous infusion of moisture. Therefore, the impact of having a tropical connection streaming into the developing MCS is that it makes the heavy rain producing system an <u>even heavier</u> rain producer. Many of the worst flash floods ever occur with MCSes which form in theta-e ridges and are accompanied by a tropical connection.

In our case study, now look at the 850 mb theta-e analysis twelve hours later:

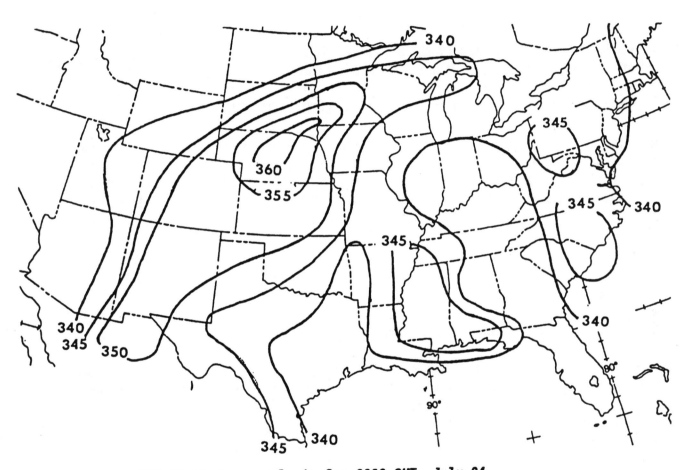

850 MB theta-e analysis for 0000 GMT, July 24

Figure 92. The 850 mb theta-e analysis for 00Z on July 24th. Notice how the ridge has intensified from roughly Nebraska into Minnesota. The result was that the convection that was over Minnesota some 12 hours earlier, intensified as it grew into an MCS, and the Minneapolis area received up to 11.1" of flash flooding rainfall.

(continued)   **PAGE 171**

Important Points About Using Theta-e for Forecasting Organized Convection

• An 850 mb (or 700 mb for western mountainous areas) theta-e ridge or maximum is not necessary to have thunderstorms; a theta-e ridge by itself does not assure thunderstorms; if thunderstorms do develop in a theta-e ridge, then they are likely to merge into clusters with the clusters then merging to form an organized convective system which we call a mesoscale convective system, MCS.

• If in a theta-e ridge and thunderstorms are expected, the surface moisture-flux convergence (SMC) chart typically shows where the first storms will form, namely, in or near a maximum of SMC or in a ridge of SMC, because the chief forcing for thunderstorms is in the lower levels of the troposphere.

• When an MCS is forming in a theta-e ridge, always check the water vapor imagery weather satellite image for a tropical connection into the developing MCS. This plume of warm moist air from the tropics seeds the convective system with additional moisture, resulting in copious rainfall and a flash flood threat.

• Whereas single-cell thunderstorms not in theta-e ridges tend to move with the mean surface-to-500 mb flow, or, for a first approximation, with the 700 mb flow, an MCS in a theta-e ridge typically moves with the 1000-to-500 mb thickness pattern except when the thickness lines diverge, which is called difluent thickness, in which case the MCS remains nearly stationary or propagates backwards.

• The MCS continues as long as the 850 (or 700) mb theta-e ridge is within the thickness pattern; when the thickness pattern (also called the "thermal wind") carries the MCS away from the theta-e ridge, then the MCS starts to die.

Other Uses of Theta-e Analyses and Forecasts

Although using theta-e charts as guidance in forecasting many of the heavy rain/flash flood threats is a major breakthrough in meteorology, various types of theta-e charts are used also to forecast some other weather events:

• heavy rain/snow in western North America

• thundersnow

• fronts aloft

• hurricane movements after landfall

(continued)

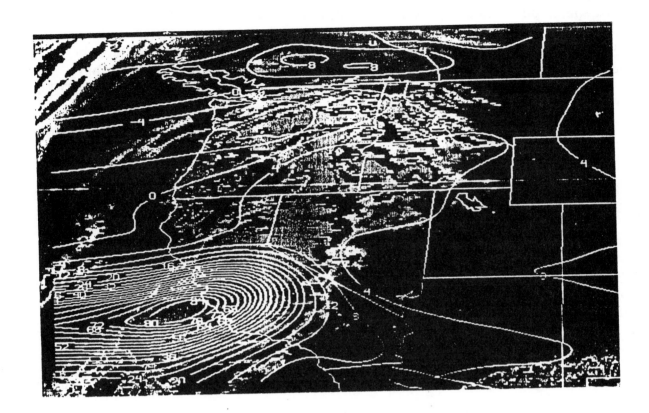

Figure 93. A 700 mb theta-e advection chart superimposed on weather satellite imagery.

For west coast heavy rain/heavy snow events caused by a major weather system, especially in the winter and spring, the 700 mb theta-e advection analysis and forecasts give rather good guidance in showing where the heaviest precipitation is likely to fall, namely, within the ridge axis or in the theta-e gradient just north of it. This technique works from central America northward, including Alaska.

An advection chart shows the change in theta-e for a time period, using for twelve hours with this type of usage. Thus, we are using not a theta-e chart but a chart showing the 12-hour increase of theta-e. A decrease of theta-e would represent drier and/or cooler air and would not be conducive to enhancing precipitation. What happens is that the cloud tops tend to grow higher in the advection ridge. There may be thunderstorms embedded in the steady precipitation but this does not necessarily occur. In or just north of this ridge the clouds do, however, show some convective development, growing higher than they otherwise would, producing more precipitation.

(continued)   **PAGE 173**

Using Theta-e to Forecast Thundersnow

Thundersnow is significant because of its heavy snowfall rates. When a theta-e ridge is superimposed on a synoptic-scale snowstorm, a potential for thundersnow exists. Although warm season convection is quasi-vertical, wintertime convection is often at an angle, and is referred to as SLANTWISE CONVECTION. The cloud tops may be under 20,000 feet high, but the convection may be 25,000 to 45,000 feet long, but occurring at an angle. A useful tool in anticipating possible thundersnow is a THETA-E SOUNDING.

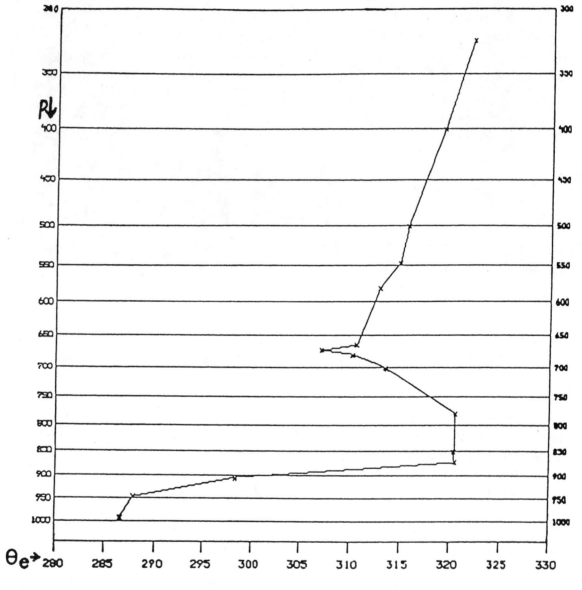

Figure 94. A Theta-e Sounding.
The vertical coordinate is millibars or could be the logarithm of millibars, and the horizontal coordinate is the theta-e value in degrees Kelvin.

(continued)

A theta-e sounding is constructed by taking the air parcel at each level of interest, such as for every 25 or 50 mb, raising the air until the moisture is all condensed out, typically to about 200 mb, and then bringing the air parcel back down dry adiabatically to 1000 mb. For example, to compute the 675 mb theta-e, go to the regular sounding and take the parcel up until all the moisture is condensed out (which we can do graphically on a thermodynamic diagram), then bring it down to 1000 mb at the dry adiabatic lapse rate, and plot its value on the theta-e sounding at the 675 mb level. Connect all the theta-e values for all the levels and analyze the slope of the sounding curve. WHERE THETA-E IS DECREASING WITH HEIGHT, THE AIR IS DESTABILIZING. If convection were to develop, this is where it would be originating.

The reason why decreasing theta-e with height is what we look for in the troposphere is because there are four ways to destabilize the local atmospheric environment to make the area more conducive to convective development: warm the air in low levels, increase the moisture in low levels, cool the air aloft and dry the air aloft. Any of these or a combination of these allows parcels that have been given a lift to remain warmer than the environment and thus keep rising to form convective clouds and their subsequent showers and/or thunderstorms.

From figure 93 we see that the atmosphere is destabilizing from about 775 mb through about 675. Convection, which typically starts at or near the surface in the warmer season, would start aloft, at around 775 mb, which would be about 7,000 to 8,000 feet up. This is an example of ELEVATED CONVECTION. Thus, we can have convection that is both elevated and slantwise.

Now that we know that when theta-e decreases as we rise through the troposphere we are destabilizing that local environment, we now need to determine if there exist a lifting mechanism and sufficient moisture so that we have the conditions necessary for convection: lift, moisture and instability (without a strong capping inversion aloft).

If we could generate theta-e soundings across the continent and then look at a cross-section of where decreasing theta-e with height is located and how this region is moving, we would have a guidance tool for anticipating the possibility of thundersnow.

The complex weather graphic on the next page is such a theta-e cross-section.

(continued)

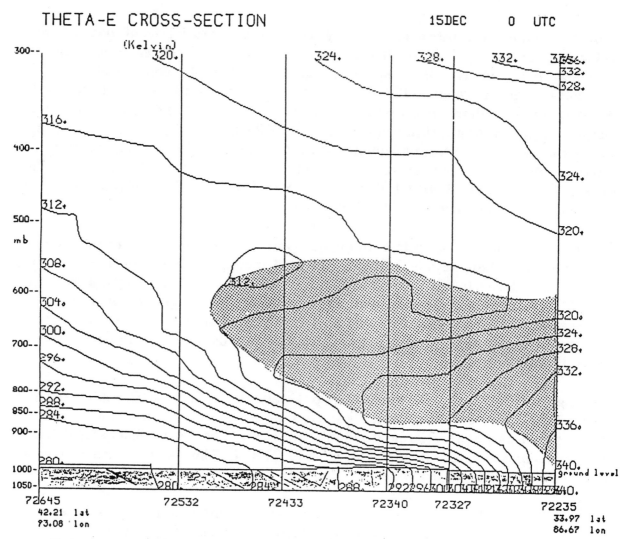

Theta-e cross-section supplied by James Moore, St. Louis
University, from their analysis program.

Figure 95. A Theta-e Cross-section. The vertical coordinate is pressure, in millibars,
and the numbers at the bottom are location identifier for weather stations. Notice at the
lower right is the latitude and longitude for a point in the southeastern U.S., and at the
lower left is the latitude and longitude for a point in the upper mid-west. Thus, the
cross-section runs from the southeastern to upper mid-west region of the country. The
station i.d.s, such as 72645 for Green Bay, Wisconsin, are given to identify locations
along the cross-section. The theta-e lines from the theta-e soundings are labelled in
degrees Kelvin (°K). The shaded-in area is where theta-e values are decreasing with
increasing height.

Thus, in this complex type of theta-e weather map, we see by looking at the shaded
area, where the potential for slantwise convection exists. The shaded area is moving
upwards and towards the mid-west.

(continued)

PAGE 176

In this particular case, a major winter storm was affecting Missouri, and when the "nose" of the shaded area moved into Missouri, thundersnow broke out, resulting in several inches more snow than would have otherwise occurred from the synoptic-scale low pressure system itself. A video-loop of this type of analysis in, e.g., hourly or three-hourly increments would be quite useful to show the progression of this elevated area of instability.

Empirical studies have shown that the decreases of theta-e with height should be at least 5 K degrees, and when they are 10 K degrees or greater, significant convective potential is generated.

Using Theta-e for Fronts Aloft

Although most people are familiar with weather maps showing frontal boundaries on surface weather maps, these fronts also extend for some depth into the troposphere.

It is useful to look for fronts at 850, 700 and even as high as 500 millibars, because such an analysis can be useful in forecasting some types of convection.

When the air gets colder and/or drier at any level in the atmosphere, it lowers the equivalent potential temperature or theta-e for that level. Thus, the front, or leading edge of colder and/or drier air can be found at any level by looking for the leading edge of lower values of theta-e.

Here are two examples of when a front aloft may be a significant factor in convective weather.

Consider an intrusion of cold air flowing over the Rocky Mountains into the Plains. The cold front aloft at about 500 mb would cause cold air advection aloft, which destabilizes the mid- and upper-troposphere, and may lead to convection, or could cause stronger updrafts which lead to more severe convective weather.

Another example occurs when a surface cold front is advancing, trying to dislodge hot air. This is more common in the summertime when the hotter air is more entrenched and the cold fronts are typically weaker than in other seasons. So, the cold front is moving against the hot air but slows down because of the entrenchment and build-up of the hotter air. However, aloft at say 700 mb, the cooler air is still advancing. Ultimately, the front aloft overshoots the front at the surface. The leading edge of this upper front is the leading edge of lower theta-e values. By cooling in mid-levels, this destabilizes the atmosphere and sometimes leads to the creation of a pre-frontal squall-line of thunderstorms. Thus, there are sometimes situations in summertime when a cold front can generate a line of thunderstorms some 100 to 150 miles in advance of its location at the surface, and have another line of thunderstorms along the surface front itself. A theta-e cross-section every one to three hours would therefore be a useful tool for forecasting such thunderstorm potential.

(continued)

Using Theta-e to Forecast Hurricane and Tropical Storm Movements After Landfall

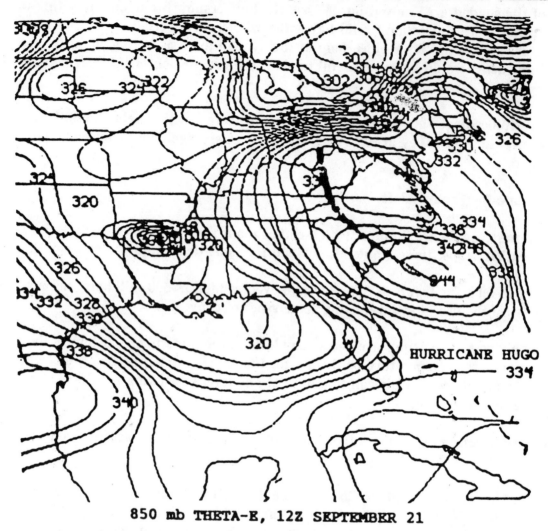

850 mb THETA-E, 12Z SEPTEMBER 21

Figure 96. The 850 mb theta-e analysis showing a pre-existing theta-e ridge from Charleston, SC to Charleston, WV, and Hurricane Hugo 12 hours before landfall, bringing in its own high theta-e air.

We know that organized convection feeds on concentrations of warm, moist air. These concentrations show up as theta-e maxima and theta-e ridges. Hurricanes are also a type of organized convection; they are a type of mesoscale convective system. We know that they form typically over tropical oceans in areas of high theta-e air.

When these tropical cyclones move inland, they lose access to their chief source of energy, the warm ocean surface and the warm, moist air above it. To maintain their heavy rainmaking ability, they seem to move into a pre-existing theta-e ridge over land, at least initially. As they move into higher latitudes, the strong westerlies...winds aloft...tend to take over as the chief steering influence for their movements.

(continued)

In the Hurricane Hugo case in figure 96, note the theta-e maximum off the South Carolina coast. This represents the eye or center of the hurricane. Hurricane Hugo is moving inland, transporting its own high theta-e tropical air. This theta-e air must be distinguished from any pre-existing theta-e ridges near the landfall area. In this case, a pre-existing 850 mb theta-e ridge was in place from South Carolina into West Virginia. Although all the computer weather forecast models predicted that Hugo would hit the mid-Atlantic coast and then turn sharply to the right, striking New Jersey, the New York City area, Long Island and New England, instead Hugo moved into and through the theta-e ridge from Charleston, SC to Charleston, WV.

The theta-e analysis has been used since Hugo, typically showing hurricanes moving into pre-existing theta-e ridges. A notable hurricane-theta-e interaction was noted in 1992 when Hurricane Andrew crossed southern Florida, travelled through the Gulf of Mexico and then made its second landfall, striking the Louisiana coast. After hitting the coast, Andrew ran into a theta-e TROUGH, i.e., a concentration of low theta-e value air. Andrew abruptly veered rightward directly into a theta-e ridge.

In conclusion, the 850 mb theta-e analysis appears to be a useful guidance product for how a hurricane is likely to move during the approximately 24-hours after making landfall: **if a pre-existing theta-e ridge is in the proximity of the landfalling hurricane, then the storm is likely to move into the ridge initially.**

El Nino and Theta-e

El Nino is a sudden warming of a vast area of equatorial Pacific Ocean surface (and for at least some depth below the surface) water, in the middle of the Northern Hemisphere Pacific Ocean. El Nino may start in Southern Hemisphere waters off Peru and rapidly work its way northwestward into the south-central Northern Pacific Ocean. El Nino gets its name for the Christ Child, since it typically starts about November and peaks in December through March. (El Nino means little baby boy.) Sometimes it is referred to as ENSO, for El Nino Southern Oscillation.

El Nino does not occur every year. The El Nino event of 1992-1993 was especially interesting, because it persisted through the summer of 1993 and appears to have played a role in the disastrous mid-west floods of that year, because it created a tropical connection that persisted through the summer, with that continuous mid- and upper-tropospheric moisture injection feeding into persistent 850 mb theta-e ridges over the mid-west United States.

The cause of El Nino is unknown. Some type of dynamic heating process is suspected. Thus, El Nino remains a fascinating mystery of oceanography.

(continued)

When such a vast ocean surface warms up...sometimes by more than 5 Fahrenheit degrees, it warms the air above it. Warmer air can hold more moisture than when it was cooler; consequently, this warm air absorbs more water vapor from the ocean. Much of this moisture works its way up to mid-levels of the troposphere (700 to 500 mb), and some of the moisture is transported to the upper-troposphere (above 500 mb, up to 300 to 200 mb).

Next, we would want to know how the moisture gets transported across the Pacific into North America in tropical plumes. We know that tropical connections occur throughout the year around the globe, but when El Nino occurs, we have intense and persistent tropical connections, with major, continuous infusions of moisture from the tropical North Pacific into North America in the mid- and upper-troposphere.

There are two chief sources of this transport: the sub-tropical jet-stream and anticyclonic outflow aloft from organized convection in the tropics.

Jet-streaks of the sub-tropical jet readily carry the air and its moisture from the source region for this tropical moisture east-northeastward across the central and eastern Pacific and over the North American continent.

The other major source of this moisture plume is in the Intertropical Convergence Zone (ITCZ). There are typically large high pressure systems over the North Atlantic and North Pacific Oceans, and there are also large highs over the South Atlantic and South Pacific Oceans. The low pressure systems move through and around these highs. The circulation around a high is clockwise in the Northern Hemisphere and counterclockwise in the Southern Hemisphere. This results in air coming together or converging near the equator, with climatological statistics showing us that the greatest convergence is a few degrees latitude north of the equator. This is the axis of the Intertropical Convergence Zone. The ITCZ axis migrates some to the north and south, but stays north of the equator. Most hurricanes form in the ITCZ since it is a zone of converging, rising and very warm tropical air...thus, it is air of a high-value theta-e environment. Hurricanes form out of organizing convection which is an MCS, mesoscale convective system. Since air is converging and rising into the MCS in low and middle levels of the troposphere, the air must come out of the system and diverge aloft. It does so as anticyclonically-curved plumes of air, which also contain the moisture.

Thus, each of these MCSes in the tropics, including those that become hurricanes, generate their own tropical moisture plumes.

These MCSes form in regions of high values of low-level theta-e.

In conclusion, when El Nino occurs, the tropical connections are more intense and prolonged, and if they stream into MCSes over North America forming in theta-e ridges, the heavy rain/flash flood potential from these MCSes is enhanced.

MORE SPECIFICS ON USING THETA-E FOR PREDICTING HURRICANE MOVEMENTS:

Because more weather observations are available over land than over the ocean, it is easier to generate theta-e analyses over land than over ocean areas. Theta-e may be useful in hurricane forecasting as following:

●Separate the 850 mb theta-e envelope that moves with the hurricane from any pre-existing 850 mb theta-e ridge over land. As the hurricane approaches land, it tends to move into the theta-e ridge and maintains its heavy rain producing factory even when it has been downgraded into a tropical depression low-pressure system. Although the hurricane and then its remnants tend to move into a pre-existing theta-e ridge, the system will likely be steered more by the mid- and upper-level winds as it moves into higher latitudes, especially from about 40°N or higher.

●In the absence of a pre-existing and well-defined 850 mb theta-e ridge over land near where the hurricane is heading towards, the hurricane's own 850 mb theta-e ridge is usually still useful in short-term forecasting. The ridge typically "pokes" in the direction towards which the system is moving. Thus, analyzing the storm's own 850 mb theta-e envelope of warm, moist air shows how the storm is likely to move for up to 12 to 18 hours.

The initial history of using the 850 mb theta-e analysis with a landfalling tropical cyclone shows the following:

●In 1989, Hurricane Hugo, which was predicted by the computer forecast models to hit the Carolinas and then move up the east cost into the New York City area and New England, instead moved into a pre-existing theta-e ridge that stretched from Charleston, South Carolina to Charleston, West Virginia. Hugo moved from Charleston, S.C. to Charleston, W.V.

●In 1990, Klaus and Marco merged, moving out of the eastern Gulf of Mexico as Marco. Although the models had the storm center moving east of the Appalachians across eastern Georgia, Marco went directly into an 850 mb theta-e ridge west of the mountains and gave portions of Georgia significant flash flooding.

●In 1991, Hurricane Bob travelled directly up a theta-e ridge off the east coast, directly into New England.

These were the only tropical storms to strike the mainland within that time-period, and the theta-e analysis proved helpful in all three.

However, only three cases are not a compelling argument. Successive uses of this type of analysis through 1995, demonstrated its practicality, In 1995, the path of Hurricane Erin was easily predictable through using 850 theta-e from the Gulf states into New England.

The heavy rains and flash flooding occurred as Erin continued to feed on high-value theta-e air (i.e., on a concentration of warm, moist air), as she moved through a pre-existing theta-e ridge.

MCSes forming over land areas in low latitudes and moving out over the ocean can become tropical cyclones. The MCSes can originate over Texas, Africa and Asia, for example. MCSes form only in theta-e ridges. Unlike air mass or single-cell thunderstorms, most of whose life-spans average from about 20 to 60 minutes, a mesoscale convective system persists for many hours, in many cases over 9 hours. Therefore, an MCS needs an energy source to sustain it, which is the concentration of warm and moist air which comprises the theta-e ridge.

When an MCS moves out from the land to over the ocean and the conditions there, as outlined in earlier chapters of this book, are favorable for tropical cyclogenesis, then if the MCS holds together sufficiently long, it may evolve into a tropical storm and subsequently likely reach hurricane status.

Indeed, if you study closely the enhanced infra-red weather satellite images over equatorial Africa during the hurricane season, you observe that most of the hurricane seedlings that move into the Atlantic as easterly waves originate as mesoscale convective systems.

Moreover, as a tropical cyclone forms in the Gulf of Mexico, Caribbean Sea, the rest of the low-latitude North Atlantic Basin, the low-latitude Pacific Basins and the Indian Ocean, it mushrooms as an MCS before growing into a tropical storm, in most of the tropical cyclogenesis episodes.

The relationship of concentrated high-value theta-e air and tropical cyclones is therefore established (the air comprising tropical cyclones is high theta-e air, since these systems are a type of organized convection), but using theta-e ridges and projected theta-e ridges to forecast the likely movement of tropical cyclones is still experimental in the early 21st century, and should be viewed as an engaging attempted use of theta-e which requires more rigorous investigation.

Much of the pioneer work on theta-e and its uses was developed by Roderick Scofield who worked for the weather satellite branch of the U. S.'s weather service.

HOW TO COMPUTE 850 MB THETA-E FROM A SOUNDING ON A SKEW-T

850 mb theta-e (or any level theta-e) can easily be determined from the sounding on a skew-T, log P diagram.

Take the 850 mb temperature on the temperature curve and the 850 mb dewpoint on the mixing ratio curve and raise the temperature dry adiabatically (along or parallel to the closest dry adiabat on the chart), and simultaneously raise the dewpoint (it is conserved in dry adiabatic processes) along or parallel to the nearest mixing ratio curve until both raised lines intersect. This is the Lifted Condensation Level (LCL). Cloud bases may appear here. Now that this parcel has been dry adiabatically cooled to its dewpoint so that it is saturated, continue raising it moist adiabatically, i.e., along or parallel to the closest moist adiabat, until essentially all the moisture has been condensed out. This is where the moist adiabats become parallel to the dry adiabats. On the standard skew-T diagram, this is at 200 mb. Then take that same parcel down or parallel to the closest dry adiabat to 1000 mb. This is the parcel's 850 mb equivalent potential temperature. Convert it from Celsius to Kelvin (add 273 degrees) for convention. Note: on the skew-T, it is unnecessary to take the parcel dry adiabatically down from 200 mb to 1000 mb to find its theta-e; note that the same dry adiabat along which the parcel would be brought down, also extends to the top of the chart, and is labelled at both bottom at top; therefore, simply raise the parcel to 200 mb and then follow the dry adiabat to the top of the chart to read the equivalent potential temperature value, afterwhich converting it to Kelvin. Doing this for soundings in your interest area gives you values you then plot on a map and analyze, looking for theta-e ridges, maxima and gradients.

46. OMEGA DIAGNOSTICS, including Q-VECTORS and PIVA/NIVA

Q stands for QUASI-GEOSTROPHIC THEORY. Quasi-geostrophic theory states that the air tends to move towards geostrophic balance, and when it is not, i.e., when there is an AGEOSTROPHIC COMPONENT OF THE WIND, vertical motions develop. Geostrophic balance is when the forces (or forces per unit mass: accelerations) which cause the wind are in balance, with the result being the wind blowing parallel to the height contours on an upper-level chart. For example, the pressure-gradient force which causes air to move, is balanced by the Coriolis force due to the earth's rotation, which causes the air to turn to the right in the Northern Hemisphere and to the left in the Southern Hemisphere (see section 2d and chapter 19). When the flow is curved but above the planetary boundary layer, then three forces are in balance to cause the wind to blow parallel to the height contours: the pressure-gradient force, the Coriolis force and the centrifugal force. The centrifugal force is a "center-fleeing force" which, because of the curvature in the flow, establishes a component of movement causing the air to try to move away from the center of rotation. The centrifugal force may be a response to a centripetal force which causes air to try to move in towards the center of rotation.

In summary, for the wind to be geostrophic...in geostrophic balance...all of the forces that cause the wind must be in balance. When the forces are out of balance, we have situations such as those described in chapter 19 for jet-streak-induced ageostrophic circulations. That is, suppose we have fairly straight flow above the planetary boundary layer so that there is no frictional force. Then the wind is a balance of the pressure-gradient force and the Coriolis force. When either of these forces is temporarily stronger than the other in time and space, then the air is forced to blow across the height contours. For example, when the pressure-gradient force is stronger than the Coriolis force (see chapter 19), the air blows from high heights to low heights. Because of the theorem of conservation of mass applied to air, we cannot create or destroy air; therefore, the air has to go somewhere. The areas in which the area is converging ("piling up") when crossing the contours, is an area from which these extra parcels will then rise or sink, and where the air is being depleted from (from where the air is diverging), the lost parcels will be replaced by air from above or below. Thus, vertical motions are established. The atmosphere is actually trying to get back into geostrophic balance.

In our example, that part of the pressure-gradient force that is temporarily stronger than the Coriolis force is called the ageostrophic component of the wind. The total or resultant wind is the combination of its geostrophic and ageostrophic components. Ageostrophic means "not geostrophic". When the Coriolis force is stronger than the pressure-gradient force, than that component of the Coriolis force that is stronger than the pressure-gradient force is the ageostrophic component of the wind.

The point of this discussion is that one set of causes of vertical motion is when ageostrophic wind components are established, and this happens when the forces that cause the wind are temporarily out of balance.

(continued)   PAGE 183

On the synoptic scale, not the convective scale, a famous meteorological equation has been derived that gives the dynamic forcing mechanisms for vertical motions in the atmosphere. This equation is called THE OMEGA EQUATION, because the lower-case Greek letter omega, ω, is the chosen symbol for vertical motion, i.e., motion following the air parcel. These air parcels are small bundles, about one cubic meter in volume.

The omega equation does not define the mechanical causes of lift or sink, such as air being forced to rise up and over higher terrain, but it does give the dynamic causes.

Here is the omega equation in physical terms. The terms on the right-hand side are what cause the vertical component of the wind. There are more than four terms, but they are at least an order of magnitude less than (at least one-tenth less than) the four main terms, so we can effectively ignore them.

The Omega Equation:

For synoptic-scale vertical motion:

Upward or downward motion =   differential vorticity advection
- **+ thermal advection**
- **+ deformation of the horizontal component of the geostrophic wind**
- **+ deformation of the vertical component of the geostrophic wind**
- **+ minor miscellaneous forcings**

Differential vorticity advection (see previous chapters relating to vorticity) refers to the vertical component of spin or vorticity of an air parcel, i.e. the component of spin about a vertical axis. Fluid dynamics show us that when there is greater positive vorticity advection aloft, say at 500 mb, than there is near the surface, the fluid spins up, rises. Thus, e.g, increasing positive vorticity advection with height causes air to spin up, to rise. Recall from previous chapters in this book, that positive vorticity is air spinning from left-to-right about that vertical axis, as if we were above the Northern Hemisphere looking down at the air parcels and their vorticities in the Northern Hemisphere.

The thermal advection term essentially states that by itself, warm air advection is rising air, and cold air advection is sinking air. As warmer air is moving in (advecting), it rises above the cooler air, and as colder air moves in, it sinks below the warmer air.

The third and fourth terms are more mathematical. Deformation of the wind means that the air is essentially diverging aloft, and therefore, from the theorem of conservation of mass, these air parcels are replaced by air from above or below, therefore giving rise to vertical motions. Sometimes these deformation terms are significant. Most of the time, the differential vorticity and thermal advection terms are the major players.

(continued)

Quasi-geostrophic theory also states that low pressure systems and their associated short-wave troughs aloft first form as areas of positive vorticity. The storms do not develop into major storms unless thermal advections then take place, to enhance the vertical motions. Low-level (below 700 mb) warm air advection must occur to the east of the short-wave trough axis, with cold air advection occurring to the west of this axis. The warm air rises and the cold air sinks underneath the warm air it is displacing. Eventually, the system occludes, i.e., the air all mixes around and up and the storm dies. The short-wave trough aloft can grow, even through the entire depth of the troposphere, before dying. And if the strong thermal advections do not get established after the vorticity maximum develops, then the short-wave trough and its surface low "fizzle out".

Now that the quasi-geostrophic theory has been addressed, let us return to the omega equation. The omega we are computing is a very small number. For example, if we want to compute the 700 mb vertical velocity, a strong upward or downward component is on the order of 5 to 15 microbars per second. At 700 mb, 1 microbar/sec is approximately 1.12 centimeters per second. A mathematical conversion will therefore show that a strong upward or downward vertical velocity at 700 mb on the synoptic scale is less than one-fifth of a mile per hour! Yet, if a lift of say 5 to 15 microbars/sec is occurring over hundreds of miles out to the north and east of the low pressure center, and the air is saturated or nearly saturate, then that rising moist air will form clouds and subsequent precipitation. In using the differential vorticity term and the thermal advection term of the omega equation, and ignoring the other terms since they usually are at least one order of magnitude less than the vorticity and thermal advection terms, we find various combinations of advections possible that would give us rising air or sinking air. Unfortunately, since we are dealing with very small numbers for the advection terms, an error in them could yield the wrong result in the sign of the resultant vertical velocity. This is why the Q-vector approach has been invented.

However, before discussing Q-vectors, it is necessary to understand the resultant vertical motions based on the forcing terms of differential vorticity advection and thermal advection.

- If we have increasing positive vorticity advection (PVA) with height, air spins up.

- If we have decreasing negative vorticity advection (NVA) with height, air spins down.

- If we have low-level warm air advection, air rises.

- If we have low-level cold air advection, air sinks.

(continued)

Now, if we have increasing PVA with height AND low-level warm air advection, we have two terms contributing to causing air to rise, so the result is the dynamical combination for the greatest upward vertical motion.

If we have decreasing NVA with height AND low-level cold air advection, we have two terms contributing to causing air to sink, so the result is the dynamical combination for the greatest downward vertical motion.

But when we have increasing PVA with height, which causes air to rise, AND low-level cold air advection, which causes air to sink, what will be the resultant vertical velocity?

And when we have decreasing NVA with height, which causes air to sink, AND low-level warm air advection, which causes air to rise, what will be the resultant vertical velocity?

This is when Q-vectors help, because they mathematically combine both right-hand side forcing terms of the omega equation and give the resultant vertical motion. This forecast guidance tool is quite helpful in situations such as the two above when competing forcing mechanisms present a confusing analysis, and the forecaster is trying to determine which of the advective contributors to vertical motion is the stronger.

For example. suppose a vigorous rain or snow storm is passing through your area, and the cold front associated with the low pressure system has just passed. Now you are experiencing cold air advection, which causes sinking, diverging air. However, the 500 mb vort max in its 500 mb short-wave trough is still to the west of you, so your area is receiving PVA, which causes air to rise if it is stronger PVA aloft than in the lower levels.
If the average relative humidity from the surface through 500 mb behind the cold front is still 90% or greater, the rain or snow would continue if the resultant vertical motion is still upward. However, if the cold air advection overpowers the effect of the differential PVA, then the result is downward motion and clearing skies. In the case of a major snowstorm, your area could therefore either receive another, say, six inches, or it could clear out. A correct prognosis protects against a "busted" forecast!

Thus, we want to know the result of the dynamic and mechanical forcings for lifting and sinking of air parcels: will the air be rising or sinking? Moreover, we need to know if there is ample moisture available so that if the air is rising, that area would experience cloudiness and subsequent precipitation.

The Q-vector scheme mathematically combines the two most significant terms on the right-hand side of the omega equation, the differential vorticity advection and the thermal advection terms, and expresses the result as one value. When displayed graphically, this complex approach produces simplified weather maps of Q-vectors that show us whether air is rising or sinking, based on the dynamical forcings for vertical motion.

(continued)

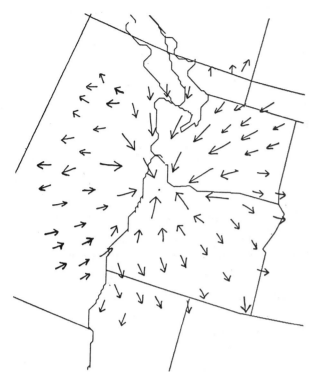

Figure 96. A Plot of 500 mb Q-vectors.
What arises out of the Q-vector mathematics is that **an area in which the Q-vectors are converging is where air is rising, and an area in which the Q-vectors are diverging is where air is sinking.**

Notice how the Q-vector arrows are pointing towards (converging on) northwest Oregon. This is the maximum Q-vector convergence area; therefore we would expect the greatest upward vertical motion of air parcels in that area.

The entire region that covers much of Washington, the western part of Oregon and just off the coast of both states is the overall area of convergence of Q-vectors, which is therefore the overall area of rising air.

To the east and south of that region, the vectors are diverging, which represents the region of sinking air.

Where the greatest Q-vector convergence is found, in northwest Oregon, the combined effect of the differential vorticity advection and the temperature advection is to create the strongest upward vertical velocities.

Some of the area, e.g., to the west just offshore, may be experiencing differential PVA but also cold air advection, but the differential PVA, which causes air to spin up, would be stronger than the effect of the cold air advection, which causes air to sink, so that the resultant is still rising air, as indicated by converging Q-vectors.

We can look at plots of Q-vectors at 850 mb. 700 mb, 500 mb and 300 mb, to see if air is rising or sinking at any or all of the levels, and we can look at Q-vector plots for layers...e.g., for the 850 mb through 500 mb layer and for the 500 mb through 300 mb layer...to determine the sign (upward, neutral or near-neutral, or downward) of the vertical motion through each layer. What we look for are areas of converging Q-vectors, which indicate rising air, and areas of diverging Q-vectors, which indicate sinking air. Next, we look at analyses or prognostications of the available moisture, such as the surface-to-500 mb average relative humidity chart, so that we forecast the sky condition relative to cloudiness and any precipitation probability.

(continued)

Note: the convergence and divergence of Q-vectors should not be looked at as being the convergence and divergence of the wind, i.e., of air parcels, What we are analyzing is the convergence and divergence of an abstract mathematical property which helps us to determine what the atmosphere is doing for synoptic-scale vertical motions.

This interesting Q-vector usage does not stop with the above type of chart, however, There is a set of superior Q-vector graphics that meteorologists enjoy using, which are the result of mathematically computing the actual values of convergence and divergence of Q-vectors. These charts are easier to read than looking at plots of Q-vectors and determining areas of their convergence and divergence.

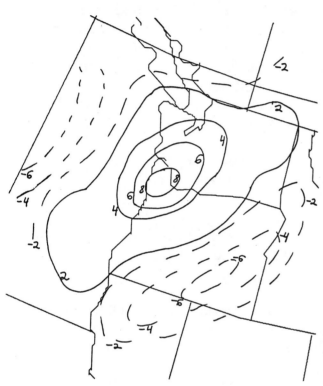

Figure 97. The 500 mb Divergence of Q-vectors. More specifically, this weather map shows the 500 millibar divergence of Q-vectors times -2 with a contour interval of 4 times 10 to the minus 17 power in units of meters per kilogram of mass per second. The Q-vector divergence is a negative number, and the Q-vector convergence is a positive number.

Although the mathematical derivation is complicated, the interpretation of the graphical display is simple: where there is convergence of Q-vectors (solid lines), we have rising air, and where there is divergence of Q-vectors (dashed lines), we have sinking air. Keep in mind that we are looking at the results of the dynamical forcings for synoptic-scale vertical motion. Any mechanical forcings, such as upslope and orographic lifting caused by air being forced to rise up and over rising terrain, need to be added to the results of the dynamical forcing.

Any weather maps of convergence/divergence of Q-vectors that you may obtain could vary how the display is given. For example, one type of presentation gives all solid contours, with positive values for divergence of Q and negative values for convergence (negative divergence) of Q. What you must determine is which areas are areas of convergence of Q-vectors and which areas are areas of divergence of Q-vectors, so that you can infer where air is rising and where air is sinking, respectively.

(continued)

One of the benefits of using Q-vectors is that meteorologists have learned that the role of warm air advection is many times more significant than the role of increasing PVA with height in causing air to rise. Some series of Q-vector charts actually divide the vorticity and thermal advections into each component's contribution to vertical motion, to show which is a greater contributor.

There is yet another use for Q-vectors, which is provable through the Q-vector mathematics. If you overlay the 850 mb Q-vector plot onto the 850 mb isotherm analysis, you can identify areas where a front is strengthening (FRONTOGENESIS) and where a front is weakening (FRONTOLYSIS). Knowing this is significant, because a frontal zone is a zone of air parcel convergence, and when a front is strengthening, the baroclinicity is likely to increasing. What this means is that vertical motions are likely increasing, so that the threat for precipitation is enhanced. When frontogenesis is occurring, the isotherm packing is tightening, i.e., the isotherms are getting closer together.

Thus, the procedure is to overlay the 850 mb Q-vectors and 850 mb isotherms for the same time. Here is how you analyze for frontogenesis and frontolysis:

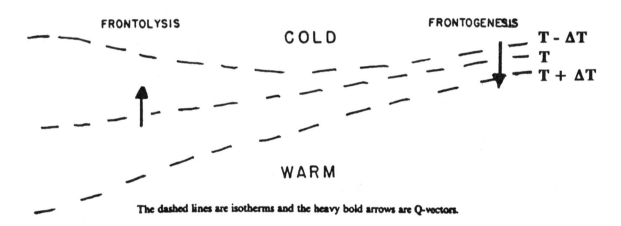

Figure 98. Analyzing for the Frontogenetic Function of Q-Vectors. The dashed lines re isotherms and the heavy arrows are Q-vectors, all at the same level in the lower troposphere. Where the Q-vectors cross the isotherms and are pointing from cold to warm air, we have frontogenesis; where the Q-vectors cross the isotherms and are pointing from warm to cold air, we have frontolysis.

From the Rocky Mountains westward over North America, use the 700 mb isotherms and Q-vectors, and east of the Rockies use the 850 mb isotherms and Q-vectors.

(continued)

Sometimes, on a wavy quasi-stationary front, frontogenesis leads to cyclogenesis as an incipient wave forms on a kink of the front, and this wave continues developing into a low pressure system that may become a major storm. Thus, for example, in the colder part of the year, a major snowstorm may develop within a region of strong frontogenesis as depicted by the frontogenetic use of Q-vectors.

As a typical meteorologist could say about this entire unusual meteorological abstraction called "Q-vectors", "This is really neat stuff!"

Finally, there is what may be called a "quick and dirty" Q-vector-type analysis that can be done for anyone wanting a Q-vector analysis but having access to only the basic charts. This is called the PIVA/NIVA technique:

The PIVA/NIVA Approach to Graphically Solving the Omega Equation

PIVA stands for Positive Isothermal Vorticity Advection;
NIVA stands for Negative Isothermal Vorticity Advection

PIVA/NIVA is a unique approach for graphically solving, to a first approximation, the omega equation. PIVA/NIVA combines both major right-hand, forcing terms of the omega equation.

Instead of advecting the 500 mb vorticity by the 500 mb geostrophic wind, using the height lines (see chapter 18), PIVA/NIVA advects the vorticity by the 1000-to-500 m b thickness lines. Another abstract meteorological property called the THERMAL WIND flows parallel to the thickness contours, with cold air to the left and warm air to the right of the thermal wind. The thermal wind is not a real wind. It is a vector which represents the difference between the geostrophic wind at two different levels.

Consider the following:

(continued)

Figure 99. The fictitious THERMAL WIND, which shows how veering (winds shifting in direction in a clockwise sense) of the geostrophic wind with increasing height implies warm air advection through that layer, and backing (winds shifting in direction in a counterclockwise sense) of the geostrophic wind with increasing height implies cold air advection through that layer.

V_{ug} = upper-level geostrophic wind

V_{lg} = lower-level geostrophic wind

V_{th} = thermal wind = $V_{ug} - V_{lg}$

WARM AIR ADVECTION   COLD AIR ADVECTION

V_{ug} = 220° at 25kt V_{ug} = 160° at 25kt

V_{lg} = 160° at 25kt V_{lg} = 220° at 25kt

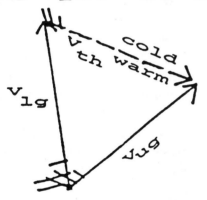 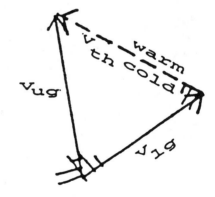

Therefore, veering (clockwise in direction) winds with height imply warm air advection.

Therefore, backing (counterclockwise in direction) winds with height imply cold air advection.

THE ABOVE APPLIES ABOVE THE PLANETARY BOUNDARY LAYER.

(continued)

PIVA/NIVA assumes that if there is PVA at 500 mb, we most likely have weaker PVA in the lower troposphere because the winds and wind shear are stronger aloft. Thus, we are assuming that when we have PVA at 500 mb we have differential PVA. Then we can advect the 500 mb vorticity by the 1000-to-500 mb thickness lines, i.e., advect the vorticity by the thermal wind, and are loosely combining graphically the two main forcing terms of the omega equation.

We would look for areas of PVA as advected in by the thermal wind, which may show a somewhat different positive vorticity advection thrust than that given by advecting the positive vorticity by the geostrophic wind. An example of how this technique is used is for east coast snowstorms. The heaviest snow tends to fall where the greatest PVA occurs as advected in by the thermal wind using the PIVA/NIVA technique.

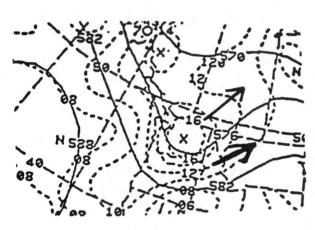

Figure 100. A PIVA/NIVA Chart. The solid lines are the thickness lines for the 1000-to-500 mb thickness (see chapter 18), and the dashed lines are the 500 mb absolute vorticity, with each X marking the location of a vorticity maximum, and each N marking the location of a vorticity minimum. The arrows show how the "thermal wind" is directed, parallel to the thickness contours.

The arrows were placed to show where positive vorticity advection was occurring as transported by the thermal wind, at the time of this chart.

That region, ahead of the "VORTMAX" (vorticity maximum) is where the greatest dynamic lift would be expected.

Thus, a PIVA/NIVA analysis or prog is used the same way as is a convergence/divergence of Q-vectors analysis or prog, respectively.

The Q-vector and related PIVA/NIVA charts do not replace other weather maps showing vertical velocities and features related to vertical motion; but they do enhance the data set.

Keep in mind that forecasters place a strong emphasis on looking for the PVA areas, which is appropriate, but sometimes overlook the warm air advection areas. Some Q-vector analyses programs break up the forcings into the role of the differential PVA and the role of the thermal advection, and often the warm air advection is a greater contributor to lift than is the vorticity role.

EXAMPLES OF WHERE USING Q-VECTORS CAN BE HELPFUL IN FORECASTING;

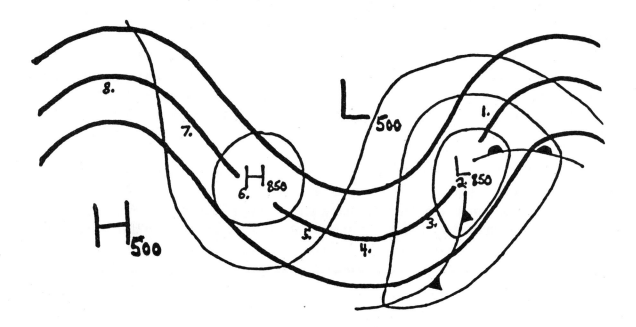

Figure 101. A common situation: surface (or 850 mb) highs, lows and fronts (lighter, thinner lines) and the 500 mb contours and flow, with the 500 mb low and high centers (darker, thicker lines). The table below gives the resultant synoptic-scale vertical motion from the 850 mb thermal advection and 500 mb vorticity advection at each locale.

LOCALE	VORTICITY ADVECTION	TEMPERATURE ADVECTION	NET VERTICAL MOTION
1.	PVA	WARM	MAX UP
2.	PVA	0	UP
3.	PVA	COLD	?
4.	0	COLD	DOWN
5.	NVA	COLD	MAX DOWN
6.	NVA	0	DOWN
7.	NVA	WARM	?
8.	0	WARM	UP

Where the low-level warm air advection and/or 500 mb PVA contribute to lift (locales 1, 2 and 8), the result is therefore rising air. At locale 1, both thermal and vorticity advections are combining to each produce lift, we at locale 1 we find the greatest upward vertical velocities.

Where the low-level cold air advection and/or 500 mb NVA contribute to sinking air (locales 4, 5 and 6), the result is downward motion. At locale 5, where we have the combined effect of thermal and vorticity advections for sinking air, we find the greatest downward vertical velocities.

But at locales 3 and 7 we have a dilemma. At locale 3, we have cold air advection behind the cold front, which should cause sinking air, but we still have 500 millibar positive vorticity advection, which should infer rising air. What is the result? If there is ample moisture and the resultant motion is still upward, then we can still get another half-foot of snow, e.g., even behind the cold front; however, if the cold air advection is stronger than the effect of the PVA so that the air is sinking right behind the cold front, then the snow will stop and we can forecast gradual clearing.

Thus, in situations such as these, it is helpful to use Q-vectors to determine what the net or resultant vertical motion will be (up, down or none, and if up or down, the magnitude) so that we can decide whether there will still be snow or rain at locale 3.

Locale 7 poses a similar dilemma…low-level warm-air advection returning around the high pressure center, but still NVA occurring aloft. However, we are more likely to encounter considerable moisture at 3 than at 7, so that Q-vectors would be a more significant help for locale 3.

Note: convergence and divergence of Q-vectors is NOT the same as convergence and divergence of the wind! Q-vectors refer to a mathematical abstraction that does have physical meaning, and convergence and divergence of this abstraction also have physical meanings!

The thermal advection term of the omega equation is actually the negative of the LaPlacian of the thermal advection (if you study calculus, you know what this is). It has physical meaning. The same is true for Q-vectors. If we try to ascribe a physical explanation of a Q-vector, it is the following: a Q-vector is the change with time of an acceleration per unit depth of air parcels; a Q-vector can also be defined as the vector rate of change of the temperature gradient, following an isobaric (geostrophic) trajectory, and vertical motions are related to this vector rate of change. Thus, the mathematics become somewhat abstract, but if you are a student of the math, or are interested in studying "dynamical meteorology", you will discover the secret of the beauty of the math, which is, the mathematics describe the physical realities of atmospheric behavior. Only when the equations are meaningful to us, that is, when we can visualize and conceptualize what they say physically, is when we see the science of meteorology through an additional perspective, and we can therefore appreciate and enjoy the weather even more!   **PAGE 194**

(The following is a more technical explanation of the Q-vector mathematical formulation. This section may be skipped without missing the essence of the Q-vector discussion as given in this chapter's previous pages.)

Two meteorological scales of vertical motion we are concerned with for forecasting are the synoptic scale and the convective scale.

On the synoptic, or larger of these scales, a strong 700 mb upward vertical velocity would be a value of +3 microbars per second, or greater. A 700 mb vertical velocity of minus 3 microbars per second, or greater, in the downward sense, would be a strong synoptic scale sinking motion. A microbar/second at 700 mb is about 1.12 centimeters per second. Thus, a strong vertical speed at 700 mb on the broad-scale synoptic scene is something stronger than about one tenth of a mile per hour! Compare this with the convective scale, in which updrafts and downdrafts can be greater than 50 miles per hour. Indeed, for updrafts to support grapefruit-sized hailstones, they must be on the order of 125 to 150 mph.

$$1 \text{ bar} = 10^6 \text{ dynes/cm}^2 \quad 1 \text{ millibar (mb)} = 10^{-3} \text{ bar} = 10^3 \text{ dynes/cm}^2$$

$$1 \text{ microbar} = 10^{-6} \text{ bar} = 10^0 = 1 \text{ dyne/cm}^2$$

For large sweeping areas of broad-based vertical motion, the synoptic scale vertical motion field is used for forecasting major weather systems, clouds and precipitation or the lack thereof, and deriving some mesoscale inferences.

We may analyze the vertical motion at a specified height, i.e., looking at $w = dz/dt$; more commonly, we use the isobaric coordinate system to analyze the vertical motion of parcels past a specified pressure level, $\omega = dp/dt$. Because 700 mb usually averages about 10,000 feet above sea-level and, east of the Rocky Mountains, in the "meaty" area of synoptic scale systems, the vertical velocities at this level have become commonly used in the forecasting challenge.

Physically, the difference between $\frac{dp}{dt}$ and $\frac{\partial p}{\partial t}$ is as follows.

$\frac{dp}{dt}$, the LaGrangian or total time derivative of pressure, is the change in pressure of a parcel of air if you are moving along with the parcel.

$\frac{\partial p}{\partial t}$, the Eulerian or partial time derivative of P, is the local rate of change of pressure: what you would measure in one spot if you read the barometric pressure change.

The total derivative is the sum of the partial (local) derivative and the horizontal and vertical advections of the property.

The OMEGA EQUATION is a diagnostic equation for the total time derivative of pressure. Its beauty is that the synoptic scale vertical motion field can be determined without actually measuring the vertical motion itself. A problem with the omega equation is that the values for dp/dt are so small that a small error in one of the determining terms of the omega equation could change the sign of dp/dt at that location. Thus, meticulous care is vital to ensure accurate values, assuming the original weather observations are accurate. In reality, the search for actual values is not as operationally feasible as the subjective uses of the equation to determine whether upward or downward vertical motion is occurring on the synoptic scale below the level of nondivergence.

A form of THE OMEGA EQUATION is given below:

$$\underbrace{\left(\sigma\nabla^2+f_0^2\frac{\partial^2}{\partial p^2}\right)\omega}_{A} = \underbrace{f_0\frac{\partial}{\partial p}\left[\mathbf{V}_g\cdot\nabla\left(\frac{1}{f_0}\nabla^2\Phi+f\right)\right]}_{B}+\underbrace{\nabla^2\left[\mathbf{V}_g\cdot\nabla\left(\frac{-\partial\Phi}{\partial p}\right)\right]}_{C}$$

f_0 = constant Coriolis parameter; Φ = geopotential = $\int_\bullet^z g\,dz$;

$\sigma = -\frac{\alpha}{\theta}\frac{\partial\theta}{\partial p}$, a static stability parameter where θ = potential temperature and α = specific volume

THE TERMS OF THE OMEGA EQUATION:

TERM A : proportional to ω; is actually the three-dimensional LaPlacian of omega

TERM B : proportional to differential vorticity advection; this term is proportional to the rate of increase or decrease with height, of the advection of absolute vorticity

TERM C : the two-dimensional negative of the LaPlacian of the thickness advection; this term is proportional to the thickness advection; with warm air advection, Term C is positive

Note: The right-hand side of the equation actually contains several terms for dynamical forcing of synoptic-scale vertical motions; however, the forcing by differential vorticity advection and thickness advection are at least an order of magnitude higher than other factors; therefore, these other factors are typically relatively insignificant and are therefore obviated, allowing us to drop them.

WHAT THE OMEGA EQUATION SAYS:

The omega equation says that upward vertical motion will result when there is increasing positive vorticity advection with height and/or when there is warm air advection. Decreasing negative vorticity advection with height would also cause air to spin up.

Thus, downward vertical motion will occur when there is decreasing PVA or increasing NVA with height, and/or cold air advection.

Of course, care must be used in this form of omega diagnostics because the above are not the only causes of vertical motion on the synoptic scale in the troposphere. Moreover, terms B and C can sometimes work against each other, in which case the predominating contributor determines the resultant vertical motion field.

Realistically, the omega equation is helpful as a subjective diagnostic tool. Operationally, a forecaster would subjectively determine what contributions to the vertical motion are being made by terms B and C as follows. He or She would obtain the absolute vorticity advection at 1000 mb and at 500 mb over the area of interest. If the vorticity advection is positive and has a higher value at 500 mb than at 1000 mb, then positive differential advection of geostrophic vorticity (increasing PVA with height) is occurring through this layer, causing air parcels to spin up. Then the forecaster would look at the 850 mb chart to determine if any temperature advection is occurring. The stronger the warm air advection, the greater the contribution is likely to be to upward motion. Obviously, the differential NVA and cold air advection would likely contribute to downward vertical motion.

The surface geostrophic vorticity chart gives the surface geostrophic relative vorticity after determining what the surface wind would be if it were geostrophic (the frictional component is subtracted out). Thus, $2\Omega \sin\phi$, the vorticity of the earth, would need to be added to the relative vorticity values of this chart to obtain the absolute vorticity. It is easier to use one of the applications programs which determine the vorticity field at various levels. Ideally, we would need to determine the average vorticity advection in the column, or better yet, the rate of change of vorticity advection as we ascend, to determine mathematically how the differential vorticity advection is contributing to vertical motion on the synoptic scale.

Because the values of ω are so small, on the order of at most several microbars per second, we would need meticulous observations to not induce errors in calculating values for itself. The sign of ω could easily be miscalculated. Thus, the usefulness of the omega equation is in identifying two fields (differential vorticity advection and low-level temperature advection) that contribute to the vertical motion field, and being able to infer the vertical motion field from 1000 to 500 mb without actually measuring it.

Simply having positive vorticity advection at 500 mb does not mean that there is upward motion; observations imply that there probably is, but 500 mb PVA alone will not cause upward motion. Because the 500 mb level is close to the level of nondivergence (about 550 mb), the vorticity advection is more closely related to short wave motion at that level. It is the differential PVA (increasing PVA with height through the layer) that likely will contribute to upward motion.

Recent research has well documented the importance of the role of low-level warm air advection in synoptic and mesoscale storm development, because of its contribution to upward motion.

It can be shown that, in the middle troposphere, the forcing caused by vertical differential absolute vorticity advection is very nearly cancelled by the forcing caused by the LaPlacian of the thermal advection, in many cases. This has led to the development of **Q-VECTOR DIAGNOSTICS** (Q stands for Quasi-Geostrophic).

DEFINITION OF Q-VECTOR:

A Q-Vector is defined by:

$$\vec{Q} = \left[\frac{\partial \vec{V_g}}{\partial x} \cdot \nabla\left(\frac{\partial \Phi}{\partial p}\right), \quad \frac{\partial \vec{V_g}}{\partial y} \cdot \nabla\left(\frac{\partial \Phi}{\partial p}\right) \right]$$

The above equation says that a Q-Vector is equal to the rate of change of the horizontal potential temperature gradient, which develops in an air parcel moving with the geostrophic wind if the vertical velocity were zero. This is not always true. The Q-Vector is useful because it gives an approximation of the ageostrophic horizontal wind in the lower branch of the circulation that develops in order to maintain the thermal wind balance in a developing synoptic disturbance.

THE Q-VECTORS GRAPHICALLY SHOW THE SYNOPTIC-SCALE VERTICAL MOTION RESULTING FROM THE TWO MAIN FORCING TERMS OF THE OMEGA EQUATION: NAMELY, DIFFERENTIAL VORTICITY ADVECTION AND THE LAPLACIAN OF THICKNESS ADVECTION.

HOW TO USE Q-VECTOR ANALYSIS:

The magnitude of a Q-vector is roughly proportional to the strength of the ageostrophic horizontal wind. What we look for is the convergence and divergence of the Q-vectors, because the convergence of Q-vectors implies synoptic-scale upward vertical motion, and the divergence of Q-vectors implies synoptic-scale downward vertical motion. On computer we can generate plots of Q-vectors at various levels in the atmosphere, but looking at these plots alone, as in the first diagram on the following page, it is somewhat of a challenge to infer convergent and divergent areas; therefore, we want to look at the analysis of the convergence/divergence of the Q-vectors.

(Note on the actual values of convergence/divergence of Q-Vectors: Although the actual values of Q-Vectors may not in themselves be as important as perhaps the gradients of the convergence/divergence of Q-Vectors, we can say something useful about these values in a qualitative way: consider two synoptic storms, each with the same amount of moisture available for precipitation; the storm with a significantly higher value of Q-Vector convergence than the other storm would imply that it will yield heavier precipitation. Also, do not "advect" Q-Vector convergence/divergence field beyond about the first two to three hours, because the Q-Vectors are continually changing as the differential vorticity advection and thickness advection each changes (there is also deformation of the geostrophic wind, which is a forcing term for vertical motion); rather, use the actual initial analysis of the field and prognostications of the field to infer vertical motions.)

TYPICAL WINTERTIME CASE WHERE USING THE Q-VECTOR APPROACH IMPROVES FORECASTING THE LOCATION OF THE HEAVIEST SNOW

Many forecasters have made the mistake of keying-in on only the vort max and its movement in forecasting where the heaviest rain or snow will fall from a major low pressure system; however, the vorticity contribution to synoptic-scale lift is often-enough not the main dynamic forcing mechanism for lift: the role of warm-air advection must be determined, because if adequate to copious moisture is present in the region of strong warm air advection, then the greatest precipitation may fall there rather than where the greatest positive vorticity advection is occurring. The region of strongest warm-air advection may be some two hundred or three hundred miles away from the area of greatest PVA; therefore, the forecaster choosing to consider the PVA without determining the role of the warm-air advection may have a "busted" forecast.

In studying many winter storms in recent years, this author's finding and opinion is that for major low pressure systems that have good thermal advections underway and are not well into the occlusion process, the role of the low-level warm-air advection is often a stronger dynamic mechanism for lift than the role of differential vorticity advection.

Therefore, with the Q-vector set of analyses, one may consider the contribution to lift as determined by the Laplacian of thermal advection, and the contribution due to differential PVA, to see which may be the more important factor.

Q-vectors will not help when considering mechanical causes of lift, such as upslope flow and, for lake-effect snows, frictional convergence from saturated air coming from over the water to over land where it must also rise as it moves over a higher elevation, thereby condensing even more snowfall from the clouds.

The following is a typical case where the Q-vector approach makes for a better forecast of where the heavy snow can be expected.

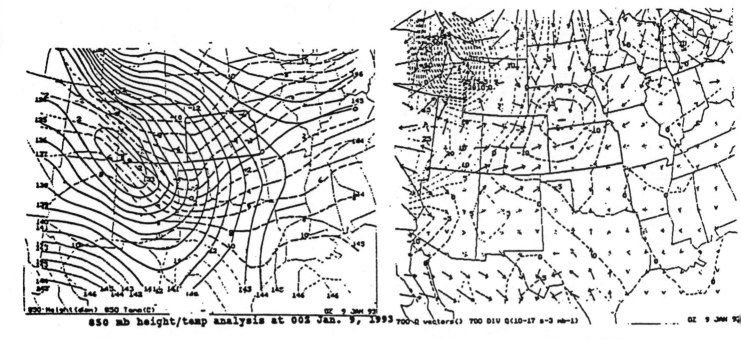

850 mb height/temp analysis at 00Z Jan. 9, 1993

700 mb Q vectors and Div Q field
00Z Jan. 9, 1993.

The 850 mb analysis at 00Z showed strong warm-air advection from Texas into Nerbraska. The 700 mb Q-vector depiction shows the strongest negative divergence (convergence) of Q-vectors over Nebraska and northern Kansas.

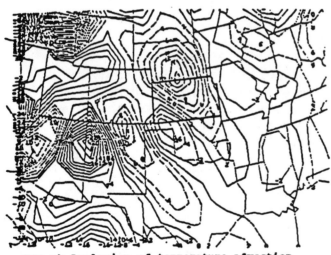

700 mb Laplacian of temperature advection.

00Z Jan 9, 1993

The 00Z analysis of the 700 mb Laplacian of thermal advection indicates where the greatest contribution to lift is (Nebraska and northern Kansas), and, after looking at the vorticity analysis (on next page), leads to the conclusion that the vertical motion in this storm at this time is primarily thermally-forced.

(continued)

Interestingly, the forecast models predicted a significant vorticity
maximum at 500 mb, and these forecasts verified. For example, below is
the 12-hour 500 mb height and vorticity prog for 12Z, showing the
greatest positive vorticity advection over Oklahoma. Notice from the
actual observed 12Z 500 analysis that the model's forecast was quite
good, with the actual greatest PVA over Oklahoma.

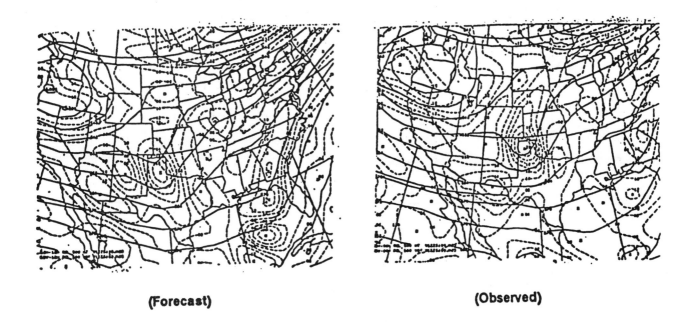

(Forecast)   (Observed)

If a forecaster used traditional forecasting techniques, he/she might
have forecasted the heaviest snow and/or rain across Oklahoma, especially
since the surface-to-500 mb moisture was copious from Texas into Kansas
and southern Nebraska. Furthermore, the models were verifying the vort
max and PVA quite nicely. Even the 24-hour prog, below, showed the
greatest PVA into MIssouri and Arkansas, which might entice the
forecaster to then carry the heavy snowfall into northern Arkansas and
Missouri.

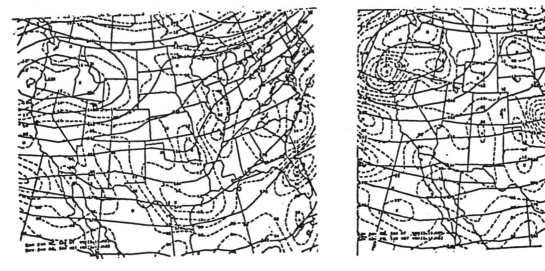

(continued) (Forecast)   (Observed)

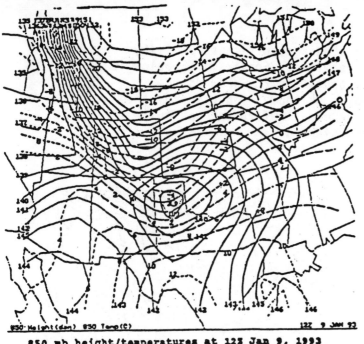

By 12Z, the low-level warm-air advection pattern was obvious across the Central Plains.

Note that the low is in the Texas panhandle and was moving into Oklahoma. Based on the vorticity considerations alone, the heaviest snow and rain would still be expected to fall from Oklahoma into southeast Kansas and into Missouri.

850 mb height/temperatures at 12Z Jan 9, 1993

However, the 12Z analysis of the Laplacian of thermal advection shows the greatest lift occurring over Kansas and Nebraska.

700 mb height and Laplacian of the temperature advection at 12Z Jan. 9, 1993

THE HEAVIEST SNOW FELL IN SOUTH-CENTRAL NEBRASKA, within the region of greatest thermal forcing for lift. Although it is possible that there may have been some mechanical forcing in the form of upslope, the heavy snow band extended outside any possible upslope area, into northeast Kansas to the northwest Missouri border region. The January 8th-9th storm produced 19" of snow in McCook, Nebraska, 17.2" in Topeka, Kansas and 12" in Kansas City, Missouri, all outside the region where the models forecasted the greatest PVA, and the models' 500 mb progs verified, yet exactly in the region where the Laplacian of thermal advection showed the greatest lift due to thermal forcing alone.

The "bottom line" is this: a forecaster must look at all the dynamic causes of lift (such as low-level warm-air advection and differential vorticity advection) and all the mechanical causes of lift (such as upslope and frictional convergence), in conjunction with the available moisture (average surface-to-500 mb relative humidity) available, to forecast where the heaviest precipitation is most likely. 500 mb positive vorticity advection alone is not the answer! In fact, it appears that the role of low-level warm-air advection may be the greatest synoptic-scale dynamic cause of lift in the earth's weather. **PAGE 202**

SOME ADDITIONAL COMMENTS ON Q-VECTORS AND
QUASI-GEOSTROPHIC (Q-G) THEORY

Q-Vectors, like the thermal wind, are not physical realities; they do not exist. However, they arise mathematically and help to explain the results of physical processes in the atmosphere. Thus, they are useful diagnostic tools.

Q-Vectors were invented by British meteorologist B.J. Hoskins in 1978. They started to enjoy special attention in the 1980's when Stanley Barnes at NOAA's Environmental Research Laboratory at Boulder, Colorado began developing software to enable the generation of Q-Vector displays on personal computers.

Ascribing a "physical" definition of the mathematical Q-Vector, it can be described as the change with time of an acceleration per unit depth of air parcels. A Q-Vector can also be defined as the vector rate of change of the temperature gradient, following an isobaric (geostrophic) trajectory . Vertical motions are related to this vector rate of change.

In manipulating the mathematics of Q-Vectors to look at it in various forms, we find that we can also explain the Q-Vector in this more easily visualized concept as explained by Sanders and Hoskins (1990): The Q-Vector can be obtained by travelling along the isotherm with the cold air to the left, and observing the vector change of the geostrophic wind. Then rotate this vector change 90 degrees clockwise and you obtain the direction of the Q-Vector. Its magnitude is proportional to the magnitude of the vector rate of change multiplied by the strength of the temperature gradient.

These vectors graphically show the combined effects of differential vorticity advection and the LaPlacian of thickness advection (essentially, thermal advection) as given in the omega equation.

Diagnostically, as described earlier, the divergence of the Q-Vectors (layer-averaged to be rigorously correct) depicts the synoptic-scale vertical motion field. Moreover, Q-Vectors themselves, when they point from cold to warm air (when overlaying the thermal field on the Q-Vector field), would infer a tightening of the thermal gradient and therefore frontogenesis (and, frequently, cyclogenesis if in increasing baroclinicity).

Important note: The convergence/divergence of Q-Vectors is not the same as convergence/divergence of the wind! The level-of-nondivergence principle does not apply. In other words, do not confuse the Q-Vector divergence field with the wind divergence field.

OVERVIEW OF QUASI-GEOSTROPHIC (Q-G) THEORY AND ITS IMPLICATIONS ABOUT THE SYNOPTIC SCALE:

When the temperature and geostrophic wind fields are not in phase with each other through a depth of the atmosphere, then Q-G adjustments which result in vertical motions must occur.

Temperature and vorticity advections cause imbalances in the distribution of mass and momentum in a weather system. The atmosphere therefore counteracts the geostrophic component of the advective changes in temperature and vorticity by causing either upward motion to cool the air or downward motion to warm the air, adiabatically, while simultaneously adjusting the vorticity back towards being geostrophic (Barnes, 1987). These adjustments are for synoptic-scale systems and last for relatively long time-periods (many hours to a few days). Note that Q-G Theory is synoptic scale because the governing equations of motion, as applied in the forecast models, are essentially larger scale.

A Q-G Theory application that has been used even before the Q-Vector concept was invented discusses the forecast approach about developing cyclones. In the early stage of cyclogenesis in baroclinic zones, vorticity advection appears to play a dominant role; as the system develops to maturity, then the thermal advection appears to become the dominant agent for development.

SUMMARY ON QUASI-GEOSTROPHIC OMEGAS:

The omega equation does not explain the atmospheric physics of WHY the atmosphere is trying to generate large-scale vertical motions. We must look at the baroclinic systems producing vertical motions.

The troposphere tries to be in hydrostatic balance, which is relatively easy, and in geostrophic balance, which is difficult. In baroclinic systems, the advections of temperature due to geostrophic motions alone will drive the system towards an imbalance in its distributions of thermal energy and momentum. To compensate for these effects, the atmosphere generates vertical circulations on a large scale, that redistribute thermal energy and momentum back towards its preferred geostrophic balance. This is done by changing the vorticity structure of the mass field and by changing the temperatures of parcels through adiabatic ascent or descent.

Only in truly barotropic systems is this balance achieved for awhile. The troposphere is typically frequently perturbed by latent heat releases, diurnally-oscillating fluxes of radiant energy, frictional drag caused chiefly by terrain and by turbulent motions, long-term ocean-atmosphere energy exchanges, and other sources of perturbance. The result is quasi-geostrophic vertical motion patterns that are continually changing in response to geostrophically-induced imbalances and to all other imbalancing effects. Therefore, the omega equation, which is derived from first principles and simplifying approximations, gives us a way to determine where and how significant are these resultant vertical circulations.

47. POTENTIAL VORTICITY AND POTENTIAL VORTICITY CHARTS

In several previous chapters in this book, we discussed vorticity (spin) of air parcels, and we discussed the components of that spin if you separate the spin into the rotation about a vertical axis and the rotation around a horizontal axis. We also defined positive and negative vorticity, relative vorticity compared with absolute vorticity, and the advection or movement of positive and negative vorticity (air parcels moving with their components of spin).

Potential vorticity is even more complex. It is related to absolute vorticity and stability of the atmosphere. Stable and unstable atmospheric environments have been defined elsewhere in this book also. If parcels keep accelerating upward or downward (and can also move with a horizontal component) after given an initial push, then they are in an unstable environment. If the parcels return or try to return to their originations, then they are in a stable environment.

The stratosphere is a very stable environment. This is because of the ozone found in the stratosphere which absorbs ultraviolet radiation from the sun, consequently heating up that layer.

As we rise through the atmosphere, we find that the heaviest gasses that comprise our atmosphere are more concentrated in the lowest part of the atmosphere, and by the time to get to the top of earth's atmosphere, which is about 1000 kilometers (a little over 600 miles up), all that is left are molecules and atoms of the lightest gas, hydrogen, before we then enter into outer space. It is interesting that half the weight of the atmosphere is below about 500 millibars...below about 18,000 feet up...with the other half from 18,000 feet...about 3 1/2 miles...height up to about 600 miles height! At the 500 mb level, there is still 500 mb of air pressure above you.

The stratosphere is the warm layer of the atmosphere above the troposphere. Its average vertical extend is about 40 to 50 kilometers, ranging from an average lower elevation of about 10 km (about 6 miles) to about 50 to 60 km (to about 30 to near 40 miles). Many of the oxygen molecules in the stratosphere are broken apart by solar ultraviolet radiation into oxygen atoms. Oxygen atoms combine with some of the oxygen molecules that were not broken up, to form ozone:

$$O_2 \xrightarrow{\text{ULTRAVIOLET}} O + O$$

$$O_2 + O \longrightarrow O_3$$

Figure 102. The creation of ozone in the stratosphere.

(continued)

This ozone is the same as ozone that is created where we live by some of our industrial and burning activity, but the ozone in the stratosphere is significant because it plays a major role in cyclogenesis and possibly in the generation of the largest of tornadoes.

The ozone in the stratosphere is why we have a stratosphere. Ozone itself absorbs ultraviolet radiation from the sun and heats up, which warms the stratosphere. There are pockets of ozone, including extensive-sized concentrations of ozone, which migrate through the stratosphere.

Occasionally, in the vicinity of jet-streams, some stratospheric air, which carries with it its ozone, plunges into the upper troposphere and can continue downward to as far as 700 mb and sometimes even lower.

On rare occasion, fingers of a jet-stream jet-streak surge toward the ground and actually skip off the ground. This results in a sudden squall, usually lasting from under a minute to no more than a few minutes, and may seem to occur out of nowhere with clear skies. The wind at the surface may exceed 100 mph, causing damage, and would disappear as swiftly as it started.

This phenomenon was first studied after being reported in deserts of the southwest U.S. when a strong jet-streak was digging into and around the base of a long-wave trough aloft. Other cases from across the country were then reported, and eventually, through the analysis of "potential vorticity", there was proof that these excessive, short-lived windbursts are indeed (narrow) fingers of the jet-stream plunging to and hitting the surface of the earth.

Stratospheric air intrusions into the troposphere can be followed by measurements of the ozone amount (called OZONE MIXING RATIO, such as parts per million of ozone), and by the potential vorticity analysis. The results of a major research project, published in the Journal of Geophysical Research, proved that both ozone and potential vorticity are each a tracer of stratospheric air. Later, meteorologists discovered that there are major weather aspects of an intrusion of air downward from the stratosphere.

Mathematically, potential vorticity, commonly referred to as POT VORT by weather forecasters, is effectively absolute vorticity divided by a measure of how stable the air is. There is a THEORY OF CONSERVATION OF POTENTIAL VORTICITY, which states that the potential vorticity of the air is conserved in adiabatic, frictionless processes. One such process is taking air out of the warm stratosphere and bringing it down dry adiabatically, which means if warms at the dry adiabatic lapse rate, with virtually no friction involved, into the troposphere which is much less stable than the stratosphere. Keep in mind that the temperature warms for some distance upward as we rise through the stratosphere, so that if we try to generate convection by forcing air parcels to rise there, and we know that these parcels themselves cool as the rise, then the parcels on their own will not rise but sink because they will be cooler than the stratospheric environment. Therefore, the stratosphere is very stable.

(continued)   **PAGE 206**

From the theory of conservation of absolute vorticity, when we take air from the stable stratosphere and bring it downward into the less stable troposphere, it must conserve its potential vorticity, Since pot vort is essentially absolute vorticity divided by the stability, the mathematics show that when we decrease the stability we need to increase the absolute vorticity to keep the pot vort the same, i.e., to conserve the pot vort of the air parcels.

The stability is measured by how close "isentropic surfaces", discussed in the next chapter, are to each other vertically. When air is stable, these surfaces are close, and when unstable or less stable, they ar farther apart...their distance is greater, This therefore increases the value of the denominator; therefore, the value of the numerator, the absolute vorticity, must increase. The "bottom line" of this complicated discussion, is that, because of the theory of conservation of potential vorticity, **when air comes out of the stratosphere into the troposphere, it GENERATES POSITIVE ABSOLUTE VORTICITY.** Positive vorticity is also called cyclonic vorticity, because the component of spin about a vertical axis is cyclonic (from left to right in the Northern Hemisphere. We know from the previous chapter's discussion on the omega equation, that when we have greater positive vorticity advection (PVA) aloft than in low-levels, air spins up, rises. Therefore, by creating a major increase in the upper- and mid-tropospheric PVA, we can have a greatly increased upward vertical velocity.

This is critical, because if it happens over a developing low pressure system, that enhanced lift can turn that storm into a major storm. Meteorologists call such a process BOMBOGENESIS, because the low's pressure drops rapidly...the system is said to DEEPEN rapidly...and the storm becomes a major precipitation producer. Many of the worst winter snowstorms occur when stratospheric intrusions occur over them.

Thus, **pot vort advection from a stratospheric intrusion is a significant factor that separates a routine low pressure system from a vigorous, major low pressure system, because it generates positive vorticity advection aloft in the troposphere, which can significantly increase upward vertical motion via differential positive vorticity advection.**

As some pot vort intrudes the troposphere, it is replenished in the stratosphere by solar heating, chiefly through ultraviolet radiation, of the ozone.

After formulating the theory, the next step is to generate operationally useful weather maps of the potential vorticity field, and interpreting where the upward motion would be generated.

(continued)

POTENTIAL VORTICITY CROSS-SECTION

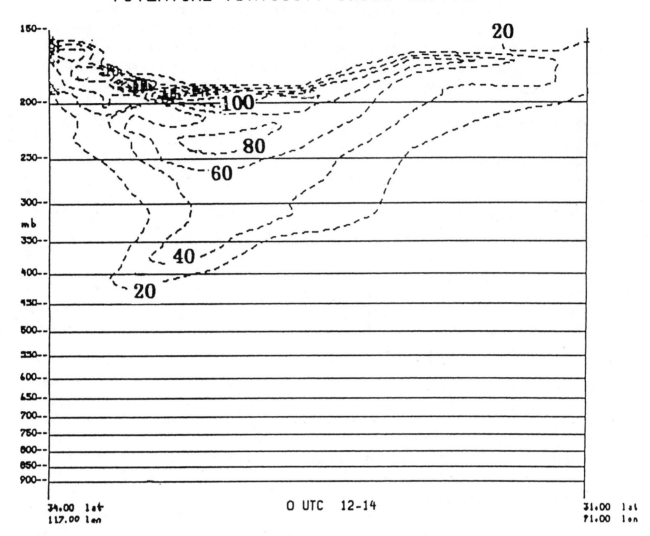

Figure 103. A Potential Vorticity Cross-section. The time is for 00Z on December 14th. Units are times 10 to the -6 power in degrees Kelvin per millibar per second. A second form of units used is called the potential vorticity unit or PVU. One PVU is equal to 10 of the traditional pot vort units as given on the above pot vort map. Thus, 40 of the traditional units would equal 4 PVUs.

Looking at the latitude and longitude settings from the lower left to the lower right of the map, notice that a cross-section was selected from the U.S. central Gulf of Mexico coastline area through the southwest U.S., to look for pot vort through that region. At 00Z on December 14th, air from the stratosphere, with its potential vorticity, was surging downward into the upper- and mid-troposphere over the southwest U.S. The leading edge of it was likely below 450 millibars. To the east (to the right on this chart) of the pot vort, positive vorticity is being created, and the PVA is generating upward vertical motion there.

(continued)

PAGE 208

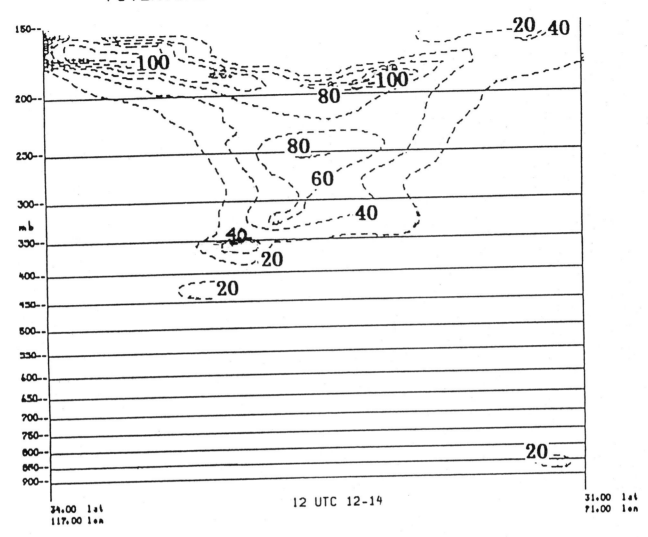

Figure 104. The Pot Vort Map Twelve Hours Later.

Now, at 12Z on December 14th, twelve hours later, the pot vort has moved to the east-southeast, moving over the southern Rocky Mountains and entering over the southern plains states. At this time, a low pressure system was developing to the east, and if the pot vort reaches over that low, it would likely cause significant intensification of the storm.

(continued)

PAGE 209

POTENTIAL VORTICITY CROSS-SECTION

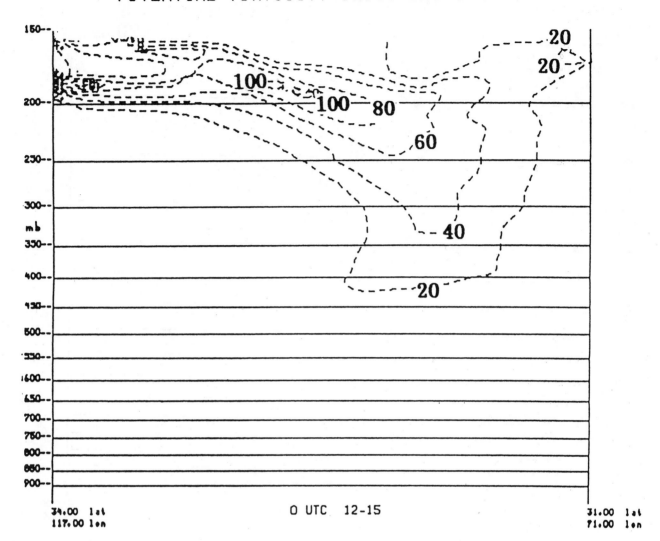

FIgure 105. The pot vort continues eastward, and is now generating significant PVA aloft over the mid-west, causing a low pressure system in that area to rapidly intensify.
It is now 00Z on December 15th. The significant cyclogenesis resulted in a major snowstorm for the mid-west, that then moved to the east coast.

The storm was more intense that it otherwise would have been, because of the infusion of stratospheric air with its potential vorticity over and into the storm. From the omega equation (chapter 40), we know that the increased PVA aloft created by the pot vort, caused increased upward vertical motion in the storm, and led to the cyclogenesis.

Sometimes, pot vort advection into the troposphere precedes strengthening PVA and cyclogenesis by up to about 12 hours.

(continued)

Potential Vorticity and Sudden Upper-Tropospheric Warming

In the warmer part of the year, the mid-latitude polar tropopause is closest to 200 mb, and is lower, closer to 300 mb, in the colder part of the year. Watch for sudden apparent warm air advection on the 300 mb chart in the colder season and 200 mb chart in the warmer season.

If the warm advection materializes abruptly and does not appear to have a temporal connection with a vertically-growing short-wave trough through the troposphere, then this sudden appearance of warmer air may be air intruding from the stratosphere, and warming even more dry-adiabatically as it descends. Thus, the warm air advection is coming from above.

The magnitude of this warm air advection is typically several Celsius degrees within 12 hours, typically in the vicinity of a jet-streak.

Thus, if you do not have access to any potential vorticity weather maps but do get the upper-level charts with their temperatures or isotherms, look for sudden warm air advection at and below any jet-streaks, if that advection dow not have a spacial and temporal connection to warm air rising from lower levels, as it would in a short-wave trough that is well-developed throughout the depth of the troposphere. There could also be pot vort advection with such a well-developed trough, in which case the trough would likely intensify more.

There are other types of potential vorticity analyses, such as pot vort analyzed on isentropic (see next chapter) surfaces and cross-sections. The main point is to determine if pot vort exists coming downward from the stratosphere, and how and where it generates upward vertical motion as it generates positive vorticity advection aloft.

HERE IS A MORE TECHNICAL VERSION OF THE SAME CHAPTER ON POTENTIAL VORTICITY AND POTENTIAL VORTICITY CHARTS

Potential vorticity plays an important role in the generation of vorticity in cyclogenesis, especially along the polar front, and also is useful in tracing intrusions of stratospheric air deep into the troposphere in the vicinity of jet-streaks.

$$\text{POTENTIAL VORTICITY} = \frac{-(\zeta_\theta + f)}{\frac{\partial P}{\partial \theta}}$$

Units are in $10^{-6} \, K \, mb^{-1} \, s^{-1}$

(An alternate expression gives potential vorticity in potential vorticity units (PVUs), in which 1 PVU = 10 of the standard units above. The discussion that follows uses the standard units. Some forms of the equation also include the gravitational acceleration, g, in the numerator on the right-hand side, although that can be divided out as it was above.)

Potential vorticity (usually referred to as "pot vort" for short) is the absolute vorticity divided by a stability parameter. In considering the measure of stability, note that as the slope of a temperature sounding increases, the difference between the same two potential temperature (theta) surfaces increases. Thus, when the distance between two isentropic surfaces increases, the atmosphere there is becoming more unstable. In an unstable atmosphere, any generation of pot vort is low. When the isentropes are tightly packed, the air is stable and the pot vort generation can be high.

Pot vort is an important aspect of stratospheric meteorology. We understand how deep convection can infuse tropospheric air into the stratosphere. By tracing air movements by their potential vorticities we can follow the intrusion of stratospheric air into the troposphere.

Although some potential vorticity is created in the troposphere, it is relatively insignificant compared with the pot vort generated in the stratosphere where it is an order or more of magnitude greater than it is in the troposphere.

Stratospheric potential vorticity is created when the air becomes more stable; e.g., warming of parts of an ozone layer will create pot vort. Solar ultraviolet radiation plays the major role in heating stratospheric ozone. In the stratosphere, many oxygen atoms are divided by ultraviolet photons into monatomic oxygen. Some of these single atom oxygens combine with regular oxygen molecules that have not been broken up, to form tri-atomic oxygen, called ozone.

$$O_2 \xrightarrow{\text{ULTRAVIOLET}} O + O$$

$$O_2 + O \longrightarrow O_3$$

Ozone has absorption wavelengths for incoming ultraviolet
radiation and therefore warms up. Stratospheric warming is a
spatial and temporal variable. When and where it occurs, it
generates potential vorticity.

Warming in the stable stratosphere also occurs as the air there
sinks (adiabatic warming). Pot vort comes "down", moves along,
the isentropic surfaces from the stratosphere into the
troposphere.

Thus, potential vorticity gets depleted from the stratosphere, but
it is also being replenished through stratospheric warming.

Potential vorticity is a conservative property of small parcels of
air (about a cubic meter). Thus, it can be used as a tracer of
air, i.e., to follow the paths taken by air parcels. We can
therefore follow stratospheric air intruding into the troposphere,
and observe potential vorticity generating vorticity in the
troposphere. Uccellini has argued that an intrusion of
significant stratospheric potential vorticity deep into the
troposphere can indicate by up to about 12 hours in advance that
significant positive vorticity advection is being generated which
will lead to major cyclogenesis when along the polar front.

Thus, we need to analyze for three-dimensional pot vort and
consider the argument that 3-D potential vorticity advection may,
at least some of the time, be more significant to analyze than is
the customary positive vorticity advection.

Uccellini   uses a value of 10 x 10 e-06 units as the leading
edge of stratospheric air, when it is intruding the troposphere.

Consider the following three potential vorticity cross-sections.

POTENTIAL VORTICITY CROSS-SECTION

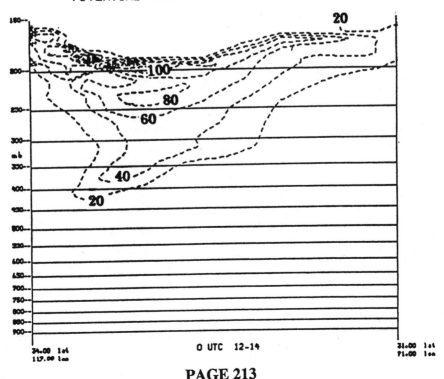

O UTC 12-14

These pot vort cross-sections in time increments of 12 hours show an intrusion of stratospheric air into the upper and middle troposphere. There should also be tropospheric residential potential vorticity, but it is an order of magnitude less than that of stratospheric origin.

The pot vort advection generated positive vorticity in the mid and upper troposphere, which then strengthened a short-wave and its surface low to be a major winter storm ("bombogenesis"). The PVA aloft was increased considerably to become much higher than the PVA in low-levels, thus strengthening the forcing of synoptic-scale lifting by differential vorticity advection (reference the omega equation). Sometimes, pot vort advection into the troposphere precedes strengthening PVA and cyclogenesis by up to about 12 hours.

POTENTIAL VORTICITY CROSS-SECTION

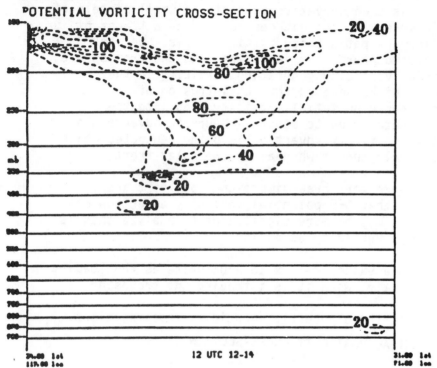

12 UTC 12-14

POTENTIAL VORTICITY CROSS-SECTION

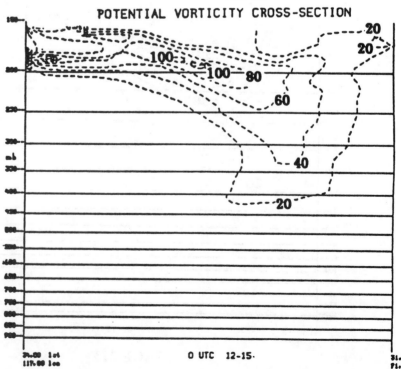

0 UTC 12-15

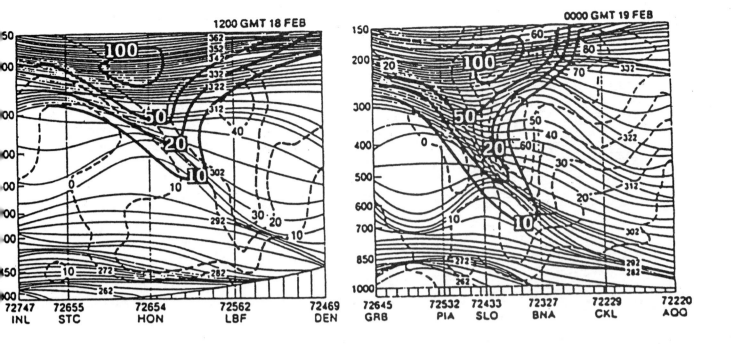

The above analyses shows a major intrusion of potential vorticity
from the stratosphere deep into the troposphere, associated with a
jet-streak and a developing cyclone. The heavy solid lines at the
pot vort. isopleths where 10 = 10 x 10 e-06 K per mb per sec; the
light solid lines are isentropes in degrees K; and the dashed
lines are the geostrophic windspeed in meters per sec computed
from the horizontal thermal gradient in the plane of the cross-
section (from Ucellinni et al.   ). The analysis on the right
is 12 hours after the left-side chart.

Notice that in a period of 12-hours, as the potential vorticity
advects three-dimensionally southeastward and downward, the
leading edge of the stratospheric air plunges from 500 mb down to
700 mb (using 10 as the threshold value for stratospheric air).
This major plunge of pot vort created significant positive
vorticity which intensified a developing cyclone into a major
winter storm. By the time the pot vort intrusion reached the East
Coast, it was down to the 850 mb level and helped create major
cyclogenesis.

Pot vort analyses infrequently show narrow tongues of
stratospheric air reaching the surface, especially over higher
mountainous terrain such as the Rocky Mountains. Unexplained
short-lived (no more than a few minutes) bursts of surface wind,
sometimes to extremes gusting to about 100 mph, are apparently
caused by **fingers of the jetstream darting to and skipping off the
ground.** Danielson of NCAR noted this phenomenon in the desert
southwest when a strong jet-streak digs into the base of a sharp
long-wave trough. This rare meteorological phenomenon can occur
anywhere. (Hopefully, a finger of a descending jet will
eventually be detected by one of our profiler sounders.)

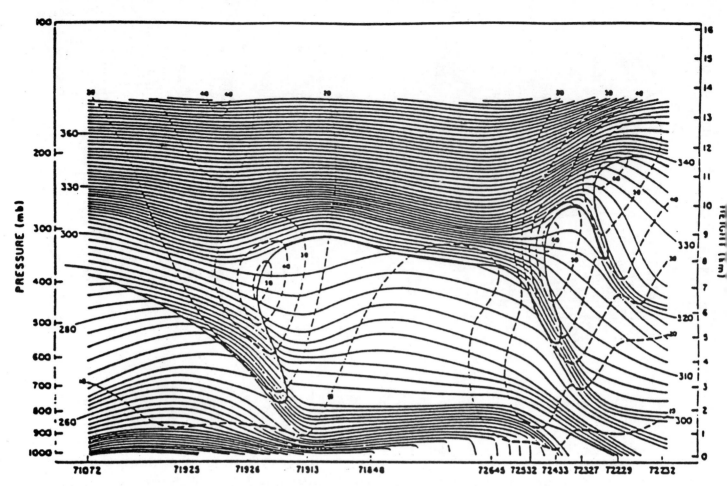

This cross-section, from Resolute, Canada to Louisiana, shows
three regions of overlapping tropopause leaves. The heavy solid
line is the pot vort value of 10 units. The thin solid lines are
potential temperature isolines in degrees Kelvin, and the thin
dashed lines are isotachs in meters/second.

The above analysis demonstrates how stratospheric air and its
potential vorticity extrudes from the stratosphere through jet-
streaks where tropopauses overlap each other (where the higher
mid-latitude tropopause leaf overlies the lower polar tropopause,
and where the higher tropical tropopause overlies the lower mid-
latitude tropopause...and, when an arctic tropopause develops,
where the polar tropopause leaf overlies the lower arctic
tropopause). Between each set of tropopause leaves lies a
jetstrem. It can be argued that the tropical tropopause is
associated with the tropical Hadley cell of the general
atmospheric circulation, and the mid-latitude tropopause is
associated with the indirect Ferrel cell which is forced in part
by the tropical and polar Hadley cells, and the polar tropopause
is associated with the polar Hadley cell; where these tropopauses
overlap we find the jetstream jet-streaks and the intrusion into
the troposphere of potential vorticity in stratospheric air.

Thus, potential vorticity is associated not only with cyclogenesis
when the pot vort enters the troposphere and generates positive
vorticity, but it is also associated with tropopause folding and
the jetstream because it is in these regions where it moves from
the stratosphere into the troposphere.

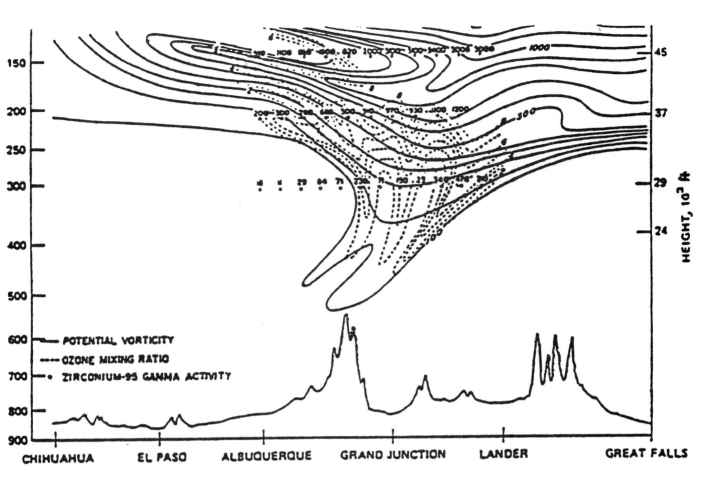

The above graphic is taken from a study done by Danielson et al.
and published in the Journal of Geophysical Research back in 1970.
It shows how potential vorticity can be used as a tracer of air
because of its conservativeness (changing relatively slowly).
More rigorously stated, potential vorticity of small air parcels
is conserved in adiabatic, frictionless conditions.

Three tracers of air are depicted in this study. The ozone and
radioactivity were detected essentially by research aircraft.

The potential vorticity can be easily computed using the absolute
vorticity divided by the stability parameter as shown by the
equation on page 212. The ozone measurements are displayed as
ozone mixing ratio values. The radioactivity is that of
zirconium-95 gamma radiation left over from the 1950's above-
ground nuclear bomb tests and activities. All three tracing
parameters originate in the stratosphere and appear to be extruded
into the troposphere in essentially the same regions --namely, in
jet-streaks (overlapping tropopauses areas).

Thus, pot vort (as well as these other tracers) can be used to
study from where, and hopefully also how, air from above the
troposphere enters the lower levels. From that starting point of
understanding, we can hopefully learn the implications for
humanity and our weather.

POTENTIAL VORTICITY AND SUDDEN UPPER TROPOSPHERIC WARMING:

Watch for sudden apparent "warm-air advection" on the 300 mb analysis in the colder half of the year, and on the 200 mb analysis in the warmer half.

If the warm advection materializes abruptly and does not appear to have a temporal connection with a vertically-growing short-wave trough through the troposphere, then this sudden appearance of warm air may be air intruding from the stratosphere. Look for the presence of a jet-streak since the descending air would be entering the troposphere in the descending air regions of jet-streaks.

This stratospheric air is warmer than the air of the upper troposphere and would be warming up further due to adiabatic descent. This manifests itself on a 300 mb or 200 mb chart as "warm-air advection", even though the warm air is coming from above. It may be possible to distinguish this warm advection from the warm advection associated with deep tropospheric short-wave troughs that extend throughout the depth of the troposphere in their mature phase. The trough-related warm advection would show a continuity in space and time associated with lower-level forcing (forcing in the lower and/or middle troposphere). In major cyclones, such as the "bombogenesis" episode in the eastern U.S. in March 1993 (the famous "snow hurricane"), potent lift occurred due to a combination of isentropic lift associated with warm advection, and lift caused by very strong differential positive vorticity advection, and lift caused by a major intrusion of stratospheric air with its potential vorticity deep into the lower troposphere into the storm. The pot. vort. advection generated extremely high values of positive vorticity in the troposphere which combined with the already strong differential PVA to greatly increase the magnitude of the upward vertical displacement of air.

Because, in part, of the stratospheric air intrusion contribution to the PVA and consequent increased lift, thundersnow occurred without unstable air. The slantwise convection was imposed by intense lift caused by the combination of potent synoptic dynamic forcings.

Thus, sudden significant warm advection (several degrees Celsius within 12 hours) below a jet-streak, when moving into a developing low pressure system, can contribute significantly to cyclogenesis. However, this warm-air advection must be distinguished from the warm-air advection originating in the low or mid troposphere, which also contibutes to lift.

48. ISENTROPIC CHARTS

The word "isentropic" means "equal entropy". Entropy is a measure of disorder in a system. Unfortunately, the term is more of a misnomer when used in meteorology. "Isentropic analysis" should be called "potential temperature analysis", since these charts are based on data referring to 1000 mb, which is the potential temperature reference level.

The potential temperature is commonly referred to as theta, θ, which should be distinguished from the equivalent potential temperature, theta-e (θ_e), referred to in chapter 39, which combines the temperature and dewpoint and references it to air brought back down dry-adiabatically to 1000 mb.

Isentropic analyses can be helpful because under many circumstances, air flows along theta surfaces rather than along isobaric surfaces. Theta, or potential temperature, surfaces usually slope, and air will move laterally as well as vertically, up or down theta surfaces.

So, just what is a theta surface? Isentropic techniques employ two types of analyses: theta surfaces and isentropic cross-sections.

To create a theta surface weather map, picture a temperature sounding and then picture the sounding cooling throughout a time period of say twelve hours.

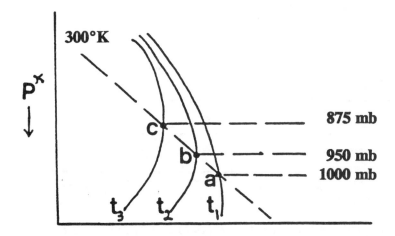

Figure 106. Soundings showing cooling over a 12-hour period, to identify the height of the 300 degrees Kelvin isentropic surface. P is pressure, increasing downward (pressure is the vertical coordinate here) and each t is for a time period, with t_1 being the original time, t_2 six hours later and t_3 six hours after t_2. To find the height of the 300°K isentropic (potential temperature) surface, start at 1000 mb and 300°K on the sounding and go up the dry adiabat until the sounding it reached. Initially, in this example, the 300°K surface is at 1000 mb. Six hours later the sounding has cooled, so the 300°K isentropic surface is at 950 mb. And six hours after that, further cooling of the environment raises that isentropic surface to 875 mb.

(continued)   PAGE 219

Figure 107. Below is an actual sounding. The solid line sounding is the temperature curve gotten from an ascending weather balloon. The dashed line sounding is the dewpoint curve. Across the bottom of each sounding diagram is the temperature in degrees Celsius. To covert to Kelvin, add 273°. The logarithm of pressure is the vertical coordinate.

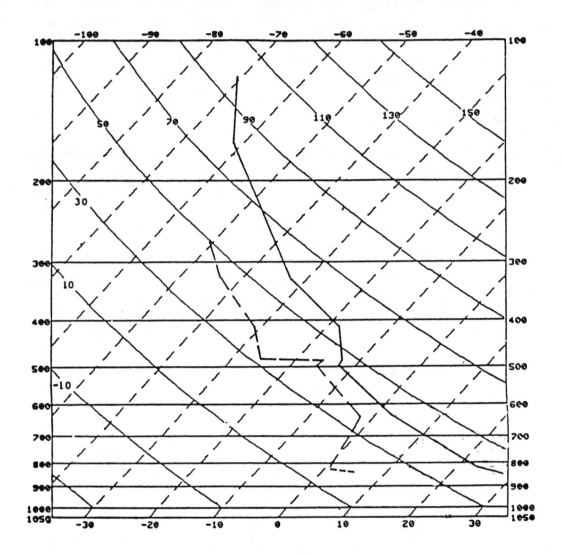

Notice how the temperature lines are not vertical but are skewed to the right. This makes it easier to read, and meteorologists can also use such a chart to compute energy related to rising and sinking air parcels.

Because the vertical coordinate, the ordinate, is the logarithm of pressure, and the horizontal coordinate, the abscissa, is the temperature but it is skewed to the right, this diagram is known as a **SKEW-T, LOG P DIAGRAM.** It is a **THERMODYNAMIC DIAGRAM.**

(continued)

Thermodynamic diagrams would also have curves for the dry and moist adiabats, and curves for the moisture amount, called "mixing ratio" of the water vapor. Air rises along the dry adiabat (it cools at the dry adiabatic lapse rate [see chapter 20]), until it cools to its dewpoint, at which time it becomes saturated. If air is then still rising, it cools at the moist adiabatic lapse rate, which is less than the dry adiabatic lapse rate because the heat of condensation is released by the parcel as the vapor forms into clouds and possible subsequent precipitation from the coalescing cloud particles.

By the time the parcels reach about 200 mb, the moist adiabats parallel the dry adiabats, since virtually all or all of the moisture will have been condensed ("squeezed") out of the rising air parcels by then.

The term "adiabatic" means that during a physical process, such as air parcels rising on their own because they are positively buoyant, or air parcels being forced to rise by some dynamic and/or mechanical forcing such as two thunderstorm outflow boundaries colliding or a cold front forcing air to rise as it advances, no heat is added to or taken away from the parcel. In reality, very meager heat is generated through friction of the air molecules and larger parcels, but that is considered meteorologically insignificant. These parcels are on the order of a cubic meter volume. Other adiabatic processes involve sinking of the air and lateral movements of the air. Thus, if no heat energy is added to or taken away from a parcel undergoing a physical process such as the ones just discussed, then that motion is called ADIABATIC.

Returning to our discussion on isentropic surfaces, here is the listing of isentropic surface values that we know, empirically, work, based on the season of the year.

Season	Low Level Potential Temperature
Winter	290-295 K
Spring	295-300 K
Summer	310-315 K
Fall	300-305 K

Figure 108. Low-level potential temperature surfaces (isentropic surfaces) for mid-latitudes based on the season of the year. These work most of the time. Sometimes, several values have to be picked to assure getting a useful analysis.

Even though mountainous regions such as the Rocky Mountains do not have a 1000 mb level (it would be below the ground!), isentropic charts interpolate for where the 1000 mb level, which is the potential temperature reference level, would be if the higher terrain were not present.

(continued)   PAGE 221

Figure 109. The Skew-T, Log P Thermodynamic Diagram. The five sets of lines are the logarithm of the isobars, the skewed isotherms, the dry adiabats, the moist adiabats (sometimes called the saturation adiabats) and the mixing ratio lines. When air parcels are unsaturated and rising, they rise (cool) along the dry adiabat upward; when the parcels are saturated after cooling to their dewpoint temperature, they rise (and continue) cooling along a moist adiabat.

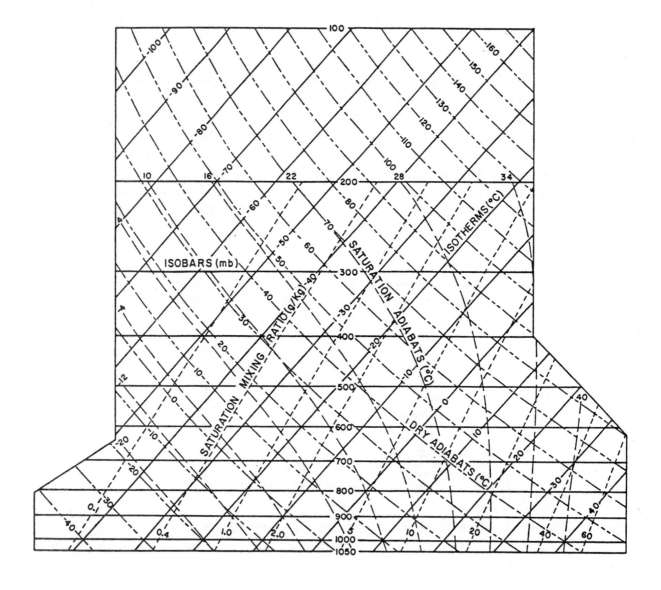

(continued)

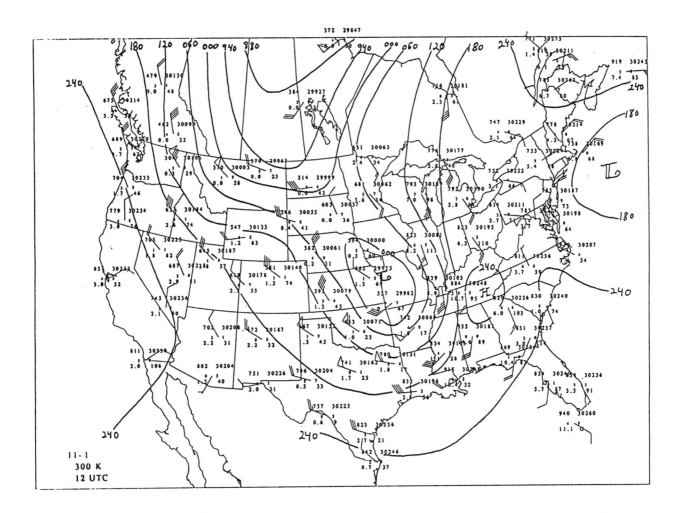

Figure 110. A 300°K Isentropic Surface for 12Z on November 1st. The solid lines are streamlines, analogous to contours of height on a pressure-level chart. The air flows along the streamlines. The units plotted in the upper right of each station model plot are actually units of energy per unit mass, and the units plotted in the upper left are millibars, which indicate the height of the 300°K surface, i.e., starting at 1000 mb on the Skew-T, log P diagram, and following a dry adiabat until it hits the temperature sounding, how high must we rise to find the height of the 300°K isentropic (potential temperature) surface.

Interpret this chart this way: air flows along the streamlines and also rises from lower levels, indicated by high pressure values in millibars, to higher levels, indicated by low pressure values in millibars. Thus, for example, air is flowing northward and rising from Alabama to Wisconsin and is also rising through that fetch. Why? The air is flowing northward because the streamlines are south-to-north in that region and the pressure rises, meaning the isentropic surface rises, from 955 mb over Alabama to 793 mb over Green Bay, Wisconsin.

(continued) **PAGE 223**

Another interesting point about isentropic surfaces is that isobars effectively serve as isotherms. Thus, the 955 mb reading over Alabama represents air that is much warmer than the 793 mb reading over Wisconsin. This makes sense because the air cools as it rises.

Thus, we can use this unique type of weather map to show both horizontal and vertical motions of air parcels.

Other information can be plotted around the station location plots, such as mixing ratio of water vapor, the relative humidity, and the wind direction and speed.

Suppose we are studying an 850 mb chart which shows dry air over our region. The temperature-dewpoint spread is, say 12 Celsius degrees. Twelve hours later, the 850 mb chart shows the temperature-dewpoint spread over our region to be only 3 Celsius degrees. The air has moistened considerably. That additional moisture did not just "pop up". It came from elsewhere. A series of isentropic charts would show that it advected in from a particular direction and may have been in a rising air mode also.

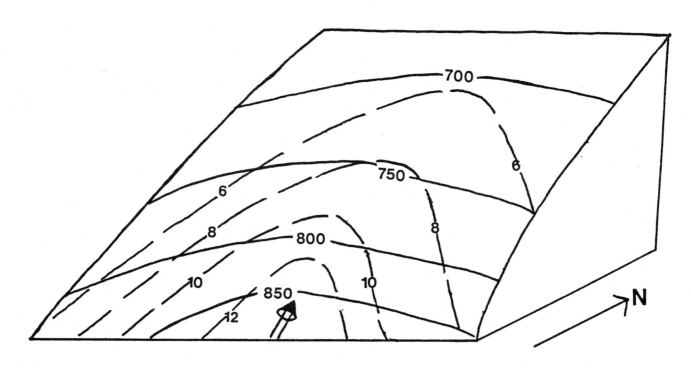

Figure 111. An isentropic surface looking northward, east of an advancing short-wave trough. The solid lines are the isobars in millibars, and the dashed lines are the mixing ratio of water vapor, given in grams of water vapor per kilogram of air (i.e., parts per thousand of water vapor). Thus, the moisture is moving northward and rising.

(continued)

An Isentropic Cross-section

The other type of isentropic or potential temperature weather map is called an isentropic cross-section.

A cross-sectional area is chosen through a baroclinic zone, such as through a jet-streak and where cyclogenesis is underway, e.g.

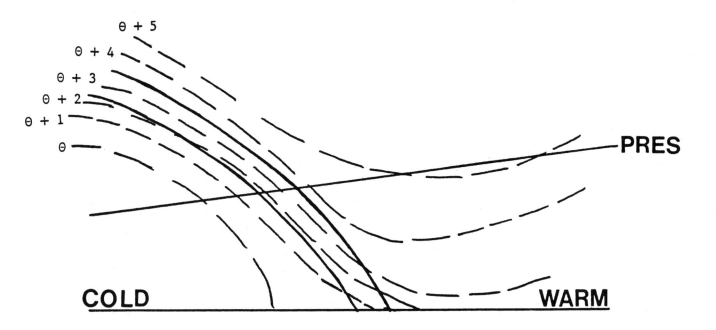

Figure 112. An isentropic cross-section taken through a cold front. The dashed lines are the isentropic surfaces with the representative pressure surfaces shown by the solid lines. The air flows along the isentropic surfaces, with sinking cold air and rising warm air. It is possible to have rising cold air and sinking warm air.

The slope of an isentropic surface in the vertical is related to the thermal wind (see chapters 24 and 46). A vertically-sloping isentropic surface means there exists a strong thermal contrast in that region. The isobars, acting as isotherms, would be tightly packed. When isentropic surfaces tilt up or down significantly, we have a frontal zone with its change of wind speed with height.

(continued)

Moreover, where isentropes on an isentropic cross-section are packed tightly together, the air is stable, as in the stratosphere; where the isentropes are farther apart, the air is less stable. This makes sense when looking at a plotted sounding on a thermodynamic diagram. Look at figure 106. If, e.g., we cool the air aloft, which destabilizes the local atmosphere, we now have to go higher to get the level of that same isentropic surface. These surfaces spread apart as air destabilizes.

The wind components can also be overlain on isentropic cross-sections.

Thus, we can complement our isobaric upper-air charts with a series of isentropic charts which work most of the time is showing how air is moving laterally and vertically, as it transports properties such as moisture.

ADDENDUM:
Some more technical thoughts on adding charts based on an isentropic coordinate system to our menu of weather maps, from meteorologist James T. Moore who has used and taught on this topic for decades:

One must first begin with the concept of an *adiabatic* process as applied to a fictitious parcel of air with a volume of roughly 1 m^3. During an adiabatic process an air parcel will experience no heat exchange with its environment; i.e., no heat is added or taken away from the parcel. In terms of the first law of thermodynamics we write,

$$dh = 0 = C_p dT - \alpha dP \tag{1}$$

Since $\alpha = RT/P$ we can write (1) as:

$$\frac{dT}{T} = \frac{R}{C_p} \frac{dP}{P} \tag{2}$$

Following Hess (1959), if we integrate from some temperature, T, and pressure, P, to a temperature, θ, at 1000 mb, we obtain:

$$\theta = T \left(\frac{1000}{P}\right)^\kappa \tag{3}$$

where $\kappa = R/C_p$.

The temperature, θ, is physically defined as the temperature that a parcel of air would have if it were compressed (or expanded) adiabatically from its original pressure to 1000 mb. It is known as *potential temperature* and is a conservative property for parcels of air with *no* changes in heat due to such processes as solar/terrestrial radiation, mixing with environmental air that has a different temperature, and latent heating/evaporative cooling. Although these restrictions would seem to make the application of this thermodynamic variable limited there is empirical evidence that such "diabatic" heating and cooling processes are usually secondary in importance for temporal scales on the order of the synoptic.

Hess (1959) also shows that the entropy of an air parcel, ϕ, is related to its potential temperature as:

$$\phi = C_p \ln\theta + \text{const} \tag{4}$$

So a parcel which moves dry adiabatically not only conserves its potential temperature but also its entropy. A surface composed of parcels whose potential temperatures are equal is described as an equal entropy or isentropic surface. In thermodynamics we are told that entropy is a measure of the disorder of a system. However, operational meteorologists have little use for this concept. Thus, aside from using the term *isentropic,* we meteorologists prefer to use *potential temperature* as a variable rather than *entropy,* which carries more of a mystical aspect!

In the troposphere the atmosphere is, on the average, stable; i.e., $-\partial T/\partial Z = \gamma_{envir} < 9.5°C/km$, typically $\gamma_{envir} = 6.5°C/km$. In such an atmosphere the potential temperature can be shown by (5) to *increase* with height.

$$\frac{1}{\theta}\frac{\partial\theta}{\partial z} = \frac{(\Gamma_d - \gamma)}{T} \tag{5}$$

In (5) Γ_d is the dry adiabatic lapse rate and γ is the actual or environmental lapse rate. Under stable conditions $\gamma < \Gamma_d$, so $\partial\theta/\partial Z > 0$ meaning θ increases with height. If the lapse rate is neutral then $\gamma = \Gamma_d$ and $\partial\theta/\partial Z = 0$; i.e., θ is constant with height. If $\gamma > \Gamma_d$ the lapse rate is superadiabatic and θ decreases with height. Furthermore, as Rossby et al. (1937) note, the potential temperature also increases southward at about the same rate as the dry bulb temperature. So the troposphere may be envisioned as being composed of a great number of isentropic layers which gradually descend from cold polar regions to warmer subtropical latitudes. As one ascends from the troposphere into the stratosphere, where the atmosphere is very stable, isentropic surfaces become compacted in the vertical. This attribute makes them extremely valuable for resolving upper-level stable frontal zones in the presence of upper tropospheric wind maxima or jet streaks. Thus, in a stably stratified atmosphere; i.e., $-\partial T/\partial Z < 9.8°C/km$, potential temperature can be an excellent vertical coordinate--especially since it increases with height, thereby avoiding the headaches of dealing with a vertical coordinate (namely pressure) which decreases with height.

Rossby et al. (1937) and later Blackadar and Dutton (1970) note that it is necessary to "tag" a parcel with more than its potential temperature since on an isentropic surface all parcels "look alike". A second natural "tag" would be mixing ratio or specific humidity, both quantities which are also conserved during dry adiabatic ascent/descent. Another possible "tag" (see chapter 47) is *potential vorticity.* It should be no surprise, then, that the three-dimensional transport of moisture on a vertically sloping isentropic surface should display good spatial and temporal continuity. **This** has important diagnostic and prognostic implications for the movement of both moist and dry tongues in low-middle levels of the troposphere.

"It can hardly be doubted that the isentropic charts represent the true motion of the air more faithfully by far than synoptic charts for any fixed level in the free atmosphere. At a fixed level in the middle of the troposphere entire air masses may, as a result of slight vertical displacements, appear or diappear in the time interval between two consecutive charts, making that entire method of representation futile." (Rossby et al. 1937).

"While maps of atmospheric pressure at various levels have been found especially helpful in weather forecasting, the use of temperatures and humidities on such constant level charts has hardly done more than make atmospheric disturbances seem more complicated in vertical structure than surface weather analyses would indicate." (Namias, 1939).

One researcher (Spilhaus, 1938) even suggested, in a short paper for the Bulletin of the American Meteorological Society, that airplanes fly along isentropic surfaces using a "thetameter" to keep track of the potential temperature for the pilots!

49. SOME MISCELLANEOUS CHARTS

a. AVIATION UPPER-LEVEL WIND CHARTS

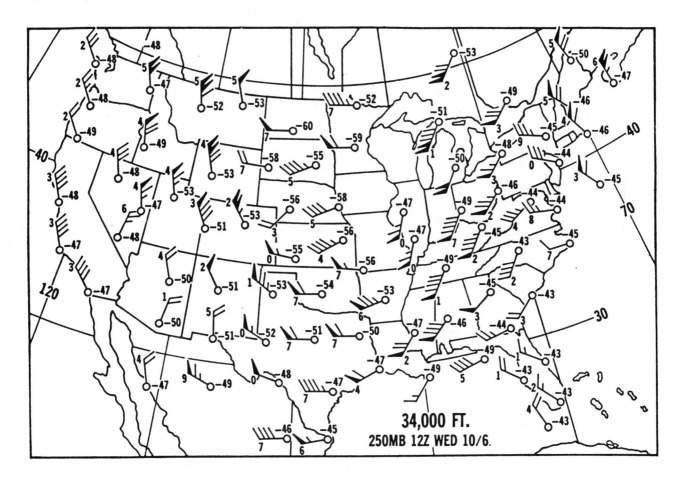

Figure 113. Upper-level wind charts are issued for various levels, such as 14,000 feet, 24,000 feet, 34,000 feet and higher, and are intended for aviation uses. The time of the analysis, or, if a forecast, the valid time of the prognostication, is given on the map. The single digit number near the station model gives the tens digit of the wind direction, For example, the "1" for Amarillo, Texas means the wind direction is from 310 degrees. The temperature in degrees Celsius is also given. Wind speeds are plotted using the standard convention: a half-line for 5 knots, a line for 10 knots, and a flag for 50 knots. Thus,

e.g., the wind depiction at left, for Pittsburgh, Pa., shows a wind from 220° at 75 knots. Winter jet-streams are strongest at about 29,000 feet, and summer jet-streams are strongest at about 39,000 feet. A part of the jet-stream shows up at 34.000 feet, and pilots flying at around that altitude can determine whether they will have a powerful head wind or tail wind for part of all of their flight. Moreover, lower-level wind and temperature charts will show if the freezing level is anywhere near these levels, although more useful are freezing level charts (see chapters 34 and 35), especially where icing is a concern, such as in precipitation.

b. MARINE WIND AND WAVE CHARTS

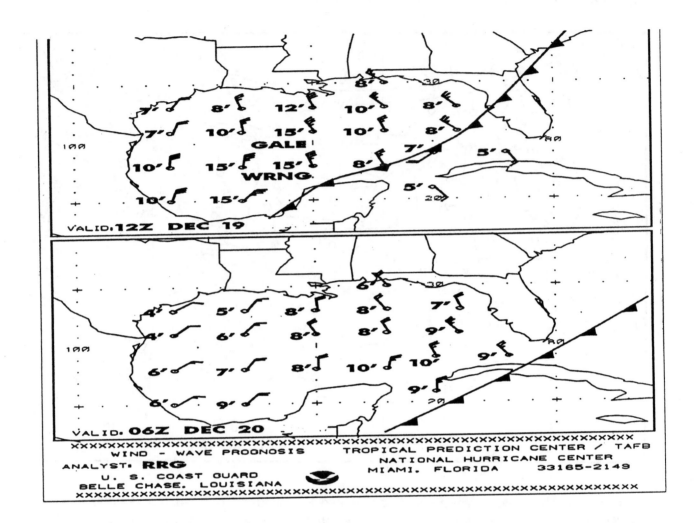

Figure 114. An Wind and Wave Prognosis Chart. This series of charts may include the original analysis or, as in this example, a forecast (prognosis) for a specific time. The wind directions and speeds are given over open waters of the oceans or, as in this example for over the Gulf of Mexico, for a large water region. The wind barbs use the same format as described on the previous page. The forecast height of the waves is given in feet, and is plotted next to the location of the wind forecast for the same location as plotted. These charts may also show important weather features that would affect the wind and the waves; e.g., in the prog above, a position of a cold front is shown for the forecasted time of 12Z on December 19th. Similar charts are available for the oceans.

c. SURFACE STREAMLINE CHARTS

VALID: 12Z DEC 19

Figure 115. A Surface Streamline Analysis. This chart shows how the air is flowing. It is easy to see areas of convergence (where air is coming together), and areas of divergence (where air is being depleted). Low-level converging air parcels "pile up" and rise, whereas diverging air is replaced by air from above. Thus, we can define areas of rising and sinking air. To have clouds and precipitation, we generally need rising air and adequate moisture, and to have clear or clearing skies, we generally need sinking air. Thus, a streamline analysis is another way to look for the synoptic-scale vertical motions, especially as a low pressure system is developing. A mesoscale surface streamline analysis locates areas of convergence that may play a role in thunderstorm development.

d. TROPICAL SURFACE CHARTS

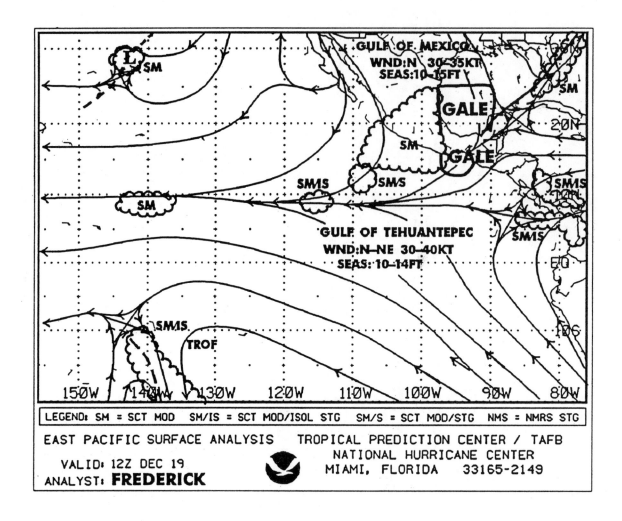

Figure 116. A Tropical Surface Analysis. Since except for tropical cyclones, the pressure gradient is weak in the tropics, there are not many isobars that can be drawn for the usual 4 millibar interval. Therfore, streamlines are drawn showing the airflow. Converging streamlines can show developing tropical cyclones. As per the legend given for the chart in this example, the areal coverage (isolated, scattered, numerous) and the intensities (moderate, strong) of thunderstorm areas can be depicted.

e. NOTE ABOUT OTHER CHARTS

With the contemporary overload of data, we can devise all sorts of charts to show items of interest. We can also create <u>composite charts</u> which superpose important features from the surface and various upper-level charts. Therefore, new graphics will continue to be invented.

There are also charts for such items as the periods of sea-waves, for the state of the ground (to determine, e.g., drought vs. saturation of the soil) and for long-range weather outlooks for out to about a month and also for the next three months. Seasonal three-month projections would shows areas where the average temperature for those three months is expected to be near average, and areas for above average and below average temperatures. The same is done for precipitation.

Ever-improving computer software allows us to generate copious displays from weather data and derived data fields. **Because of data overload, our forecasting approach is to first look at the main surface and upper-air data to see what has been happening and what is happening now for our area of interest, and then to define the forecast problem(s) or challenge(s) of the day, subsequently looking at the data and data sets relevant to that forecasting job.**

50. PROFILERS

A wind profiler is a Doppler radar pointing straight up, using the Doppler principle density changes of moving air to determine the wind at many levels in the vertical.

A wind profiler is an unattended piece of equipment which is highly sensitive. The wind direction and speed is measured in vertical increments, such as every 250 meters or every 100 meters, up to a certain height, such as about 10 miles (about 16 kilometers).

The picture shows a profiler (wind profiler Doppler radar; notice that the antenna is horizontal with a grid, and beams energy upward).

The emitted pulses of energy hit and reflect off fluctuations of radio refractive index in the atmosphere. By assuming that these fluctuations are carried along by the mean wind, and by using the principles of Doppler shift, estimates of the wind are obtained from analysis of returned power to the radar. Winds at different levels are obtained via systematic time delays in the transmitted pulses.

Using a dual planar array of coaxial, co-linear antenna, the profiler emits three beam patterns in a computer-controlled sequence, one vertical and two oblique. The system detects Doppler shifts of the atmospheric turbulence. These frequency shifts, in combination with beam position, are translated into wind speed and direction in a vertical profile.   PAGE 234

Here are examples of profiler data to analyze. Notice the time scale, in Z time (GMT, i.e., UTC) with the latest data being 03Z at the far left. The standard wind barbs are used to display wind direction and wind speed. The hand-drawn squiggly line shows a mid-level ridge passing over the station between 17Z and 18Z as indicated by the wind direction shift from northwest to southwest, and a subtle mid-level trough passed through between 21Z and 22Z as the winds shifted from west-southwest to west-northwest. Another trough passes over the site between 02Z and 03Z. Looking at data from profilers upstream shows weather features evolving and moving towards you.

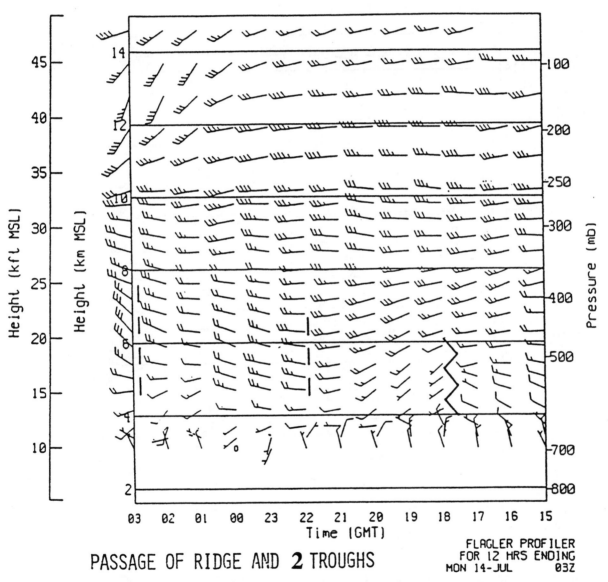

PASSAGE OF RIDGE AND 2 TROUGHS

FLAGLER PROFILER
FOR 12 HRS ENDING
MON 14-JUL   03Z

Annotated time-height cross section of profiler winds at Flagler from 1500 UTC 13 July   to 0300 UTC 14 July

Jet-streaks are defined by winds of 50 knots or greater. The outlined area aloft shows the nose of the jet-streak moving overhead at 200 mb at 19Z, with the jet-depth increasing over a few hours. A ridge between about 700 and 500 millibars passes over the station between 18Z and 19Z and a mid-level trough passes between 21Z and 22Z. Since you would expect rising air just ahead of the axis of this small trough, if there is sufficient moisture in place, you would expect a patch of cloudiness just ahead of and along the trough axis. The profilers show what the troposphere has many meso-scale short-waves (mini-troughs) and mini-ridges as well as the larger synoptic-scale ones. A summertime meso-short-wave, maybe only 50 miles wide, can trigger an area of showers and thunderstorms in mid-levels, for example. So look at profiler data upsteam from you, to see what is evolving and heading your way.

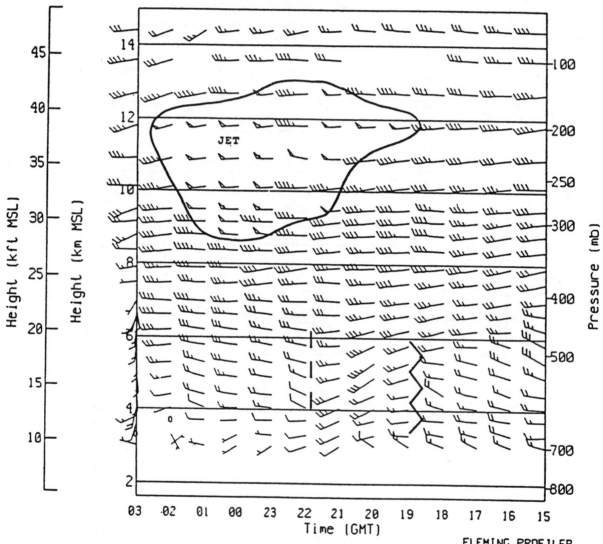

PASSAGE OF JET STREAK AND OTHER FEATURES

FLEMING PROFILER
FOR 12 HRS ENDING
MON 14-JUL   03Z

Annotated time-height cross section of profiler winds at Fleming from
1500 UTC 13 July   to 0300 UTC 14 July

Here are data from a profiler in a squall-line environment. Note that the time period between profiler soundings is a half-hour, which is more useful than hourly when thunderstorms are probable.

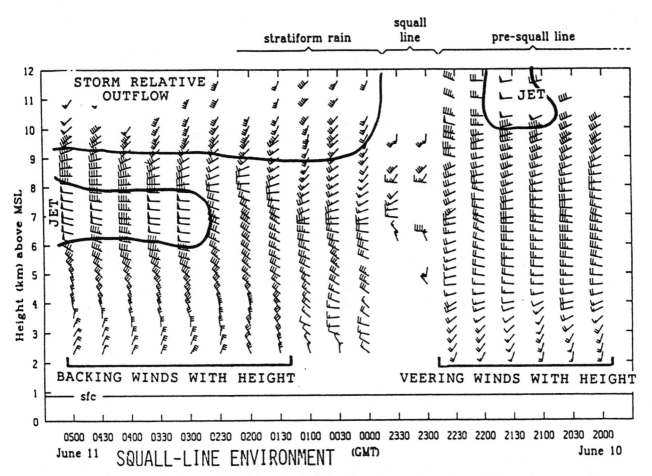

Annotated time-height cross section of profiler winds near Liberal, Kansas, from 2000 UTC 10 June   to 0500 UTC 11 June   . Note the half-hourly time interval.

Notice how the depth of the jet-stream jet-streak lowers and deepens throughout the daytime. By 23Z, the jet-streak is 300 millibars deep, extending downward to 500 mb from 200 mb. Notice the low-level backing of winds with time, which may indicate cold-air advection through those depths. This profiler site is in Colorado, so the low levels are above 800 mb.

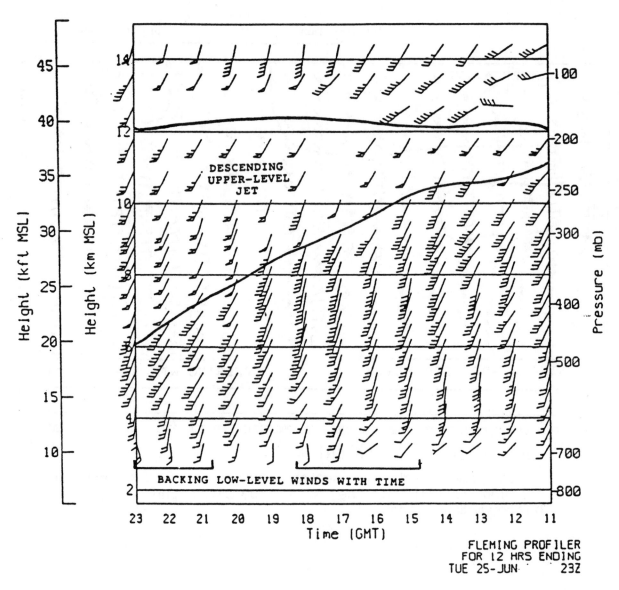

Annotated time-height cross section of profiler winds at Fleming from 1100 UTC to 2300 UTC 25 June

A thunderstorm complex passes over the profiler site in the profiler data set below.

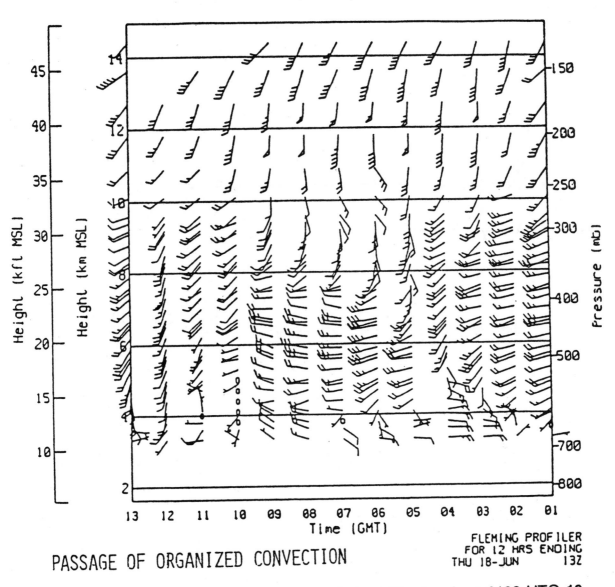

PASSAGE OF ORGANIZED CONVECTION

FLEMING PROFILER
FOR 12 HRS ENDING
THU 18-JUN 13Z

Time-height cross section of profiler winds at Fleming from 0100 UTC 18 June to 1300 UTC 18 June

In the Northern Hemisphere, winds veer (turn clockwise) with increasing height during warm air advection, and back (turn counterclockwise) with increasing height during cold air advection. Where the backing stops is the top of the dome of the cold air. As the cold front passes at the surface, which it did before 00Z, its depth is shallow, but as more cold air moves in, the depth of this cold air increases with time and then levels off.

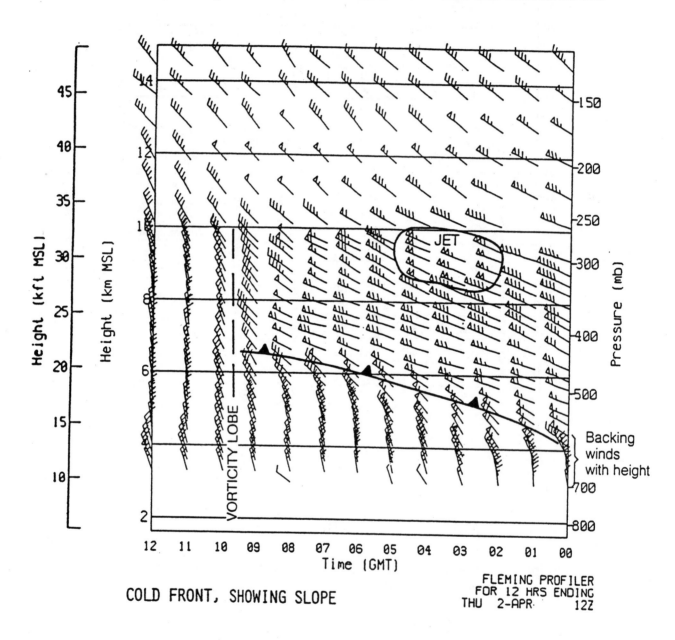

COLD FRONT, SHOWING SLOPE

FLEMING PROFILER
FOR 12 HRS ENDING
THU 2-APR 12Z

A well-developed surface low-pressure system with its associated upper-level trough shows up well in this set of profiler data. The trough tilts with height towards colder air. When the system occludes, the tilting diminishes to a vertical stacking of the surface and upper-level low. The deeper the trough through the troposphere, the better organized and more potent a system it is, everything else being about equal compared with less-deep troughs.

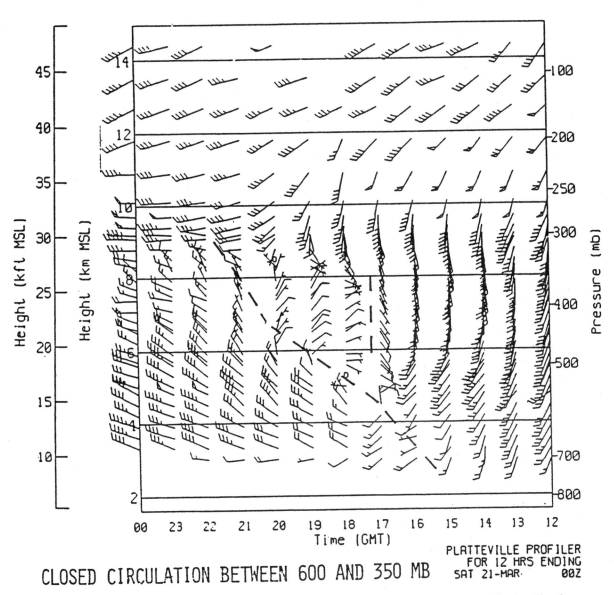

CLOSED CIRCULATION BETWEEN 600 AND 350 MB

PLATTEVILLE PROFILER
FOR 12 HRS ENDING
SAT 21-MAR   00Z

Annotated time-height cross section of profiler winds at Platteville from 1200 UTC 20 March to 0000 UTC 21 March

Quality-control checks are done via computer program to try to preclude erroneous data from being accepted as realistic data. In this example, the software prints a numeral 1 next to data that appear unrepresentative.

PAGE 242

FRI JAN 25

HKL

HORIZONTAL WIND (kt)
1 - QC CHECK FAILED OR
    NOT PERFORMED

Besides wind direction and wind speed, derived fields are data are also prepared from the profiler data. The list below shows the wealth of such weather charts that are developed from data from lots of profiler sites.

TIME SECTIONS (time vs. height):

- horizontal wind
- horizontal speed
- thermal wind
- wind speed shear
- wind direction shear
- u/v-wind components
- w-wind component
- perturbation wind
- returned power
- derived divergence
- derived vertical velocity
- derived vorticity

CROSS-SECTIONS (distance vs. height):

- horizontal wind
- orthogonal components
- w-wind component
- thermal wind
- returned power

PLAN VIEWS (horizontal area at selected atmospheric levels):

- horizontal wind
- horizontal speed
- w-wind component
- streamlines
- derived vorticity
- derived divergence
- thermal wind
- time difference of u-wind component
- time difference of v-wind component
- time difference of w-wind component
- time difference of divergence
- time difference of vorticity
- returned power

Here is an example of an 850 mb wind chart derived from data from wind profilers. Only a small number of data sites was available in these Central Plains states for this analysis.

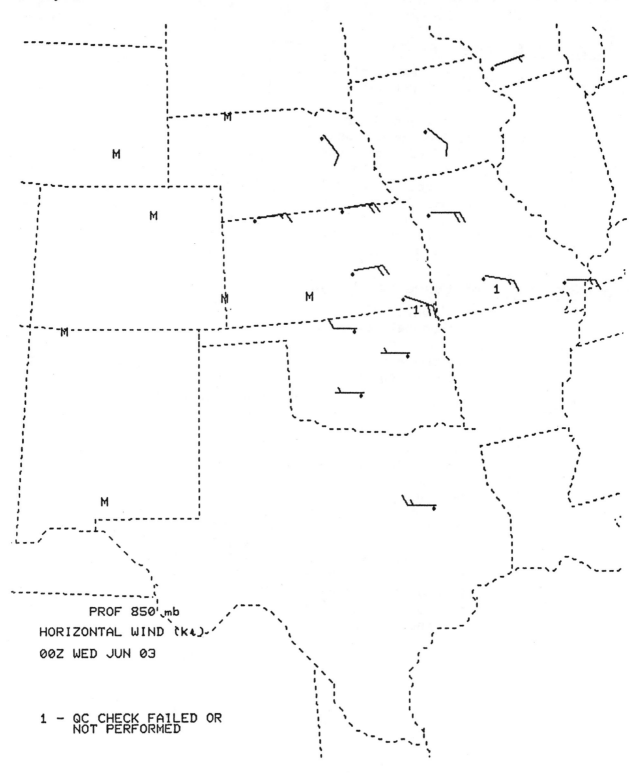

PROF 850 mb
HORIZONTAL WIND (kt)
00Z WED JUN 03

1 - QC CHECK FAILED OR
    NOT PERFORMED

Here is a regional 500 millibar wind plot from profiler stations in that region.

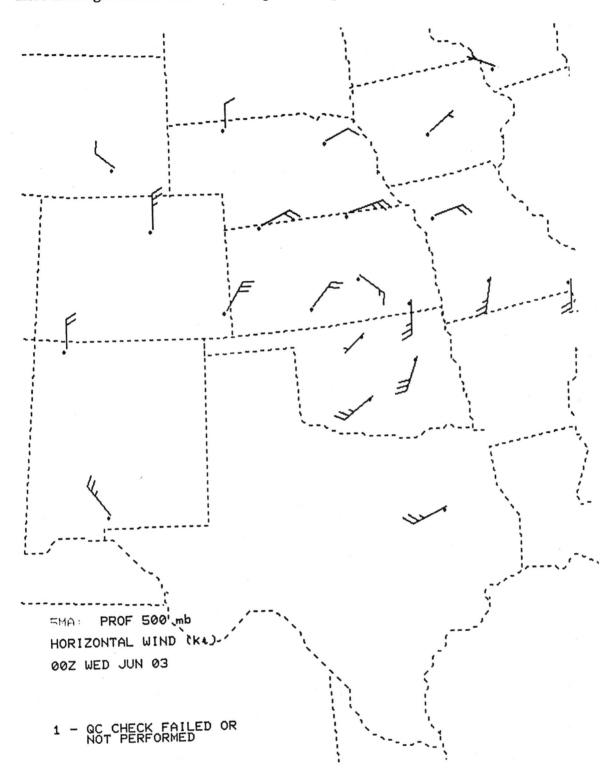

SMA: PROF 500 mb
HORIZONTAL WIND (k1)
00Z WED JUN 03

1 - QC CHECK FAILED OR
    NOT PERFORMED

Here is a 500 mb absolute vorticity plot derived from wind profiler data from a few stations. Due to no data from stations on the southeast part of this region, the software analysis program draws a jagged line there.

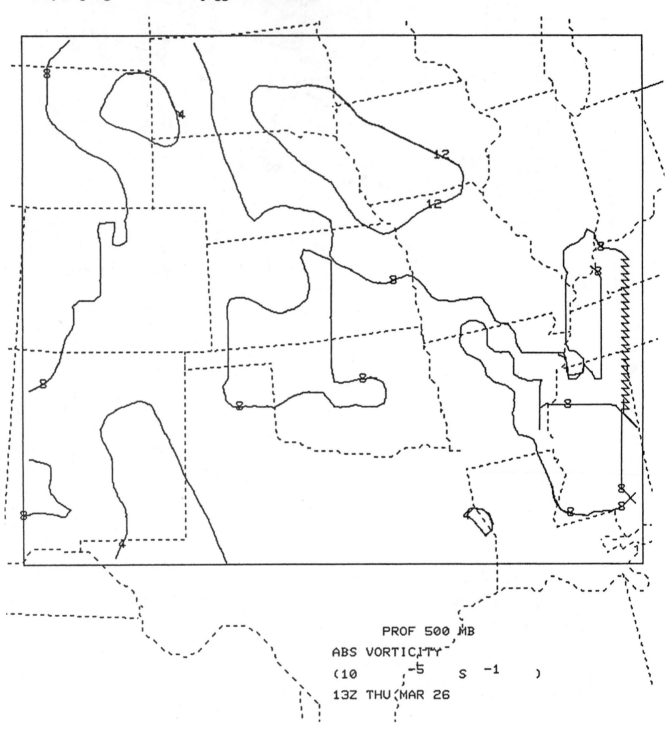

PROF 500 MB
ABS VORTICITY
(10^{-5} S^{-1})
13Z THU MAR 26

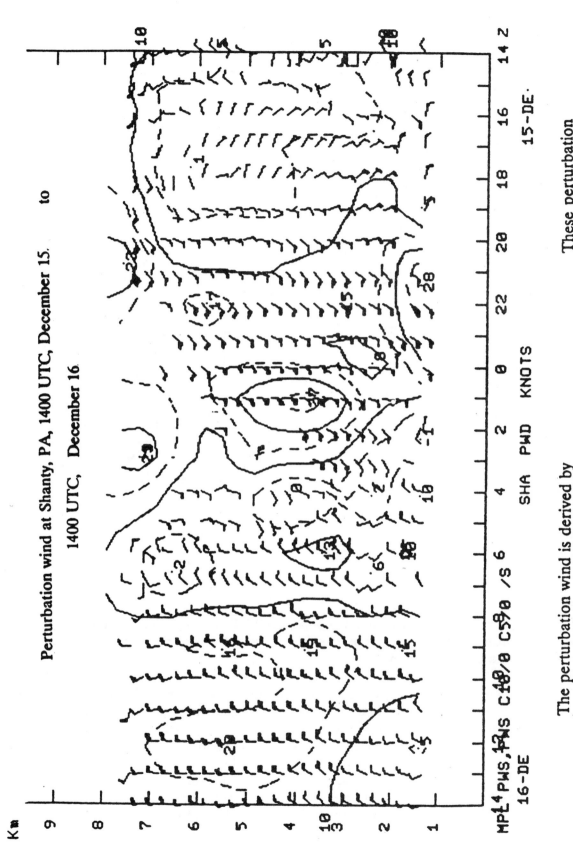

Perturbation wind at Shanty, PA, 1400 UTC, December 15 to 1400 UTC, December 16

The perturbation wind is derived by averaging the wind vector over a specific time period and subtracting the given hour from this average. The perturbation wind uses a "moving average" of all the hourly wind direction and wind speed measurements for a +12 to -12 hour period.

These perturbation winds can often reveal directional variations associated with small scale disturbances that are not apparent in the traditional wind field.

51. WEATHER RADAR

The word "RADAR" started out as an acronym for "RAdio Detection And Ranging".

During World War II, bursts of electromagnetic energy were transmitted through an antenna. The energy went out in the form of waves. The length of the wave (called the "wavelength") could be fixed so that the radar waves would bounce off (reflect off) targets of a certain size-range. Thus, for example, an energy wavelength of 23 centimeters could detect aircraft.

It was discovered by accident that precipitation, especially heavy rain and hail, often also showed up on the radar scope. Thus, radar wavelengths were experimented with to find the optimum wavelength range for detecting precipitation. Weather radars use either 10 or 5 centimeter wavelengths.

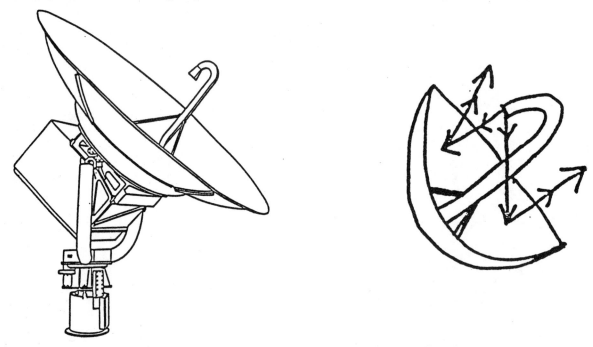

Figure 117a (left). The radar antenna within a near-parabolic dish, and figure 117b (right), illustrating how the electromagnetic energy comes out of the feedhorn and is directed to the dish which then bounces it outward.

Radar classification: The two types of radar are PULSED and NONPULSED. A pulsed radar emits bursts (pulses) of electromagnetic energy for very short time periods (short bursts), and uses the time intervals between these emitted bursts to listen for (to detect) any returned energy. When the transmitted energy hits precipitation, it is scattered, but the part that is scattered directly back to the radar is called reflection. A nonpulsed radar emits a continuous flow of electromagnetic energy and requires a second antenna next to it to detect any returned energy. Thus, it is cheaper to have a pulsed radar since only one antenna is required, but the antenna takes turns transmitting pulses of energy and listening. Most of the time, the radar is in the listening mode (between the pulses). The transmitting and receiving modes of the pulsed radar are alternated by a piece of equipment called the duplexer.

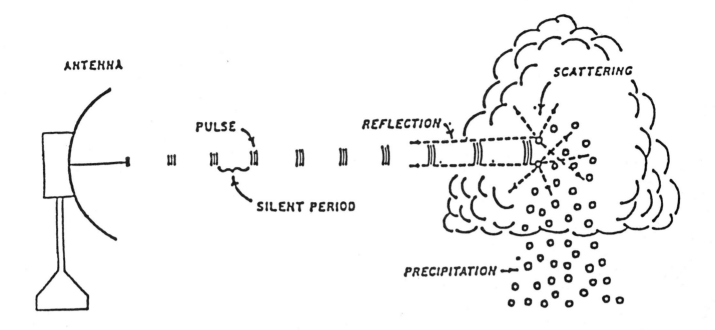

Figure 118. A schematic showing radar pulses scattered and reflected from precipitation occurring within a convective (cumulo-form) cloud.

Figure 119. The radar antenna is enclosed within a fibreglass dome called a radome. Inside the radome, the antenna is rotating as it sends out signals and listened for any returns. Returns are displayed on a radarscope or computer monitor and are called radar ECHOES.

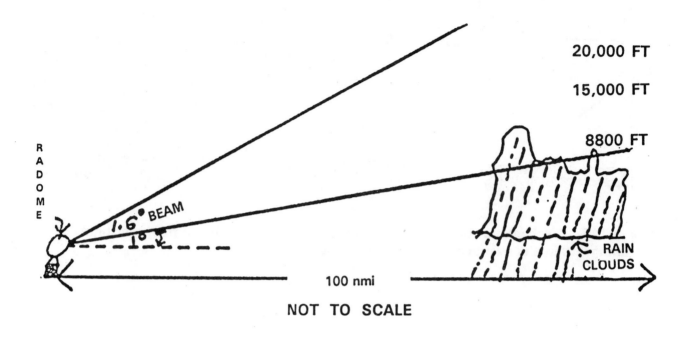

Figure 120. The radar beam goes out at a slight elevation above the horizon. The above example shows the radar signal being transmitted at a one degree elevation angle. The beamwidth itself starts out as a 1.6° beam in this example. With this radar, the beam at 100 nautical miles out extends from 8800 feet to 25,800 feet high. It is easy to see that if most echo tops are below 10,000 feet at about 100 nmi. out, then the beam is not completely filled with precipitation at that range. Thus, we have a problem of representativeness. (One nautical mile = 1.15 regular [statute] miles, so that 100 nmi. equals about 115 regular miles.)

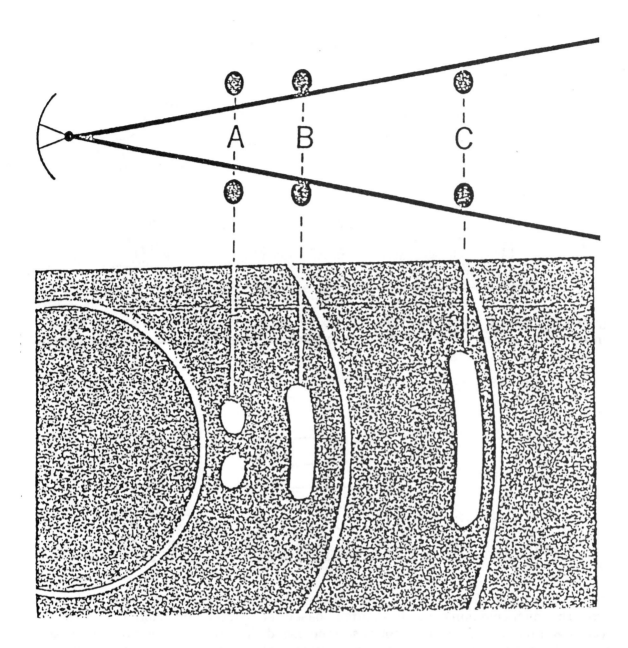

Figure 121. This figure illustrates the problem of beamwidth resolution. The figure is exaggerated to illustrate this problem. As the beam gets farther out, it gets wider. If two separate showers are within the beam width, then they will appear on the radar display as one elongated shower. At location A, as the radar antenna and beam rotate, the beam will first pick up one shower and then the other, but at B and C, if the radar beam detects both showers along or within the beamwidth, then they will appear as one rain area. Thus, it is easy to make the mistake of interpreting such radar displays as having more widespread rain than is really occurring, and then concluding that the rain area is decreasing as it approaches the radar, and then increasing again as it leaves the area! Of course, some times that will really be the case. The key in interpreting weather data sets is to look at radar, satellite and observed data to determine what is actually occurring.

<u>Refraction</u> is the amount of bending or curving of the radar beam as it gets farther from the source.

NORMAL REFRACTION

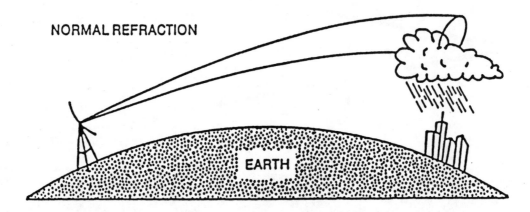

Figure 122. Normal refraction of the radar beam occurs under standard atmospheric conditions. In normal refraction, the radar beam bends slightly upward from the curve of the earth. (source: NWS)

SUPER REFRACTION

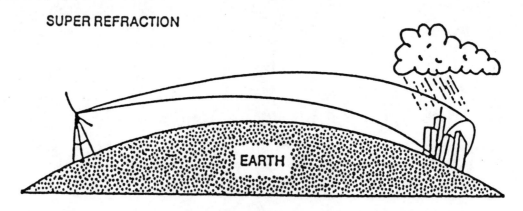

Figure 123. Superrefraction of the radar beam occurs when the beam bends back to the earth. The most common cause is a surface-based temperature inversion, i.e., when a layer of warmer air rests above cooler, surface-based air. This happens often on clear, nearly calm nights when the surface temperature cools off due to radiational cooling. After the sun comes up, the air is warmed and mixed which usually ends the inversion. (source; NWS)

Superrefraction can also exist near the earth's surface near thunderstorms, especially in their latter stage. The cold-air outflow from the thunderstorm, running along the surface of the earth, is much colder than the air it is displacing and forcing upward, resulting in a temporary temperature inversion. Another cause of superrefraction is during episodes of moisture content decreasing sharply with increasing altitude.

Thus, superrefraction occurs when the radar beam bends towards the earth, compared to normal refraction when the beam bends slightly away from the earth as it goes out from the radar antenna. When the ground targets are showing up on the radar display during superrefraction episodes, such echoes are called <u>ANOMALOUS PROPAGATION</u>.

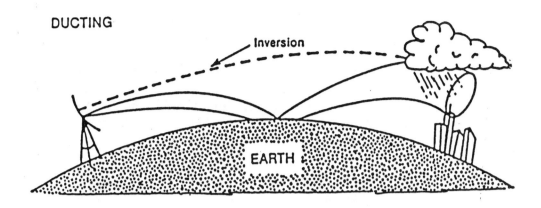

DUCTING

Inversion

EARTH

Figure 124. An extreme case of superrefraction known as ducting. <u>Ducting</u> is the radar beam superrefracting towards the earth, bouncing off the earth's surface and then refracting upwards. This can occur in extreme low-level temperature inversions, where the air near the surface is much colder than a layer of warmer air just above it. This is called a very stable condition, and permits the radar to detect targets much farther than its normal range! Most radars have a "short-range" display, which is out to 125 nautical miles, and a "long-range" display, which is out to 250 nautical miles. When no precipitation is occurring within the short range, the long range is used. The representativeness is better in the short range.

Ducting occurs with television and radio signals too. When ducting occurs, it is sometimes possible to pick up broadcast stations far beyond what you normally receive. This author, who lived and worked for awhile in the Rochester, New York area, turned on TV in the morning to watch the news and picked up a TV station from Casper, Wyoming, and listened to THEIR weather report!

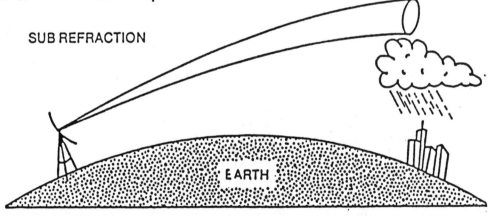

SUB REFRACTION

EARTH

Figure 125. <u>Subrefraction</u> occurs when the radar beam bends upward greater than during normal refraction. This typically occurs in hot arid regions during the hottest, driest daylight hours. It occurs where the temperature lapse rate with height is steeper than normal --an unstable atmosphere. It an also occur where moisture increases with height. Subrefraction is less common than superrefraction, and its effect is to shorten the range of the radar beam, since the beam can overshoot weather targets at shorter ranges than is normal. (source: NWS)

The intensity of the radar echo return is measured in a unit called <u>decibels</u>. The number of decibels is proportional to the rainfall rate. Thus, rainfall rates can be estimated by weather radar! Rainfall estimations based on radar data are used only for out to 75 nautical miles from the radar site; this range is called the <u>HYDROLOGIC RANGE</u> of the radar. Beyond about 75 nmi., some of the beam may be overshooting too much of any rain, which makes any rainfall rate estimates unreliable. Thus, **the hydrologic range of the weather radar is the maximum range out from the radar within which the rainfall estimates from radar data are reasonably reliable.**

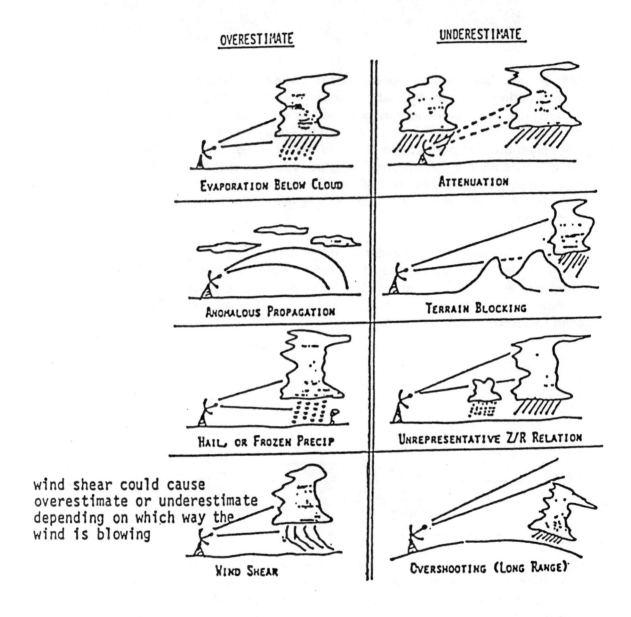

Figure 126. Conditions that would cause the weather radar to overestimate or underestimate the rainfall rate. (source: NWS)

Figure 127. The electromagnetic radiation spectrum, showing where the weather radar bands ("C" and "S") lie in relation to other forms of electromagnetic radiation.

WAVELENGTH (cm)		FREQUENCY (Hertz)
10^{-12}	cosmic rays	10^{23}
10^{-11}		10^{22}
10^{-10}		10^{21}
10^{-9}	gamma rays	10^{20}
10^{-8}		10^{19}
10^{-7}	x-rays	10^{18}
10^{-6}		10^{17}
10^{-5}	ultraviolet	10^{16}
10^{-4}	visible light	10^{15}
10^{-3}		10^{14}
10^{-2}	infrared	10^{13}
10^{-1}		10^{12}
10^{0}	EHF	10^{11}
10^{1}	SHF — K, X, S<C, L, P — radar bands	10^{10}
10^{2}	UHF TV	10^{9}
10^{3}	VHF TV FM	10^{8}
10^{4}	HF (short wave)	10^{7}
10^{5}	AM radio	10^{6}
10^{6}	LF	10^{5}
10^{7}	VLF	10^{4}
10^{8}		10^{3}
10^{9}		10^{2}
		10^{1}

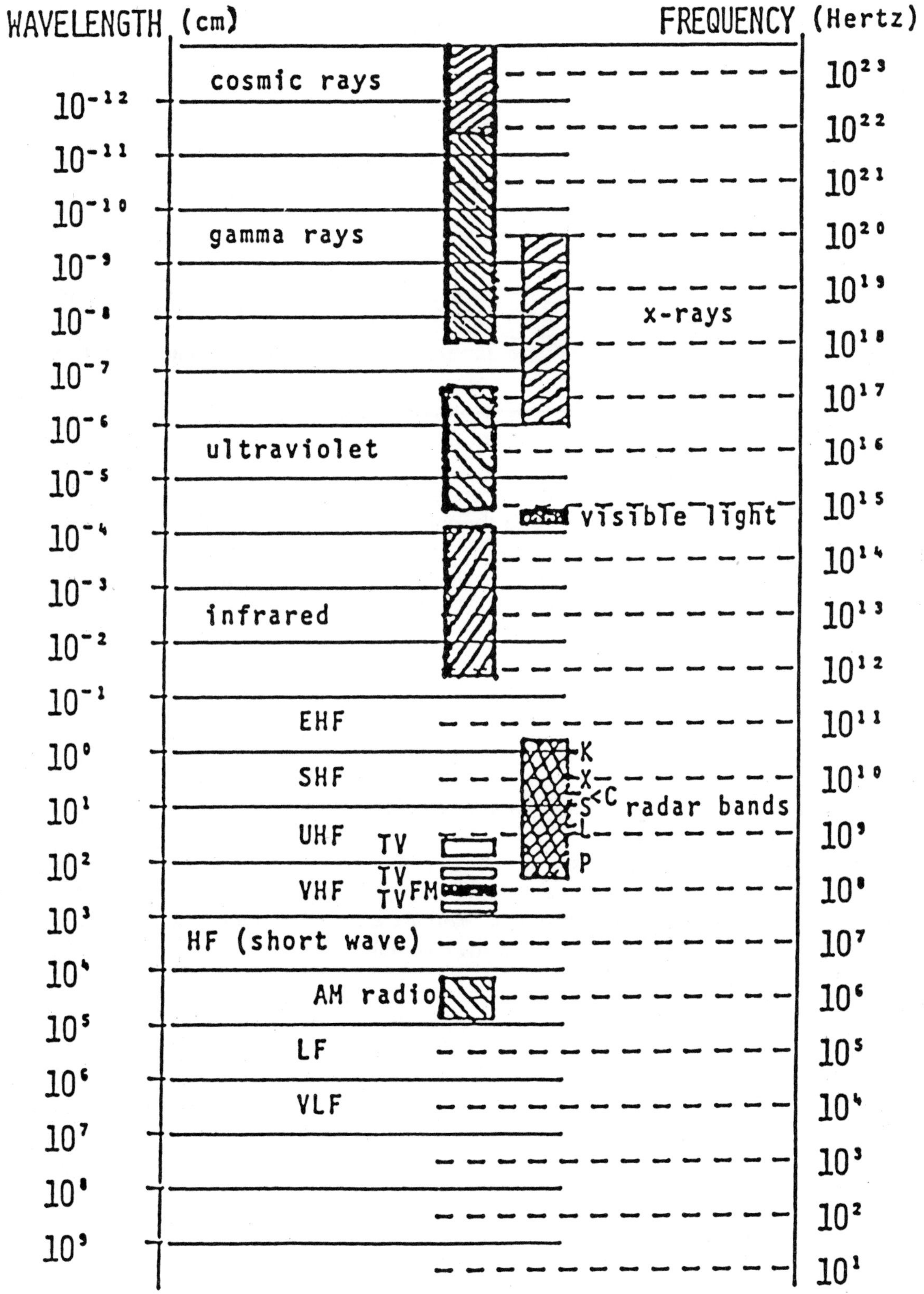

dBZ	RAINFALL CATEGORY	CONVECTIVE AMOUNT (inches per hour)
under 30	LIGHT RAIN	under 0.20" per hour
30	MODERATE RAIN	0.2" to 1.0" per hour
40	HEAVY RAIN	1.1" to 2.0" per hour
45	VERY HEAVY RAIN	2.1" to 3.0" per hour
50	INTENSE RAIN	3.1" to 4.0" per hour
55	EXTREME RAIN	greater than 4.0" per hour

Figure 128. Convective rainfall rates as estimated by weather radar, using the decibels (dBZ) value to empirically relate to the rate of rainfall. The distance out to which the reflectivity/rainfall-rate relationships are reasonably reliable is the hydrologic range of the radar, namely, about 75 nautical miles (about 85 regular miles).

The radar operator can also stop a radar antenna from rotating when he/she notices a powerful weather target, such as a strong thunderstorm, forming or already underway, and can then make the antenna tilt to scan up and down through the thunderstorm. The meteorologist would be looking for very high decibel levels within the clouds, especially aloft, since these may be signatures of flash flooding rain, hail or, when they descend, of a microburst.

Hail reflects and scatters the radar energy that hits it best of all precipitation types. Its echoes show up very brightly on the radar scope, i.e., these echoes have a very high decibel value. Snow does not reflect as well as rain or hail, because the shapes, forms and textures of the snowflakes (with air pockets in them) scatter the radar energy in many directions, with less of it returning to the radar antenna.

Radar images can appear as various brightnesses of white, or can be color-enhanced so that the lightest rain can show as green, heavier as yellow, then orange, and up to red for very heavy and purple for the most intense. Various shades of these colors can be used to further subdivide the intensities, which are the decibel levels.

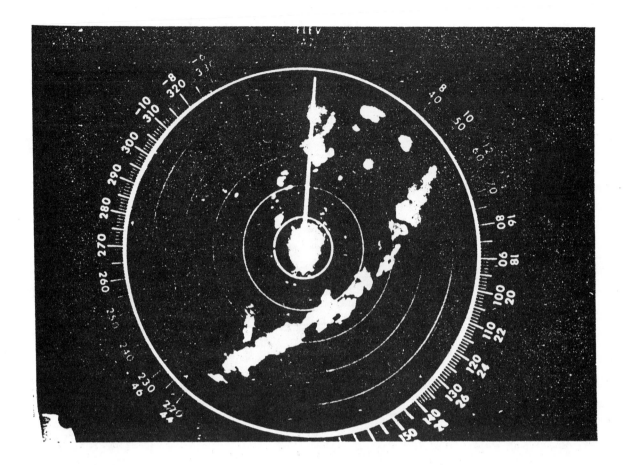

Figure 129. A radar scope showing a line of thunderstorms. In the middle of the scope is the radar site. Each concentric ring is 25 nautical miles distance from the next ring. Notice the blob of echoes in the middle where the radar site is. This is called **GROUND CLUTTER,** and is always there. It is the radar beam hitting buildings, hills, trees, etc. within several miles of the radar. In the early days of weather radar (late 1950s and 1960s), many radar sets were installed right in big cities, which resulted in lots of ground clutter where most people in the region lived, so they could not see on radar where any precipitation was right around the radar site! Learning from this experience, most of today's weather radars are located in the country, in order to minimize the ground clutter. (source: NWS)

Besides ground clutter, other "false precipitation echoes" occur when the radar shows precipitation where there is none occurring. This is anomalous propagation, which has been discussed earlier in this chapter.

Let us look at some radar signatures of severe or potentially severe weather.

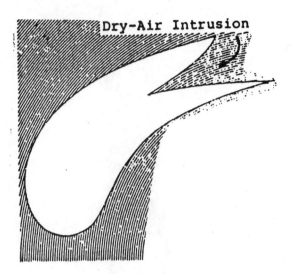

Figure 130. Here is a "V-notch", which often indicates large hail at the notch, and sometimes also a tornado. (source: NWS)

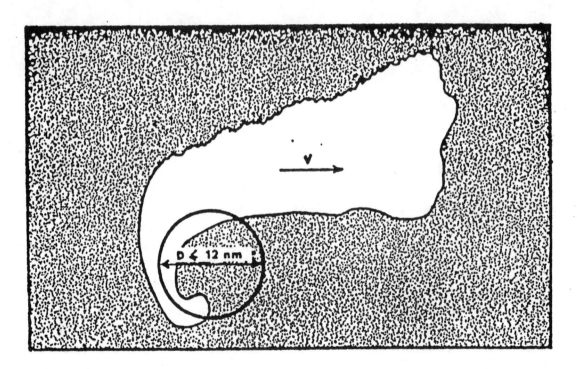

Figure 131. Here is a HOOK ECHO, which is the classic echo signature of a tornado on the reflectivity display. (source: NWS)

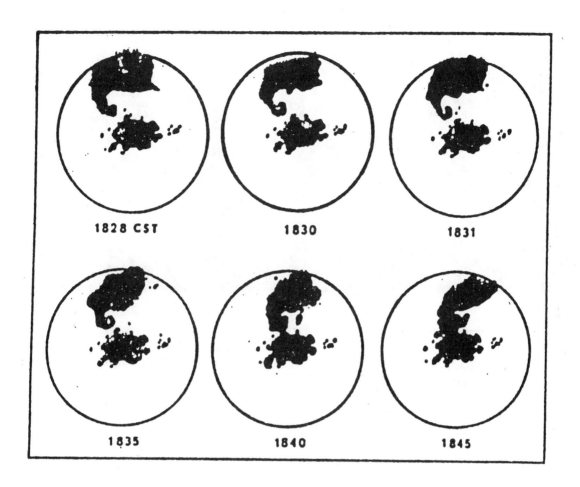

Figure 132. A time-series of radar images showing the development and movement of a hook echo (tornado) going just north of the radar site. (source: NWS)

Figure 133. A <u>line-echo wave-pattern (LEWP)</u>, which is a wavy squall-line of thunderstorms, and a <u>BOW ECHO</u>. A LEWP is typically associated with severe thunderstorms. As parts of the line merge, new and severe storms rapidly form at the merging. Where the line bows in, we have rapidly descending air no echoes) and a possible microburst of winds downward from the clouds, often in of 100 miles per hour.

BOW
ECHO

((MICRO-
BURST!)

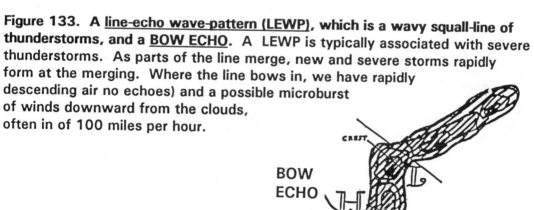

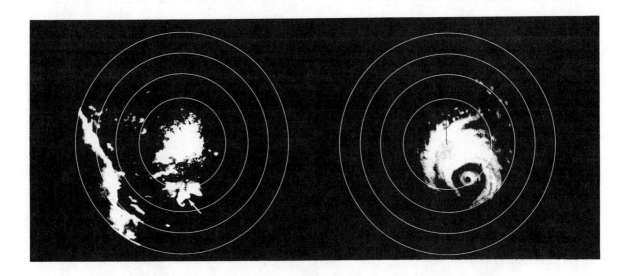

Figure 134. Radar reflectivity showing at left a hook echo (at the arrow), which is a tornado, and at right a hurricane with a double eye (no precipitation in the eye). The bright (white) areas on both displays ar rainfall, and we also find the continuous ground clutter in the middle of each picture right around the location of each radar set. (source: NWS)

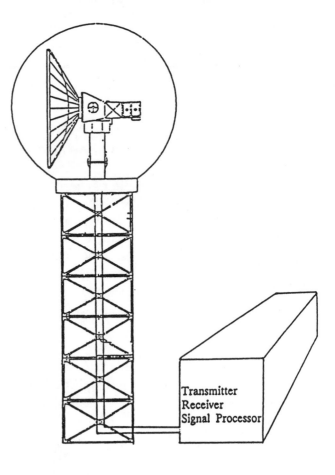

Figure 135. A schematic showing the radar dish with its feedhorn (the dish and feedhorn are the antenna) inside the radome, on a pedestal, and some electronic equipment inside the weather station.

Range-Height Indicator:

The radar antenna can keep rotating, sending out signals that look for precipitation to reflect off and try to return to the radar site. The radar antenna rotation can also be stopped so that the radar can aim in one direction at a precipitation area that may be worthy of detailed examination. For example, if a severe thunderstorm is rapidly growing, the radar can do a tilt-sequence, scanning up and down to see how high and how intense the echoes are. When high decibel levels are occurring in mid-levels of a developing thunderstorm, this heavy precipitation must plunge to the surface, meaning that such a signature may be indicative of a downburst of strong and damaging winds. Moreover, high decibel levels thorugh a deep vertical range indicate that torrential rainfall may be occurring with that storm.

Figure 136. A display on the range-height indicator (RHI).
The radar antenna has stopped rotating and is scanning up and down, looking for the vertical extent and intensities of precipitation echoes. The vertical scale of the RHI display at right is labelled in tens of thousands of feet, and the bright areas are precipitation. One cell, for example, has precipitation tops to nearly 50,000 feet. The bright areas here are convective (shower, thunderstorm) cells. (source: NWS)

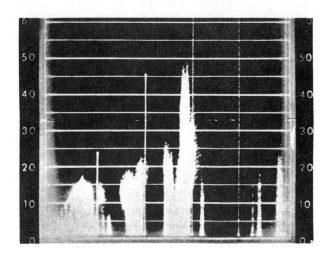

Doppler radar:

The Doppler effect is named for Christian Johann Doppler of Austria, who revealed his principle in 1842. The Doppler effect is the apparent change in the frequency of waves, such as sound waves and light waves, which occurs when the source of the waves and the observer of the waves are moving, relative to each other. The frequency increases when the source and the observer approach each other, and decreases when they move away from each other.

The Doppler part of radar uses this Doppler effect to measure the radial component of air, i.e., the component of the wind moving towards the radar site or away from the radar site. Thus, a weather radar detects precipitation echoes, and the Doppler component of the radar detects air motion.

Before discussion Doppler radar a little more, let us discuss the Doppler principle some in a little more detail.

The frequency of waves is the number of waves that pass a given point in a given period of time, such as per second. Thus, frequency is measured in cycles (number of waves) per second. The correct terminology is Hertz/second, kiloHertz/second, megaHertz/second, etc. One thousand cycles per second is one kiloHertz/second; one million cycles per second is one megaHertz/second.

The Doppler effect can occur with all phenomena that emit waves. Thus, electromagnetic waves, including radar waves, are included. When a source emitting energy in the form of waves is approaching a second object, more waves pass by the second object, thus increasing the frequency. In like manner, when the source and second object are moving away from each other, fewer waves pass by the second object, thus decreasing the frequency.

HERE IS A SIMPLE DEMONSTRATION OF THE DOPPLER EFFECT: DETERMINING THE FREQUENCY OF WAVES THAT PASS YOU WHILE IN THE WATER AT THE BEACH

This demonstration works best when the ocean is calm with perhaps gentle swells. It will work with large bodies of water such as the Great Lakes, but is more difficult to do in smaller bodies of water such as ponds. It does not work with rivers and streams.

1. Walk out into the water until it is about knee-deep.

2. Stand still and count the number of waves that pass by in a minute. You may want to repeat this several times to determine the average frequency. Frequency in this case refers to the number of waves that pass by you in a minute.

3. Very slowly but at a constant speed, walk towards the deeper water and determine the number of waves that pass by. Since you are moving towards the source, this wave number should be greater than when you were standing still. You may want to repeat walking from knee-deep water into deeper water several times in order to determine the average frequency.

4. From your deep position, walk towards the shore, counting the number of waves that pass you in a minute. This number should be lower, since you are moving away from the source of the waves. Again, you may want to repeat doing this several times in order to determine the average frequency.

Most of us probably notice the Doppler effect when an approaching and then departing train goes by. The same is true with a siren from a fast-moving fire engine, ambulance or police vehicle. For example, as the train approaches you, more sound waves are entering your ear per second, producing a higher frequency and therefore a higher pitch. As the train moves away from you, fewer sound waves reach your ear per second, producing a lower frequency and therefore a lower pitch. The same thing happens at an automobile race track. As the cars pass the observers and move away, the pitch drops.

Astronomers can tell the relative motion of stars in relation to the earth; that is, are the stars approaching or moving away from the earth, or is the earth moving towards or away form the stars, or are both the earth and the stars is question all moving towards or away from each other? Recall that visible white light is comprised of the following colors: red, orange, yellow, green, blue, indigo and violet, with red having the lowest frequency and violet the highest.

When a star is approaching the earth, the color shifts towards the violet end of the spectrum, because more light waves are entering the eye per second, therefore producing a higher frequency wave. For example, a star that normally appears as a red star may appear to become reddish-orange or orange as it approaches the earth. On the other hand, as a star moves away from the earth, the color shifts towards the red end of the spectrum, because fewer light waves enter the eye per second, therefore producing a lower frequency wave. For example, a star that normally appears yellow may appear to become yellow-orange or orange as it moves away from the earth.

Now let us move on to discuss Doppler weather radar.

Doppler radar: the movement of air parcels (the wind) creates density changes in the air, which can also be detected by weather radar and converted into a wind display. The Doppler aspect of radar allows us to have displays of the wind component coming at the radar and moving away from the radar. This is known as the radial component of the wind. This principle allows a tornado, including a developing tornado, to be detected in the clouds before it descends to the ground. Thus, the circulation is detected. The way this is done is to assign a set of colors...typically the "warm" colors of shades of red, orange and yellow, to air moving away from the radar, and the "cool" colors of shades of green, blue and violet, to air coming towards the radar. If red and green are the highest speeds, with red indicating air moving away from the radar and green indicating air moving towards the radar, and the radar display shows a small area of red next to a small area of green, then a rotation is occurring there. This could be a tornado or developing tornado, and a tornado warning will be issued, perhaps even before the twister has touched down. It may not touch down, but the warning allows people to take shelter from the potential tornado.

Sophisticated versions of Doppler weather radars also have computer software that includes algorithms (problem-solving techniques) which search for and alert the forecaster about locations of possible hail, tornadoes, wind shear, heavy rain, etc.

Thus, weather radar is a valuable took to the meteorologist. And via the internet, you can call up weather radar displays and follow the progress of storms yourself.

Surface and upper-air observations, weather maps, weather radar data and weather satellite imagery and data are used together to give us a three-dimensional and a four-dimensional (the 3 directions plus time) description of our always changing weather!

52. WEATHER SATELLITE IMAGERY

weather satellite systems

There are two types of meteorological satellites: geosynchronous and polar-orbiting. The geosynchronous satellites are placed in an orbit 22,300 miles from earth, over the equator, so that they can move from west to east, the same as the earth, at the same rotational speed of the earth at the equator, about 1000 mph. Since the circumference of the earth is about 25,000 miles, the earth, rotating at a little over 1000 mph at the equator, makes its complete rotation in 24 hours, with the geosynchronous satellites moving at the same speed, and therefore staying over the same location.

The current family of geosynchronous satellites is called GOES, which stands for "Geostationary Operational Environmental Satellite". Five GOES systems circle the globe, all over the equator. One is off the east coast of the Americas and one is off the west coast of the Americas. The others are at about the longitude of Japan (south of Japan), over the Indian Ocean and over Africa. Thus, the world is covered.

The other family of meteorological satellites is the polar orbiter series. These satellites are at a much lower altitude, about 1000 miles out, and are placed in an orbit that roughly goes from pole to pole, taking images in a swath averaging some 1500 miles across.

The main weather satellite images are visible, infrared, enhanced infrared and water vapor imagery. Images are returned to ground stations on earth, processed and enhanced to depict the weather features.

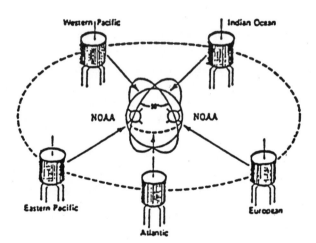

Figure 137. A schematic depicting the geosynchronous GOES weather satellites in orbits 22,300 miles out, and the polar orbiter weather satellites, currently known as NOAA satellites, in quasi-pole-to-pole orbits several hundred miles out. The GOES satellites stay over the same locations over the equator, sending images of the same part of the globe from North to South polar regions. In very high latitudes, cloud tops are displaced farther poleward by GOES satellites, which is why the polar orbiters are more useful in polar regions.

Types of weather satellite imagery:

Weather satellites have sensors that give us visible, infra-red, water vapor and other imagery of the tops of clouds and, where there are no clouds, the surface of the planet. Visible pictures are useable obviously only during the daytime. Infra-red (heat) imagery senses the temperature of the tops of the clouds or the ground, water or ice surface. The Stefan-Boltzmann Law of physics relates the emitted energy of the surface of an object to the fourth power of its absolute temperature. The more radiation emitted by each square centimeter surface area of an object, the higher the object's surface temperature.

Infra-red satellite sensors use this principle to obtain the temperatures of cloud tops. The colder the cloud-top temperature, the higher the cloud tops are. For example, for convective clouds, this enables weather forecasters to assess the severity of thunderstorms, since cooling cumulonimbus tops imply that updrafts are building the storm's clouds higher, intensifying the thunderstorm.

Infra-red imagery can be used at day and during the night, since the infra-red sensors on the weather satellites are detecting radiation emitted from the cloud tops, and this information is then converted to the temperatures of these cloud tops. Computer enhancement allows for coloring or shading the imagery based on its temperature.

Water vapor imagery is particularly clever. At the 6.7 micrometer wavelength, the water vapor in the atmosphere absorbs outgoing infra-red radiation (heat) from the earth, and then reradiates it. Sensors on the satellites set to detect this reradiated energy will show where water vapor is present between about 10,000 feet and 30,000 feet up, whether it is in cloud form or not.

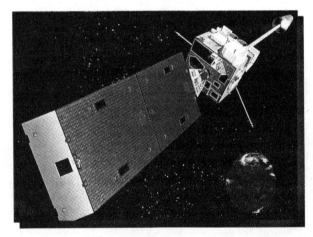

Figure 138. Weather satellites have been operational since 1960. Each new generation of satellites has improved quality of of their imagery. (source: NOAA)

A fine resolution of imagery is desired. Resolution is the smallest object that can be shown by itself. For example, a satellite image having a half-mile resolution means that the smallest object it can show in its images, say its visible pictures, is one-half mile across. Thus, if there were a lone thunderstorm that was one-half mile in diameter, it would be the smallest object that the image would show.

a. visible weather satellite imagery

Visible pictures are just like pictures taken by an ordinary camera, but are looking down from space. Since they need reflected light to show a picture of any target, the visible satellite pictures are available only during the daytime.

How well a cloud-top or snow-covered field or the ground or ocean show up depend on how much of the sun's rays they reflect back towards space. This reflectivity is called albedo. For example, the tops of a large thunderstorm will reflect back about 92% of the sunlight; thus its albedo is .92. This means that it will appear very bright on a visible satellite picture.

Fresh new snow reflects back about 88% of the sunshine impinging on it, but old snow (say 3 to 7 days old) does not reflect back as much (only 59%). A forest of pine trees or other coniferous forest hardly reflects any sunlight at all (only 12%); therefore, forested areas that are not covered by clouds show up dark on a visible picture from space. Oceans appear even darker, since their albedo is about .09.

1.	Large thunderstorm	92%	7.	Thin stratus	42%
2.	Fresh new snow	88%	8.	Thin cirrostratus	32%
3.	Thick cirrostratus	74%	9.	Sand, no foliage	27%
4.	Thick stratocumulus	68%	10.	Sand and brushwood	17%
5.	White Sands NM USA	60%	11.	Coniferous forest	12%
6.	Snow, 3-7 days old	59%	12.	Water surfaces	9%

Figure 139. The amount of sunlight reflected back towards space by various targets. The more that is reflected, the better the target will show up on the visible satellite picture.

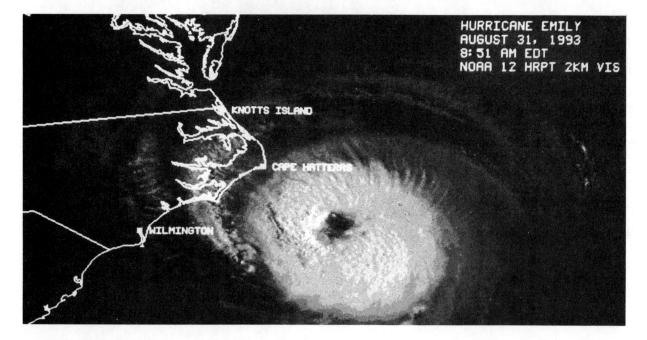

Figure 140. A visible image of a small, compact hurricane, showing its clouds and clear eye in the middle. (source: NOAA) PAGE 266

Figure 141. A Western Hemispheric full-disk visible picture view from a GOES weather satellite, showing the cloud cover and areas of clear weather. (source: NOAA)

Figure 142. A visible satellite image. The state and Canadian province borders are superimposed on the photo. Note the puffy clouds along the Kansas/Colorado border: these are the tops of thunderstorms, cumulonimbus clouds. (source: NOAA)

b. infra-red and enhanced infra-red weather satellite imagery

At night, visible pictures are not possible; therefore, infrared technology is used. Infrared images are also taken during the daytime.

Infrared radiation is a form of heat. The earth and clouds emit infrared radiation. Therefore, sensors have been developed for the weather satellites to detect the amount of radiation being emitted by the cloud tops and, if no clouds are present, by the targets below (the ground, ocean surface or snow- or ice-covered surfaces).

On an infrared black-and-white image, colder objects appear white and warmer objects appear black. Thus, if we were comparing a weather satellite picture in the visible with an image in the infrared, with both showing part of the earth and its clouds and also past the curve of the earth to show outer space, then cold outer space would appear black in the visible picture and white in the infrared image.

In meteorology, we have developed what are called "enhancement curves" which cause the infrared image to depict temperature ranges in shades of gray, white and black. Thus, we can start the enhancement at some desired temperature that would give some idea of the height of the cloud tops, and use a medium gray for say -32°C to -41°C, then a light gray for -42 to -52 degrees, etc., followed by a dark gray, then black , then white. We can set black to represent cloud tops colder than -62°C, which would mean very impressive thunderstorms if these clouds are the tops of thunderstorms. If they are, then the white, set at -80°C or colder, would represent very cold tops, i.e., very high-topped thunderstorms, likely 50,000 to 60,000 feet high and even higher (in mid-latitudes), and would be associated with the heaviest rainfall, maybe flash-flood producing, and/or the most severe weather, since these "overshooting tops", which are overshooting the rest of the thunderstorm or thunderstorm complex, represent the area(s) likely having the strongest convective updrafts.

We can also colorize these different enhancement levels, making them easy to interpret plus visually more stunning, as we observe them on computer monitors or in a color image picture.

Infrared imagery has limitations. Ground targets such as fog and snow-cover do not show up well. Thus, professional and amateur meteorologists look at both visible and infrared images during the daytime, and infrared images at night, to identify features. The infrared imagery most commonly used is enhanced infrared imagery. Moreover, another type of infrared depiction called the "water vapor imagery" is used to detect moisture in the troposphere, whether in cloud form or not, between approximately 10,000 and 30,000 feet up, which is essentially between about 700 and 300 mb. Water vapor imagery will be discussed later.

Figure 143. An enhanced infra-red satellite image. Shades of gray, and white and black are used to identify cloud top temperatures. For example, in the thunderstorm over Arkansas, the "black" area represents cloud tops colder than -62°C but not colder than -80°C. These tops may be between 40,000 and 50,000 feet high, indicating a strong thunderstorm. In the unenhanced infra-red depiction areas, colder objects, such as outer space, appear white, and warmer objects, such as the ground or tropical ocean, appear dark. PAGE 270

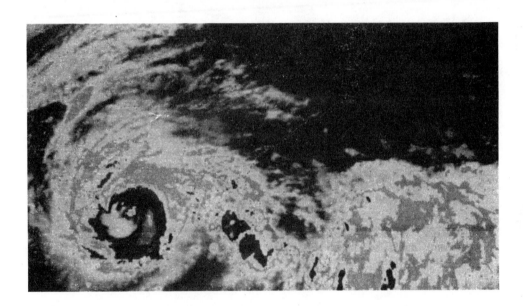

Figure 144. Compare the visible picture of Hurricane Frederic of 1979 (top) with an enhanced infrared image of the same storm (bottom) (the infrared image is enlarged somewhat to show the detail). Gray areas on the outer part of Frederic are clouds at cirrus-level, and the black area of the hurricane is the rain shield, within which a large white area represents the coldest cloud tops and most intense convective rainfall. (source: NOAA)

Thus, the most intense rainfall of the storm, which tends to correlate with the fiercest winds in the storm, can be followed in the enhanced infrared weather satellite imagery. Video-loops easily identify development, movement and diminution of storm systems.

c. water vapor satellite imagery

Figure 145. A water vapor image from a GOES weather satellite. The milky white areas are moisture in the air, not in cloud form, and the bright white areas are moisture which has condensed into clouds, most of the data being detected between approximately 10,000 and 30,000 feet up, thus the water vapor image depicts MID- AND UPPER-LEVEL MOISTURE, WHETHER IN CLOUD FORM OR NOT. ("Mid- and upper-level" refers to the middle and upper portions of the troposphere, respectively.) Note the clouds and moisture in the intertropical convergence zone just north of the equator. There is a developing tropical cyclone off the west coast of Mexico. (source: NOAA)

Here is the physical basis for water vapor satellite images. The earth receives radiation from the sun in many frequencies, short-wave and long-wave, converting that radiation to energy forms which include heat, which is a form of long-wave radiation. The earth, and clouds, emit this heat, which is the infrared radiation sensed by the weather satellites.

At the 6.7 micrometer wavelength, which is a part of the infrared band, water vapor in the air has the property of absorbing this infrared radiation. It then reemits it. Thus, a sensor on a satellite can be designed to measure the flux of radiation from targets emitting radiation at 6.7 micrometers. The amount of radiation received is proportional to the temperature of the emittor., which is the basis for enhancement of infrared images. Moreover, the more moisture in the depth of atmosphere being sensed, the brighter the area will appear on the water vapor image.

Therefore, moisture that is not or not yet condensed into cloud form appears a fuzzy or a milky light white, whereas clouds appear bright white. Areas that are relatively dry and/or are drying due to subsiding air, show up dark.

Recall that water vapor imagery sensing works essentially for the 10,000- to 30,000-foot range depth of atmosphere, essentially sensing moisture between about 700 and 300 millibars (hectoPascals).

Looking at a water vapor image is analogous to looking at a fog from the top down. The more of it there is, and/or the greater its vertical extent, the thicker it will appear.

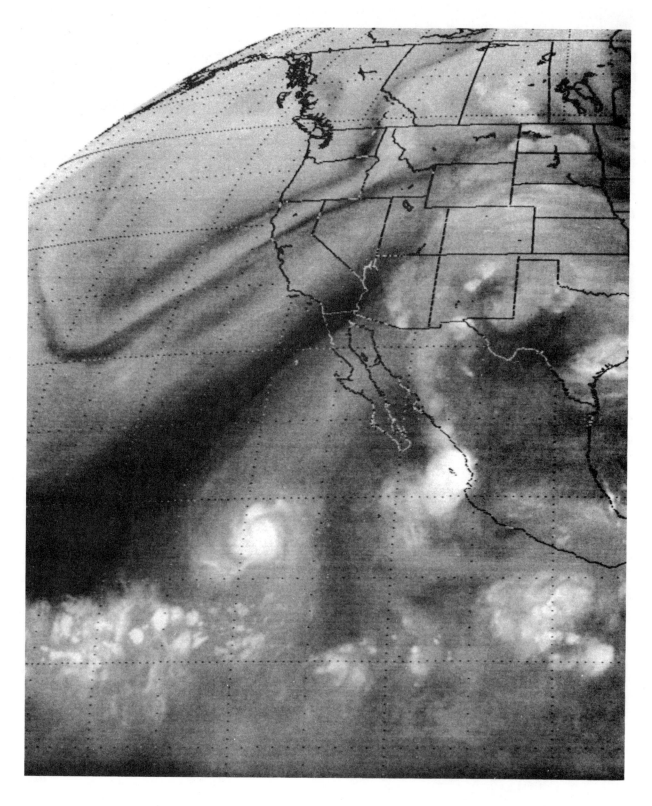

Figure 146. A water vapor image from a weather satellite. The fuzzy milky-white areas are moisture in the middle and upper troposphere, about 10,000 through 30,000 feet up, and the bright white areas are where moist air has been lifted and cooled sufficiently to form visible clouds. Dark regions show relatively dry, and often sinking, air.

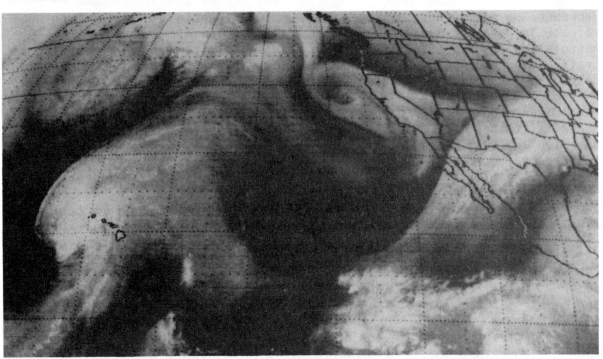

Figures 147, top, and 148, bottom. Visible satellite picture, top, and water vapor image, bottom, of Hurricane Iwa approaching the Hawaiian Islands on November 23rd, 1982. (source: NOAA)

The infrared image shows the greater extent of the mid- and upper-level moisture associated with Iwa. The water vapor image also helps to identify the location of the upper-level anticyclonic cirrroform outflow aloft, located to the north and northeast of the storm center.

PAGE 275

APPENDICES

**Appendix A. METAR/SPECI CODE FOR SURFACE WEATHER
OBSERVATIONS, U.S. VERSION**

Surface weather observations are transmitted in an international code called the
METAR/SPECI CODE.

METAR means: Meteorological Aviation Routine observation. (It originally was a
French acronym that meant the same thing.) These observations are completed just
before each hour, and are designated as the routine hourly weather observations from
airports.

SPECI means: SPECIAL observation. (It originally was also a French acronym that
meant the same thing.) A special observation occurs when at least one element of the
weather, such as ceiling or visibility or aspects of precipitation, for example, changes
such that the new condition should be reported since the change is significant. These
observations may be taken and reported at any time.

The approach this book now takes is to first present an example of a typical METAR
observation, as a means to introducing the deciphering of this weather report, and then
the rules are given for a reference.

Decode the following METAR surface weather observation:

From United States version of METAR code:

METAR KCMH 081055Z 21019G27KT 1/2SM R04R/3000FT -SN FG SCT011 OVC015
01/M02 A2945 RMK PK WND 19029/16 SLP045 T00081016

Now let us decode each block of characters.

KCMH = the observation station's location. United States stations always begin with
the letter K, Canadian stations with the letter C, and other areas with different letters.
The next three characters are the location. CMH is Columbus, Ohio. To obtain the
listing of locations and location identifiers, obtain the latest edition of the manual,
"Location Identifiers", from the Federal Aviation Administration (FAA).

081055Z = the date/time group in Greenwich Mean Time (called "Z time") (also
referred to as UTC or Universale Temps Coordinee [Universal Coordinated Time]),
which is the time at the zero degree longitude meridian (reference: Greenwich, England
time). Thus, our sample observation was taken on the 8th of the month and was
completed at 1055Z , and is referred to as the 11Z hourly observation. The last weather
element taken in a weather observation is the barometric reading.

METAR KCMH 081055Z 21019G27KT 1/2SM R04R/3000FT -SN FG SCT011 OVC015 01/M02 A2945 RMK PK WND 19029/16 SLP045 T00081016

21019G27KT = the wind direction and speed in knots (KT). Here, the wind is coming from 210 degrees at 19 knots with gusts to 27 knots. A calm wind is reported as 00000.

1/2SM = the average prevailing horizontal visibility in statute miles (SM). In our example, the visibility is one half statute mile.

R04R/3000FT = the runway visual range, giving the runway number and how far one can see down that runway in feet. Our example says that runway 04's visual range is 3000 feet.

-SN FG = the current weather in terms of any precipitation and obscuring phenomena. SN means snow and FG means fog. The minus in front of the SN means that the snow is light. Tables at the end of our example description give all the abbreviations for types of weather. Incidentally, when snow is occurring alone (i.e., snow alone is decreasing the visibility, not snow plus fog or plus blowing snow, etc.), then light snow is snow that reduces the visibility to no less than 5/8ths of a mile, moderate snow is snow that reduces visibility to from 1/2 mile to no less than 5/16ths of a mile, and heavy snow is snow that reduces visibility to under 5/16ths of a mile, i.e., to from 1/4 mile down to zero visibility.

SCT011 OVC015 = the cloud cover and ceiling. Here, the first cloud deck is scattered with bases averaging 1,100 feet above the ground, and the next deck is overcast with bases averaging 1,500 feet above the ground. This example is of low clouds. Cloud cover is reported thusly, in eights of sky-cover: "FEW" = 1/8 to 2/8 sky cover, "SCATTERED" = 3/8 to 4/8 sky cover, "BROKEN" = 5/8 to 7/8 sky cover and "OVERCAST" = 8/8 sky cover but can have BINOVC which is break(s) in the overcast. Thus, we have FEW, SCT, BKN and OVC. SKC means the sky is clear of clouds, and CLR is for automated observing stations, which are of inferior quality to human observations, and means no clouds are detected at or below 12,000 feet. The sky can also be partially or totally obscured by, for example, falling and/or blowing snow, or fog. Cloud layers are cumulative from the ground up. Thus, two or three "few" or "scattered" decks could result in the higher or highest layer being reported as broken.

01/M02 = the temperature and dewpoint in whole degrees Celsius. Unfortunately, this hurts the conversion to the most accurate Fahrenheit degree, but to compensate for this, the group at the end of the observation, T00081016, gives the temperature and then dewpoint to the nearest 0.1°C so that a more accurate Fahrenheit temperature can be determined. In our example, 01/M02 means the air temperature is 1°C and the dewpoint is minus 2°C. T00081016, which is a remark at the end of the observation, means the temperature to the nearest tenth of a Celsius degree is 0.8°C, and the dewpoint is minus 1.6°C (-1.6°C), with the 1 before the 016 indicating that the following reading is below zero Celsius. The T indicates that the temperature/dewpoint group to the nearest one-tenth degree Celsius follows.

METAR KCMH 081055Z 21019G27KT 1/2SM R04R/3000FT -SN FG SCT011 OVC015 01/M02 A2945 RMK PK WND 19029/16 SLP045 T00081016

A2945 = the barometer reading (also called the altimeter reading). 2945 means 29.45". A3015 would mean 30.15", and an A2888 would mean 28.88". The barometer reading is what the barometer would read when set to sea-level.

RMK PK WND 19029/16 = the peak wind gust since the last hourly observation. RMK means this is a REMARK added to the observation. Here, the peak wind was from 190 degrees (from the south-southwest) at 29 knots, and occurred at 16 minutes after the previous hour.

SLP045 = the sea-level pressure. Here, 045 means 1004.5 millibars (hectoPascals). A 989 would be 998.9 millibars. Sea-level pressure differs slightly from altimeter in that there is a modification to the pressure based on the temperature.

A remark that reads "A02" means that the station is an automated station, and an "A02A" means that the automated report has been augmented by a human observer. An "A01" station's reports are not as comprehensive as an A02. Automated stations are great assets in remote and smaller airports and in places where humans are not hired for night observations, but the human observer is far superior to the automated station. The human can see when some of the sensors are reporting faulty information, and the human can report such things as tornadoes, hail size, thunderstorms, information about lightning and about convective clouds that are building, for example. The human observer can report the rate of snowfall and can accurate measure snow depth. Our climatological record of over a century is slowly being deprecated by the loss of human observations. Moreover, **the best forecasts first require the most accurate and timely observations.**

On the next page is the coding for weather phenomena.

Obtain the complete METAR/SPECI code breakdown from the National Weather Service, which will also decode the remarks at the end of the observation.

METAR/SPECI coding on weather phenomena:

PRECIPITATION:
RA = rain
DZ = drizzle
SN = snow
PE = sleet
GR = hail
SG = snow grains (a snow drizzle from stratus clouds)
GS = snow pellets (partially melted and refrozen snow)
IC = ice crystals (needle of ice that float in the air on fair and very cold nights)
UP = unknown type(s) of precipitation, used only from automated observing stations

OBSCURING PHENOMENA:
FG = fog
HZ = haze
DU = widespread dust
SA = sand
BR = mist
FU = smoke
VA = volcanic ash
PY = spray

OTHER WEATHER:
SQ = squalls
FC = funnel cloud, tornado, waterspout
PO = well-developed dust/sand whirls
DS = duststorm
SS = sandstorm

DESCRIPTORS:
SH = shower (when the precipitation is showery [convective] in nature)
TS = thunderstorm
MI = shallow (e.g., with fog to indicate shallow ground fog)
PR = partial
BC = patches
DR = low drifting
BL = blowing
FZ = freezing (for freezing rain and/or freezing drizzle)

INTENSITY, OR PROXIMITY TO THE WEATHER STATION:
- = light intensity
no sign = moderate intensity
+ = heavy intensity
VC = in the vicinity of the weather station

Appendix B. THE SKEW-T, LOG P THERMODYNAMIC DIAGRAM

Meteorologists use a thermodynamic diagram for many forecast uses: to forecast thunderstorms and the probable intensity, to forecast clouds, to forecast overnight low temperatures and other useful weather aspects. On the diagram is plotted the data collected by instruments attached to weather balloons, and some of the data gathered by weather satellites. The specific data is called **sounding data**, so-named because instrumentation sounds out the vertical profile of the lower atmosphere. **A sounding is a probe of the environment, in order to acquire data for scientific analysis.**

Twice daily, and sometimes more often in potentially severe weather, weather balloons, filled with helium, are released, which ascend to about 100,000 feet, expanding as they rise. A parachute is inserted into the balloon before it is released so that when the balloon bursts, its instrument package gently lands on the surface. Powered by a battery, the instruments radio back the temperature, dewpoint and air pressure continuously as the balloon ascends. The wind direction and speed at the various levels are determined by following the motion of the balloon. The instrument package is called a **radiosonde**, because it radios back the information of the sounding.

A second method for obtaining soundings is via weather satellites. Weather satellites have sensors that give us visible, infra-red, water vapor and other imagery of the tops of clouds and, where there are no clouds, of the surface of the planet. Visible pictures are useable obviously only during the daytime. Infra-red (heat) imagery senses the temperature of the tops of the clouds or the ground, water or ice surface. The Stefan-Boltzmann Law in physics relates the emitted energy of the surface of an object to the fourth power of its absolute temperature. The more radiation emitted by each square centimeter surface area of an object, the higher the object's surface temperature.

The meteorologist takes the sounding information and plots it on a **thermodynamic diagram** in order to analyze the vertical profile of the lower atmosphere over that general location. Sounding data from all sounding sites across the globe are the chief source for upper air weather maps and computer model projections of atmospheric conditions.

The standard thermodynamic diagram used in contemporary meteorology was developed by meteorologists of the United States Air Force and is called the **Skew-T, Log P Diagram.**

The diagram is useful for forecasting convection, clouds, fog, types of winter precipitation, and often the surface high and low temperatures.

The next page shows a Skew-T, log P thermodynamic diagram.

Figure 149. The Skew-T, Log P Thermodynamic Diagram. The five sets of lines are the logarithm of the isobars (log p), the skewed isotherms (skew-t), the dry adiabats, the moist adiabats (sometimes called the saturation adiabats) and the mixing ratio lines. These are explained on the next page. When air parcels are unsaturated and rising, they rise and cool along the dry adiabat upward; when the parcels are saturated after cooling to their dewpoint temperature, they rise (and continue cooling) along a moist adiabat.

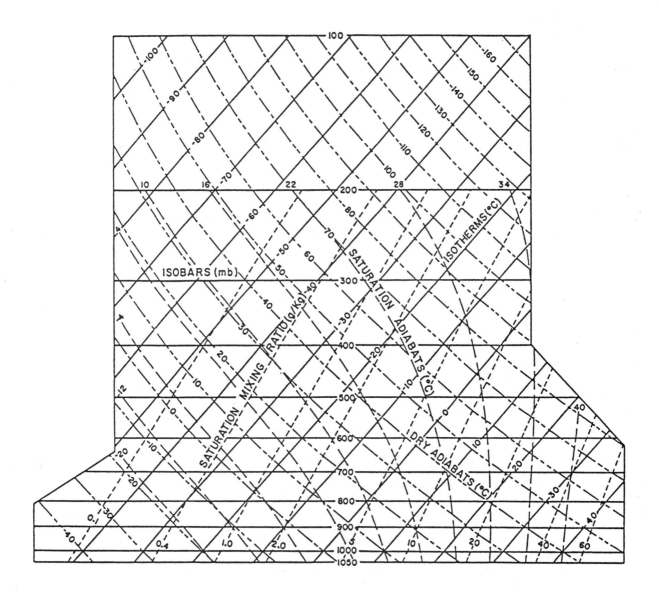

The solid horizontal lines are the pressure levels and the dashed lines sloping rightward are the lines of equal temperature called isotherms. The curved, leftward-sloping lines are dry adiabats, which is the rate of cooling of unsaturated air parcels as they rise, or warming as they descend. These are labelled "dry adiabats". The moist or saturation adiabats, which are labelled "saturation adiabats" do not slope as greatly as do the dry adiabats. As we know, air parcels rise along or parallel to a dry adiabat when unsaturated and along a moist adiabat, labelled "saturation adiabat", when saturated (i.e., when they have risen enough to cool to their dewpoints).

Across the bottom of the chart, the isotherms are labelled in degrees Celsius. On the right end of the thermodynamic diagram (not shown in figure 149) are plotted the wind directions and speeds at reportable heights, with the speed in knots. This will be shown in an example of a plotted sounding with wind information, later.

Now let us look at a plotted sounding. We have received data from either a radiosonde or satellite sounding. The temperatures and dewpoints at the various heights or pressure levels are then plotted on this diagram and the data points for the temperature profile in the vertical are connected, and the data lines for the dewpoint temperature profile in the vertical are connected.

The mixing ratio lines give the parts per thousand, actually in grams per kilogram, of water vapor that the air is holding for that dewpoint at that pressure. If the air held all the moisture it could for that temperature and pressure, then the dewpoint and temperature would be the same. This is how we compute relative humidity. Take the surface mixing ratio value that the dewpoint would give, and divide it by the mixing ratio value for the temperature, and multiply the result by 100% to express the relative humidity in percent of saturation for that temperature.

Air conserves most of its dewpoint (moisture content) as it ascends, if indeed some **forcing mechanism** is causing the air to rise. That is to say, air parcels keep or conserve their dewpoint or moisture content, for the most part, as they ascend, with only a slight dewpoint lapse rate with height. The atmospheric pressure is the sum of the partial pressure of each of its constituents. Water vapor is one of these atmospheric constituents, and its pressure is affected as it rises into lower environmental pressures. Thus, we can say that air conserves its dewpoint as these air bubbles rise, but in reality there is a slight lowering of the dewpoint during such rising.

If the rising air is not saturated, it cools along the dry adiabat (at the dry adiabatic lapse rate of about 9.8 Celsius degrees per kilometer). When saturated, it then cools at a lower rate since the rising air parcels are then releasing the **heat of condensation** as clouds and subsequent precipitation are formed. These parcels then cool at about 6 Celsius degrees per kilometer, but that drops to about 3 Celsius degrees per kilometer in the higher troposphere, and after virtually all of the moisture has been condensed ("squeezed") out, the air resumes cooling at the dry adiabatic lapse rate if it keeps rising.

The dry and moist adiabatic lapse rates are the rates at which unsaturated, and saturated, respectively, parcels of air cool as they ascend. The term, **adiabatic**, means that during a physical process, such as air parcels rising on their own because they are positively buoyant, no heat is added to or taken away from the air parcel. In reality, very meager heat is generated through friction of the air molecules and larger parcels and by entrainment of some environmental air, but this is considered meteorologically insignificant.

As long as the rising bubbles of air, about a cubic meter in volume, are warmer than the environment, they keep rising.

Figure 150. Below is a plotted sounding. The solid line sounding is the temperature curve gotten from data from an ascending weather balloon and/or from a sounder on a weather satellite. The dashed line sounding is the dewpoint curve. Across the bottom of each sounding is the temperature scale, in degrees Celsius. The logarithm of pressure, in millibars (hectoPascals) is the vertical ordinate.

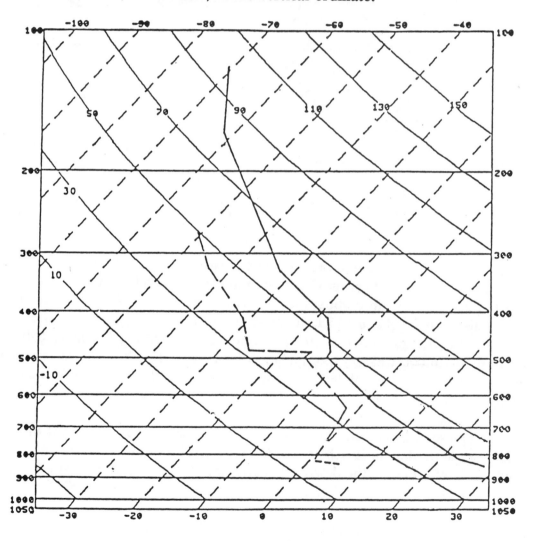

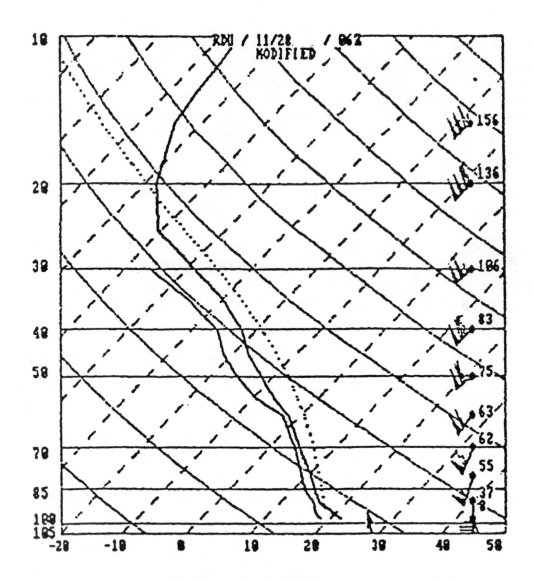

Figure 151. A sounding showing the path of the rising air parcels and the equilibrium level. This skew-T, log P diagram shows the following. At left is the pressure level, with the last zero left off, in millibars (mb). Thus, 85 means 850 mb, 70 means 700 mb, etc. This is the height to which air must rise to reach that pressure level in the atmosphere. As an approximation, for a rough average, 850 mb is about 5000 feet up, 700 mb is about 10,000 feet elevation, 500 mb is at about 18,000 feet, 300 mb is about 29,000 feet, 200 mb is about 39,000 feet and 100 mb is at about 53,000 feet...about 10 miles...up.

Look at the two solid black lines extending from the surface up. The right line extends to 100 mb, while the line to its left stops at 300 mb. The right line is the temperature sounding. The left curve is the dewpoint sounding. Thus, at 300 mb, which is about 29,000 feet up, the temperature is -40°C and the dewpoint is about -46°C.

The CAPE (convective available potential energy) is determined from the positively buoyant area. (continued)

PAGE 284

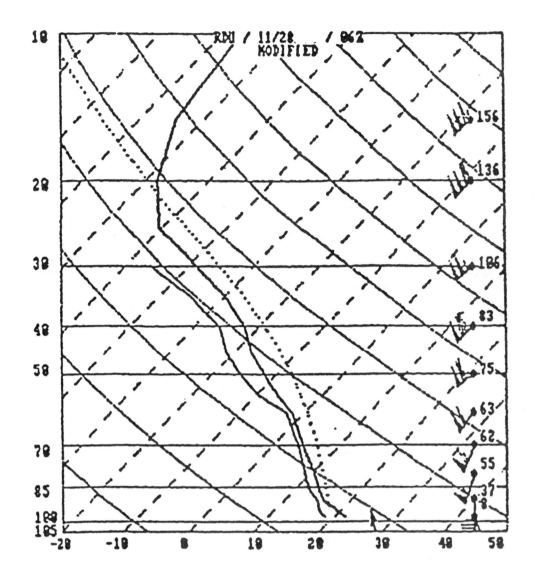

Figure 151. A sounding showing the path of the rising air parcels and the equilibrium level. This skew-T, log P diagram shows the following. At left is the pressure level, with the last zero left off, in millibars (mb). Thus, 85 means 850 mb, 70 means 700 mb, etc. This is the height to which air must rise to reach that pressure level in the atmosphere. As an approximation, for a rough average, 850 mb is about 5000 feet up, 700 mb is about 10,000 feet elevation, 500 mb is at about 18,000 feet, 300 mb is about 29,000 feet, 200 mb is about 39,000 feet and 100 mb is about 53,000 feet...about 10 miles...up.

Look at the two solid black lines extending from the surface up. The right line extends to 100 mb, while the line to its left stops at 300 mb. The right line is the temperature sounding. The left curve is the dewpoint sounding. Thus, at 300 mb, which is about 29,000 feet up, the temperature is -40°C and the dewpoint is about -46°C.

The CAPE (convective available potential energy) is determined from the positively buoyant area. (continued)

PAGE 285

The dotted curve from the surface on up is the path of rising air parcels. Since the parcels have cooled to their dewpoints at a low elevation, they rise and cool at the moist adiabatic lapse rate, and above about 300 mb, when most of the moisture has been expended, they then cool at close to the dry adiabatic lapse rate from that point and farther up.

Notice that as long as the parcels are warmer than the environment, they keep rising. That is, if the dotted line is to the right of the temperature sounding, the parcels are positively buoyant, i.e., they are warmer than the environment, and they keep rising. They actually keep accelerating, going faster and faster, until they hit the equilibrium level, which is the level at which the parcels of air are at the same temperature as the environment, i.e., at the same temperature as that shown by the temperature sounding line. This happens where the dotted line crosses the temperature sounding line, which is at about 220 millibars in our example. Thus, the equilibrium level at this time on this day at this location, which is Raleigh-Durham, North Carolina, is at the 220 mb pressure level.

Since the parcels have been accelerating, that is, increasing their vertical speed, as they ascent up to the equilibrium level, then the equilibrium level also is where the greatest upward vertical velocity of the parcels can be expected. Then, as parcels rise above the equilibrium level, notice that the dotted line shows them to be colder than the environmental temperature. Now, they are decelerating, slowing down. By the time they reach to about 100 mb, they will have stopped rising.

How high will the parcels go? Meteorologists shade in the area from the equilibrium level (EL) on down, between the temperature sounding and the rising parcel path, and call this the **positively buoyant energy area.** We then shade in the area above the equilibrium level from the temperature sounding to the rising parcel path line until that shaded area equals the shaded areas of the positively buoyant energy area. The area above the EL is the **negatively buoyant energy area.** Thus, when the negatively buoyant energy area equals the positively buoyant energy area, the parcels stop their ascent, and this is about how high the thunderstorm tops will grow to. In time, these cloud tops tend to sag back down towards the equilibrium level, especially as the updrafts weaken as the thunderstorm passes its mature stage and enters the dissipation stage.

CAPE is the area between the environmental temperature curve and the dotted curve which indicates the path of the parcels. It is the positive buoyant area. The more energy available, the greater the likelihood of having strong vs. weak thunderstorms.

An in-depth explanation of all the uses of the skew-T diagram would require a book itself! Fortunately, there is an excellent operational text on the subject, entitled, "Use of the Skew-T, Log P Diagram in Analysis and Forecasting", published by the United States Air Force.

Figure 152. Use this figure of an analyzed sounding with the description of convective operations on the next page.

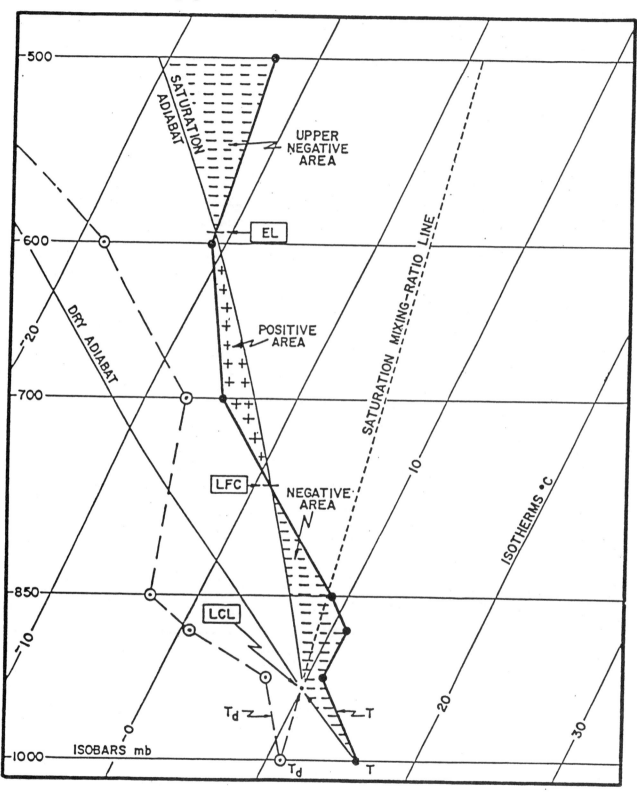

LCL -- LIFTED CONDENSATION LEVEL: Extend a line parallel to the dry adiabats upward from the surface temperature. Extend another line parallel to the saturation mixing ratio lines upward from the surface dew point. Where they cross is the LCL. This indicates where a parcel of air, lifted from the surface dry adiabatically, will become saturated. Often, if surface values are not reflective of the temperature profile or moisture content of the entire surface layer (within about 1 km) then a mean temperature and mean mixing ratio value may be chosen for determining the LCL.

LFC -- LEVEL of FREE CONVECTION: From the LCL extend a line upward parallel to the saturation adiabats until it intersects the plotted temperature curve. That point is the LFC. Under very stable atmospheric conditions, it is possible to have no LFC (the plotted temperature curve would be warmer than, or to the right of, the saturation adiabat of the LFC). The Level of Free Convection is the point where a surface-based parcel, lifted to saturation and beyond, is able to rise freely because of its positive buoyancy.

EL -- EQUILIBRIUM LEVEL: From the LFC, draw a line upward parallel to the saturation adiabats (this line MUST BE to the right of, or warmer than, the plotted temperature curve). Obviously, if there is no LFC for the sounding, there can be no EL. The point where this line crosses the temperature curve and stays to the left of the temperature for the remainder of the sounding, is the Equilibrium Level. The line may make one or more temporary crosses to the left of the temperature due to mid-level inversions, or layers of relatively more stable air, but the last point where the line crosses permanently to the left is the EL. The Equilibrium Level divides the sounding into areas of (predominantly) positive buoyancy below, and negative buoyancy above. At that level, a rising parcel of saturated air becomes colder than the environmental temperature and begins to decelerate. The parcel will theoretically come to a halt at the MPL.

MPL -- MAXIMUM PARCEL LEVEL: Continue the line from the LCL, LFC, and EL upward along the saturated adiabats (if above 200MB, follow the dry adiabats) until the amount of negative buoyancy, in area, is equal to the amount of positive buoyancy, starting at the LFC. If a parcel, lifted from surface, saturated, and brought to the LFC by lifting, rises moist adiabatically, remains saturated through the entire ascent, is not subject to entrainment or slowed by the weight of condensed water above it (left by preceding parcels), it will come to a gradual halt at the MPL.

TROP -- TROPOPAUSE: Find the lowest point in the sounding where the temperature lapse rate decreases to $2^{\circ}C/km$ and remains so for a distance of 2 km. The average lapse rate within this 2 km stratum cannot exceed $2^{\circ}C/km$. The Tropopause is the boundary layer between the troposphere below and the stratosphere above.

PAGE 288